FAST REACTIONS IN SOLUTION

Fast Reactions
in Solution

E. F. CALDIN
M.A., D.Phil.
Senior Lecturer in Physical Chemistry
University of Leeds

BLACKWELL

SCIENTIFIC PUBLICATIONS

OXFORD

FIRST PUBLISHED 1964

Printed in Great Britain by

SPOTTISWOODE, BALLANTYNE AND CO LTD
LONDON AND COLCHESTER

and bound by

WEBB, SON AND CO LTD, LONDON

Contents

Preface

Research on fast reactions in solution has developed enormously in the last fifteen years; novel techniques have been developed, and numerous reactions which would once have been called 'instantaneous' have been investigated in detail. In writing this survey, I have had in mind both the general reader who wants an outline of the field, and the research worker seeking a solution to a particular problem. I have tried to give a readable account, intelligible to senior undergraduates, of the principles and main achievements of the various methods, and also to give the researcher the information he wants on the scope and peculiarities of each technique.

Chapter 1 includes a preliminary survey of the methods, which are summarized in a table on pages 8–9. Chapters 2 to 11 outline the methods in turn and summarize their applications; these chapters are self-contained as far as possible, and cross-referenced. Chapter 12 takes up some general problems in the mechanisms and energetics of reaction.

The text was written in the main by January 1963, except the last chapter which was written six months later; the whole was revised up to August 1963. References have been included to the chapters on fast reactions in the second edition of *Investigation of Rates and Mechanisms of Reactions*, part II, edited by Friess, Lewis and Weissberger (Interscience, 1963); but this book appeared too late for me to make use of it in preparing my own.

My warmest thanks are due to the colleagues and friends who have helped me by commenting on the several chapters and in other ways; in alphabetical order they are Messrs J.Albery (chapter 9), J.Andreae (4, 5), N.Atherton (10), P.Ayscough (10), R.P.Bell (1, 2, 9, 12), E.J.Bowen (8), T.M.Connor (11), M.Fleischmann (9),

Q.H.Gibson (3), M.Heyrovsky (9), K.J.Ivin (1, 7), W.Kruse (4), A.Loewenstein (11), G.Maass (5), G.Porter (6), R.F.Prince (2, 3), F.J.W.Roughton (3), J.A.S.Smith (10, 11), B.Stevens (8), L. Sutcliffe (11), A.Walton (9), and D.H.Whiffen (10). They have greatly improved the accuracy of the text. I must also express my debt to Professor Dainton, in whose department I have been enabled to research and lecture on fast reactions; nor must I forget the late Professor M.G.Evans, who first gave me the opportunity of working in this field. The book owes its origin to a suggestion by Dr T.I.Williams, and Mr J.L.Robson was most helpful at every stage of the production. The last word must be for my wife, who not only typed a difficult manuscript but shared cheerfully the other burdens of authorship.

Leeds   E. F. C.
September 1963

Acknowledgments

Grateful acknowledgments are due to the authors, editors and publishers concerned for permission to use certain published figures. References are given in the text. The figures are those numbered 2.3, 3.3, 3.4, 4.2, 4.3, 4.4, 4.5, 5.1, 5.6, 6.1, 6.3, 7.1, 7.2, 7.3, 7.4, 8.2, 8.3, 9.1, 9.2, 9.3, 9.4, 9.5, 9.6, 9.7, 10.3, 10.4, 10.6, 11.2, 11.3, 11.7, 11.8, 11.9, 11.10, 12.2 and 12.3. Special help was received from authors who made available unpublished material for figures 3.6a (Professor Q.H.Gibson), 3.6b (Dr M.Kasparian), 5.5 (Dr J.Andreae), 8.1 (Dr B.Stevens) and 10.2 (Dr P.Ayscough).

Introduction

Historical and general introduction

For many years after the earliest investigation in 1850[1] the rates of chemical reactions in solution were studied by simple methods. The reaction was initiated by mixing the reagent solutions, and its progress was followed by titrating samples, or making measurements of some physical property, after various intervals of time. The time required for mixing and for observation had to be short compared with the half-time of the reaction. Consequently, the fastest reactions that could be measured had half-times of minutes, or at least seconds. Many reactions, especially those of ions, were immeasurably fast, and their mechanisms could not be kinetically investigated.

The situation is now entirely altered. The first major advance was the introduction of the continuous-flow method by Hartridge and Roughton in 1923.[2] This made possible the study of reactions with half-times of a few milliseconds—a reduction of the order of 10^3 or 10^4 compared with conventional methods. The limiting factor was the rate of mixing. In the years that followed, the method was steadily developed, and was applied to reactions of haemoglobin and enzymes, but it was not at once widely taken up. During the 1930's several papers appeared on fluorescence quenching, and on the photostationary state, by which very high rates could be measured; there were also some investigations at low temperatures. These were the only special techniques that had been developed by 1939 for fast reactions in solution.

By 1954, however, when the Faraday Society held a discussion on the study of fast reactions, a whole range of techniques had

[1] Wilhelmy, *Pogg. Ann.* 1850, **81**, 413.
[2] Hartridge and Roughton, *Proc. Roy. Soc., A*, 1923, **104**, 376; cf. p. 29.

emerged.[3] Some of these were developments of flow methods which made them simpler and more widely applicable. Others were radically different, in that the reaction was not initiated by mixing. Some, such as the temperature-jump and flash techniques, made use of oscillographic fast-recording gear. In others, such as the fluorescence and ultrasonic-absorption methods, a steady state was achieved, which could be observed at leisure. Others exploited the special properties of electron-spin resonance and nuclear magnetic resonance. In 1959 an international conference on fast reactions in solution held at Hahnenklee in Germany[4] showed that these new methods were being systematically used and had produced results of great interest. Rate constants can now be measured over the whole range from those accessible to conventional techniques right up to the highest values conceivable on current theories, when every encounter between reactant molecules is effective. The accessible time-range has been extended by something like ten powers of ten.

New fields of research have been opened up by these advances in technique. On the one hand, the mechanisms of reactions formerly labelled 'instantaneous', whether organic or inorganic, can be investigated, and a rich diversity of behaviour has been revealed. There is a mass of new information, on a great variety of reaction types, including proton-transfers, hydrogen-bonding, electron-transfers, complex-formations, enzyme reactions, inversions of configuration, and reactions of free radicals and of triplet states. On the other hand, the physicochemical study of rate processes in general and their energetics has been promoted, especially by studies of reactions that have low activation energies and are subject to diffusion control.

The meaning of 'fast'. The term 'fast reaction' is relative, imprecise, and ambiguous, but it is none the less serviceable. In its primary sense, it means a reaction that is fast relative to the time

---

[3] Papers on most of these techniques are to be found in *Discuss. Faraday Soc.* 1954, **17**, 114–234. (The earlier part of this discussion, pp. 1–113, relates to fast reactions in gases).

[4] The papers read at this conference were published in *Z. Elektrochem.* 1960, **64**, 1–204.

required for mixing and observation by conventional methods. A reaction with a half-time of a second or less would certainly be fast according to this criterion, though the borderline would depend on the experimental details. But a second-order reaction may have a very high rate constant under ordinary conditions and yet take place comparatively slowly if the concentrations are low enough; the highest second-order rate constant accessible by a given method depends as much on the sensitivity of the technique to low concentrations of reagent as on the least time-interval that it can resolve. Moreover, reactions that are fast at room temperature may become amenable to conventional measuring techniques if the temperature is lowered. In a loose sense, therefore, the term 'fast reaction' may be used to include reactions which would be too fast for normal methods if conducted at 'ordinary' temperatures and concentrations. These remarks are not intended as precise definitions; they serve only to indicate in a preliminary way the range of rates for which the methods described in this book are needed.

This range may now be considered more quantitatively. When conventional methods are used, rate measurements cannot be made accurately on reactions with half-times much less than 10 sec. Several of the new techniques can measure half-times down to 10^{-7} sec, and some of them to 10^{-9} sec. The range of first-order rate constants amenable to these techniques is from about 1 sec^{-1} to 10^9 sec^{-1}, so that the accessible range has been extended by about ten powers of ten.[5] The corresponding range of second-order rate constants depends on the concentration at which the minimum half-time can be measured. Values up to 10^{10} or 10^{11} l mole^{-1} sec^{-1} have been determined by several techniques, and the range extends down to meet the 'conventional' range, for which the maximum may be taken somewhat arbitrarily as around 1 l mole^{-1} sec^{-1}, which is the value for a half-time of 10 sec measured with concentrations of 0·1 M, or a half-time of 100 sec with concentrations of 0·01 M.

[5] For details see Table 1.1 below (p. 8). The half-time $t_{1/2}$ of a first-order reaction is related to the rate constant k by $k t_{1/2} = \ln 2 \approx 0.7$; for a second-order reaction, with each reactant at concentration a, $t_{1/2}$ is related to the rate constant k' by $k' t_{1/2} = 1/a$.

The range of rate constants accessible only by means of special techniques is greater than the whole of the 'conventional' range. The longest half-time that is commonly convenient to measure is of the order of one day, or 10^5 sec; by measuring initial rates it is possible to extend this by a factor of perhaps 10^2. The range of first-order rate constants accessible by ordinary methods is thus about 10^{-7} to 10^{-1} sec^{-1}, for second-order rate constants[6] it is about 10^{-7} to $1 \cdot 0$ l mole^{-1} sec^{-1}. These ranges are shorter, in powers of ten, than the new ranges whose measurement requires fast-reaction techniques (Fig. 1.1). As there is no evidence that reaction rates are

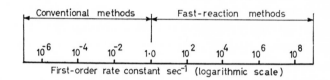

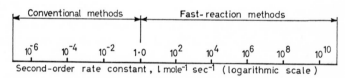

FIG. 1.1. Ranges of rate constants accessible by conventional and by fast-reaction techniques.

grouped in any way, we may expect very many reactions to have rates in the 'fast' range.

Classification of methods for fast reactions in solution

The methods to be surveyed in the following chapters may be grouped according to the general principles which they exemplify. These principles will be fully explained in their appropriate places, and will be only briefly indicated here. The classification that

[6] The great majority of the second-order rate constants recorded in *Tables of Chemical Kinetics: Homogeneous Reactions* (N.B.S. Circular 510; 1951) lie in the range 10^{-7} to $1 \cdot 0$ l mole^{-1} sec^{-1}. The lowest directly-determined value is 5×10^{-10} l mole^{-1} sec^{-1}.

follows, and the characteristics of each method, are summarized in Table 1.1 below.

(i) The rate is brought by various means into the 'normal' range, where the half-time is long compared with the times required to mix the solutions and take an observation, so that the reaction can be followed by conventional methods. Applications of low concentrations and of low temperatures are examples of such devices (chapter 2).

(ii) The reagent solutions are mixed rapidly, but matters are arranged so that the observations can be taken at leisure, or at least without special fast techniques. The thermal-maximum and quenching methods, which achieve a slight improvement in conventional methods, are among the applications of this principle (chapter 2); the continuous-flow method is another (chapter 3).

(iii) The solutions are mixed rapidly, and the reaction is then followed by fast techniques. The stopped-flow method (chapter 3) uses this principle.

The shortest half-time that can be measured by any of the preceding methods is determined by the least time of mixing, which is about a millisecond. Several principles are available by which mixing can be avoided altogether, as follows.

(iv) If a reversible reaction is initially in equilibrium, and the conditions are then suddenly altered, the reaction proceeds in one direction or the other until the new position of equilibrium is reached. For example, a sudden change of temperature has this effect on the dissociation of a weak acid. The course of the reaction is followed by a fast oscillographic method (chapter 4). A periodic change of temperature can also be effected, by means of ultrasonic waves; when the half-time of the reaction is comparable with the period of the disturbance, there is a sharp increase in the power absorbed (chapter 5). These methods make use of small displacements from equilibrium, and are called relaxation methods.

(v) Some reactions can be initiated photochemically; the absorption of radiation usually introduces a considerable change into a system, such as the production of free radicals. In some instances a single powerful flash can be used, and the reaction is

2

followed by a fast oscillographic technique (chapter 6). With the lower intensities usually used in photochemical work, other methods must be adopted, such as the rotating-sector technique, which has been applied especially to polymerization reactions (chapter 7).

(vi) When a substance is fluorescent in solution, the excited molecules have a certain mean lifetime before they emit light; this can be determined, and is of the order of 10^{-8} sec. If a substance is added which reacts rapidly with these excited molecules, so that an appreciable number of them are destroyed before emission can take place, the fluorescence intensity is reduced. From the relation between intensity and concentration, the rate constant of the reaction can be found.

(vii) Polarographic and other electrochemical processes can be arranged in which, for example, a current which would normally be controlled by the rate of diffusion of some species is affected also by the rate at which that species is produced by a reaction in solution (Chapter 9). The principle is analogous to that of the fluorescence methods (vi), in that the reaction is combined with another rate process occurring in the solution.

(viii) Fast reactions can alter the properties of systems of spinning magnetic particles, whether electrons or nuclei. Methods for determining reaction rates can be based upon electron-spin resonance (also called paramagnetic resonance) and upon nuclear magnetic resonance (chapters 10 and 11).

Reaction half-times and rate constants accessible by the various methods

The reaction half-times and rate constants accessible by the various methods are indicated, as regards order of magnitude, in Table 1.1. The smallest half-times, about 10^{-9} sec, have been detected by the ultrasonic, fluorescence, and e.s.r. methods; next come the temperature-jump and electric-impulse methods (10^{-7}–10^{-6} sec), and the flash method (10^{-5} sec). Some typical time-intervals for molecular and atomic processes are given for comparison in the Appendix, Table 13.1 (p. 293).

The upper limit for first-order rate constants that can be observed by a given method is approximately the reciprocal of the least half-time that can be measured. For a second-order reaction, however, as we have noticed, the upper limit depends also on the concentration at which the reaction can be observed, and so on the sensitivity of the technique. The maximum second-order constant that has been observed by means of each method is given in Table 1.1. It will be noticed that this is of the order of 10^9 l mole^{-1}sec^{-1} or over for many of the methods, even though for some of them the least half-time is no lower than 10^{-4} sec. The lower limits are also shown in Table 1.1.

The energetics of very fast reactions

Many reactions with activation energies around 10 kcal mole^{-1} are fast in the sense that special means are required to measure their rates, but there is nothing exceptional about their energetics. The temperature-variation of their rate constants is represented by the Arrhenius equation $k = A \exp(-E_A/RT)$, and this equation is interpreted in the normal way. The activation energy E_A represents a critical energy without which a collision will not result in reaction. The fraction of effective collisions is $\exp(-E_A/RT)$ and is quite small. The lower the activation energy, the higher is this fraction, and therefore the higher the rate constant at a given temperature. To illustrate the relation, Table 1.2 shows the second-order rate

TABLE 1.2

Second-order rate constants at 25° calculated from
$k = 10^{11}\exp(-E_A/RT)$ *for various values of* E_A,
to nearest order of magnitude

E_A (kcal mole^{-1})	14	12·5	10	7	4	(0)
k (l mole^{-1}sec^{-1})	10	10^2	10^4	10^6	10^8	(10^{11})

constants at 25° calculated from the Arrhenius equation for various values of E_A, with $A = 10^{11}$ l mole^{-1}sec^{-1} (a representative value for many reactions between an ion and a molecule).

For the fastest reactions, however, this interpretation of the Arrhenius equation breaks down. Quite a few reactions are known

TABLE 1.1

Characteristics of fast-reaction methods

'Min. $t_{1/2}$' = minimum reaction half-time in sec.
'Max. k' = maximum observed second-order rate constant in l mole⁻¹sec⁻¹.

Principle	Method	Method requires				Min. $t_{1/2}$ (sec.)	Max. k (l m⁻¹s⁻¹)
		Fast mixing	Fast obsn.	Equi-librium	Reaction type		
(i) Bring rate into 'normal' range	1 Low concentration				General	—	10^{10}
	2 Low temperature				General	—	—
	3 k_f from Kk_b			*	General	—	10^{11}
	4 Competition			*	General	—	10^{8}
(ii) Fast mixing, not fast observation	5 Thermal maximum	*			General	0·2	10^{3}
	6 Quenching	*			General	0·05	10^{3}
	7 Capacity flow	*			General	1	10
	8 Continuous flow	*			General	10^{-3}	10^{8}
(iii) Fast mixing, fast observation	9 Stopped flow	*	*		General	10^{-3}	10^{8}
	10 Accelerated flow	*	*		General	10^{-3}	10^{7}
	11 Baffle	*	*		General	10^{-3}	10^{2}
(iv) Shift of equilibrium; relaxation	12 Temperature-jump		*	*	General	10^{-6}	10^{11}
	13 Pressure-jump		*	*	General	10^{-4}	10^{3}
	14 Electric impulse		*	*	Ionic	10^{-7}	10^{11}
	15 Ultrasonics			*	General	10^{-9}	10^{11}
(v) Initiation by irradiation	16 Flash		*		Light-sensitive system	10^{-5}	10^{10}
	17 Rotating sector, etc.				Photochem. initiation	10^{-10}	10^{10}
(vi) Combine with another rate process	18 Fluorescence				Fluorescent reagent	10^{-9}	10^{11}
	19 Electrochemical			*	Ionizable reagent	10^{-4}	$> 10^{11}$
(vii) Magnetic spin resonance	20 E.s.r.			*	Free radicals	10^{-10}	10^{10}
	21 N.m.r. (proton)			*	Various	10^{-4}	10^{11}

TABLE 1.1—*continued*

Characteristics of fast-reaction methods

All values are orders of magnitude.

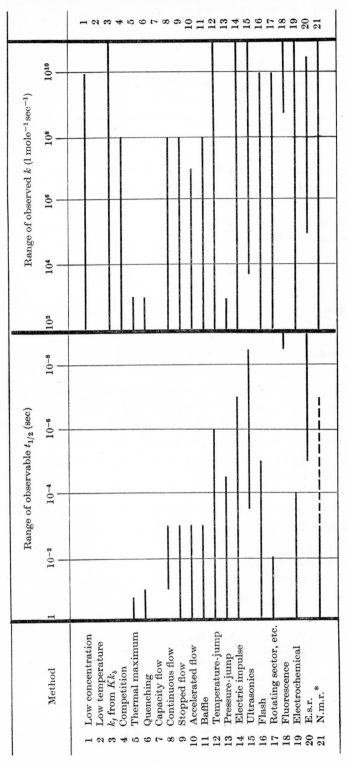

Range of observable $t_{1/2}$ (sec)

Range of observed k ($1\ \text{mole}^{-1}\ \text{sec}^{-1}$)

Method

1 Low concentration
2 Low temperature
3 k_f from Kk_b
4 Competition
5 Thermal maximum
6 Quenching
7 Capacity flow
8 Continuous flow
9 Stopped flow
10 Accelerated flow
11 Baffle
12 Temperature-jump
13 Pressure-jump
14 Electric impulse
15 Ultrasonics
16 Flash
17 Rotating sector, etc.
18 Fluorescence
19 Electrochemical
20 E.s.r.
21 N.m.r. *

* The full line refers to ^{1}H resonance; the dashed line to ^{17}O resonance.

with rate constants in the region of $10^{10}\,l$ mole^{-1}sec^{-1}, or even 10^{11} if hydrogen ions are concerned. The rate of such a reaction approximates to the rate of molecular encounter, which is determined by the velocities at which the reagent molecules move about in the solution, and may be calculated from diffusion theory (below). Such a reaction evidently takes place at practically every encounter, and is not subject to any appreciable energy barrier once the molecules have reached adjacent positions. The diffusion process, however, will require a small energy of activation, and indeed the rate is found to increase slightly with temperature, giving a value for E_A of a few kilocalories per mole. Moreover, the rate is sensitive to the viscosity of the solvent, as would be expected if it were controlled by diffusion. Diffusion control is treated in more detail later (chapter 12, p. 279), but since diffusion-controlled rate constants will be met fairly often in this book, a preliminary account will be given here.

Theory of rate constants for diffusion-controlled reactions[7]

The commonest treatment of the rate of diffusion-controlled reactions in solution was developed originally by Smoluchowski[7a] for the rates of coagulation of colloids. It is assumed that the diffusive motions of molecules can be treated like the motions of macroscopic spherical particles in a viscous fluid. The theory was extended by Debye[7c] to ionic solutions where long-range electrostatic forces must be taken into account.

Consider a solution containing two types of solute molecule, A and B. Suppose first that A or B, or both, is uncharged, so that interionic forces can be neglected. On the assumption that Fick's law for diffusion is obeyed—that is, that the rate of diffusion is proportional to the concentration gradient—it may be shown that the number of encounters per millilitre per second between A and B is

$$4\pi(D_A + D_B)(r_A + r_B)\,n_A\,n_B \qquad (1.1)$$

[7] (a) Smoluchowski, *Z. phys. Chem.* 1917, **92**, 129; (b) Onsager, *J. Chem. Phys.* 1934, **2**, 599; (c) Debye, *Trans. Electrochem. Soc.* 1942, **82**, 265; (d) Umberger and LaMer, *J. Amer. Chem. Soc.* 1945, **67**, 1099; (e) R. M. Noyes, in *Progress in Reaction Kinetics* (Academic Press, 1961), pp. 137 *seq.*

where n_A and n_B are the number of A and B molecules per ml, r_A and r_B are the radii of the molecules, and D_A and D_B are their diffusion coefficients. If reaction occurs at every encounter between A and B, the rate of encounter given by equation 1.1 is also the rate of reaction. In terms of a rate constant k_D having the units ml mole^{-1} sec^{-1}, this rate would be given by the following expression, in which N^0 is Avogadro's number:

$$k_D \, n_A \, n_B / N^0 \tag{1.2}$$

Equating the expressions 1.1 and 1.2, we find that the rate constant k_D for a diffusion-controlled reaction is given by:

$$k_D = 4\pi N^0 (D_A + D_B)(r_A + r_B) \text{ ml mole}^{-1} \text{sec}^{-1} \tag{1.3}$$

The diffusion coefficients may be eliminated from this equation by expressing them in terms of the viscosity of the solvent (η) and the molecular radii; assuming the same model as before, the Stokes-Einstein equation gives:

$$D_A = kT/6\pi\eta r_A, \quad D_B = kT/6\pi\eta r_B \tag{1.4}$$

On substituting for D_A and D_B in equations 1.3, we find for k_D:

$$k_D = \left(\frac{2N^0 \, kT}{3\eta}\right)\left(\frac{(r_A + r_B)^2}{r_A r_B}\right) \text{ ml mole}^{-1} \text{sec}^{-1} \tag{1.5}$$

$$= \left(\frac{2RT}{3\eta}\right)(2 + r_A/r_B + r_B/r_A) \text{ ml mole}^{-1} \text{sec}^{-1} \tag{1.6}$$

This equation shows that at a given temperature k_D depends primarily on the viscosity η of the solvent. Variations in the size of the molecules do not affect the calculated rate unless the radius ratio is altered; even then the term in the second bracket is not much affected. The reason for this insensitivity of the rate to molecular size is that, on the model assumed, a larger molecule will move about more slowly than a smaller one in a liquid of given viscosity, but will present a bigger target for encounter with another solute molecule; thus the effects of size on the encounter rate will largely compensate.

If the molecular radii are assumed equal, we obtain the simple expression:

$$k_D = 8RT/3\eta \text{ ml mole}^{-1} \text{sec}^{-1} \tag{1.7}$$

Converting the units of concentration to the usual moles per litre, we obtain an expression which will be cited often in this book:

$$k_D = 8RT/3000\eta \ \text{l mole}^{-1}\text{sec}^{-1} \qquad (1.8)$$

This equation predicts that the rate constant of a diffusion-controlled reaction will be inversely proportional to the viscosity; its temperature-coefficient will be comparable with that of the viscosity, and therefore small compared with that of most reactions. The numerical value calculated for k_D in water at 25°, with $\eta \approx 0.01$ poise, is 0.7×10^{10} l mole^{-1}sec^{-1}; the values in benzene and chloroform are very similar, namely 0.95×10^{10} and 1.05×10^{10} l mole^{-1}sec^{-1}. All these conclusions agree semi-quantitatively with the experimental results on very fast reactions. Equation 1.8 cannot be more than an approximation, from the nature of its assumptions, which ignore the molecular structure of the liquid and therefore the consequences of the 'solvent cage' (pp. 282–285). None the less, it provides a general guide to the effects of various factors. An observed rate constant comparable with the calculated values of k_D is a useful indication of diffusion control. It appears incidentally that reaction rates will generally not be affected within 1% by the rate of diffusion if the rate constant is less than about 10^7 l mole^{-1}sec^{-1} (p. 281).[8]

If both A and B are ions, equation 1.8 must be modified to take account of the effects of interionic forces.[7b, c, d] The result of Debye's calculation is:

$$k_D = \left(\frac{8RT}{3000\eta}\right)\left(\frac{\delta}{e^\delta - 1}\right) \qquad (1.9)$$

where $\qquad\qquad \delta = z_A z_B e^2/\epsilon kTa.$ $\qquad\qquad (1.10)$

Here z_A and z_B are the charges on the ions, e the electronic charge, ϵ the dielectric constant of the solvent, and a the distance of closest approach of the ions $(r_A + r_B)$. The factor $\delta/(e^\delta - 1)$ by which k_D is modified by the presence of charges is greater than unity for unlike charges, and less for like charges. Some values for ions of various charges with various values of a are given in Table 13.2 (see

[8] (a) Noyes, ref. 7e; cf. also (b) Schulz, Z. phys. Chem. (Frankfurt), 1956, **8**, 284.

Appendix, p. 293), from which it may be seen that the factor is not extremely sensitive to the size of the ions unless this is very small. For reactions of oppositely-charged univalent ions, it is between 1 and 10, so that k_D is between 10^{10} and 10^{11} l mole^{-1}sec^{-1}.

The plan of this book

The various methods of studying fast reactions are considered in successive chapters of this book, in the order in which the principles and methods are set out on page 5. In each chapter, the general principles of the method are first outlined, then the experimental techniques, and finally a selection of applications. The field is now so wide that the applications cannot all be covered, but at least the more important types are represented. The two great interests served by kinetic investigations—the elucidation of the mechanisms of reactions, and the understanding of their energetics—have both been kept in mind. It is hoped that the reader will be able to form an impression of the possibilities, the limitations, and the achievements of each technique—the types of reaction that it can be used to study, the outlay in special apparatus, the concentrations required, the range of rates accessible, and the reliability of the results. All these factors have to be considered in the approach to a particular problem. In the final chapter, some general topics which crop up in various places throughout the book are separately considered, in order to illustrate the contributions of studies on fast reactions to our knowledge of the mechanisms and energetics of chemical change.

CHAPTER 2

The Simpler Methods

In this chapter we consider a miscellany of methods which, while avoiding rapid observation and highly specialized techniques, make possible the determination of rate constants larger than those accessible by conventional methods.

One way of tackling the problem is to use some device to bring the rate of reaction within the normal range. Rapid mixing of the reactant solutions is then unnecessary, as well as rapid observation. This strategy leads to the following group of methods:

Use of low concentrations.
Measurement of equilibrium constant and rate of reverse reaction.
Competition methods.
Use of low temperatures.

In a second group of methods, the mixing of reactant solutions is done rapidly, but no special fast techniques of observation are used. Reactions with half-times of the order of 1 or 0·1 sec can be studied, so that those methods permit a useful though limited extension of the normal range of rates. Among them are the following[1]:

Thermal maximum method.
Quenching methods.
Capacity-flow method.
Electrolytic addition of reagent.

Use of low concentrations
Surprisingly high rate constants can be determined simply by using low concentrations of reactants, if sensitive methods of measuring

[1] The continuous-flow method (chapter 3, p. 29) might be included under this heading, but is more conveniently treated with other flow methods.

these concentrations are available. For instance, a rate constant of 4.3×10^9 1 mole^{-1}sec^{-1} has been found for the bromination of N,N-diethyl-m-toluidine in aqueous solution; this was possible because a bromine concentration as low as 10^{-8} M could be estimated from the redox potential at a bright platinum electrode, and the concentration of the free amine could be reduced to 10^{-8} M by adding sulphuric acid.[2a] Low concentrations of bromine may also be determined by measuring the limiting current between a rotating platinum cathode and a stationary platinum anode,[2b] or by generating the bromine electrolytically with a known small current.[2c] Rate constants have been determined by these methods for various aromatic alkylamines,[2a] olefinic compounds,[2c] phenols[2b 2d,] anisoles,[2d] and enols.[2e]

Photometric methods can be used to determine low concentrations of highly-coloured species.[3] A reaction which has been studied in this way is that between ferrous ion and cobaltioxalate ion in aqueous solution,[3a]

$$Fe^{2+} + [Co(C_2O_4)_3]^{3+} = Fe^{3+} + [Co(C_2O_4)_3]^{2+}.$$

Although the rate constant k for this reaction was over 10^4 1 mole^{-1} sec^{-1}, the rate was brought within the range of normal observation by the use of micromolar concentrations. When inert salts were added, up to an ionic strength (I) of about 0.01, the plot of log k against $I^{1/2}$ was linear and agreed with the predictions of the Debye-Hückel limiting law.

Low concentrations are used in a rather different way in determinations of the rates of reaction of cations with polymer radicals. An aqueous solution of acrylamide is irradiated with γ-rays from cobalt-60; this produces H and OH radicals, which add to the double bond of the acrylamide and so initiate polymerization. The growth of the polymer radical is terminated by reaction with

[2] (a) Bell and Ramsden, *J. Chem. Soc.*, 1958, 161; (b) Bell and Spencer, *Proc. Roy. Soc.*, A, 1959, **251**, 41, *J. Chem. Soc.*, 1959, 1156; (c) Dubois, *Z. Elektrochem.*, 1960, **64**, 143; (d) Bell and Rawlinson, *J. Chem. Soc.*, 1961, 63; (e) *idem, ibid.*, 726.
[3] (a) Baxendale, *Trans. Faraday Soc.* 1956, **52**, 210; (b) Pouli and MacF. Smith, *Canad. J. Chem.* 1960, **38**, 567 ($Fe^{+++} + F^-$).

cations. A steady rate of polymerization is set up, from which the rate constant for the reaction of radicals with cations can be deduced.[4] Because the concentration of polymer radicals is small ($ca.$ 10^{-8} M), this rate constant may be as high as 10^7 l $mole^{-1}sec^{-1}$ before the reaction becomes too fast to measure by normal methods such as dilatometry.

The use of low concentrations may be combined with other methods: it will be mentioned in connection with the low-temperature, quenching, flow, temperature-jump, flash, e.s.r. and n.m.r. methods.

Measurement of equilibrium constant and rate of reverse reaction

If we can measure the equilibrium constant of a reversible reaction, and the rate in one direction, then on certain assumptions we can deduce the rate in the other direction. Suppose the reaction is

$$A + B \underset{k_b}{\overset{k_f}{\rightleftharpoons}} C + D$$

The equilibrium constant, if differences of activity coefficients can be neglected, may be written:

$$K = c^e d^e / a^e b^e \qquad (2.1)$$

where a^e, b^e, etc., represent the equilibrium concentrations of A, B, etc. If the forward rate is found to follow the second-order expression $k_f ab$, and the rate of the back reaction is assumed to follow the similar expression $k_b cd$, (where a, b, etc., represent the concentrations at any time), then since the forward and backward rates are equal at equilibrium,

$$k_f a^e b^e = k_b c^e d^e \qquad (2.2)$$

Comparison with equation 2.1 shows that

$$k_b = 1/K k_f \qquad (2.3)$$

Hence the value of k_b can be found from those of K and k_f.

The rate constants of some fast proton-transfers have been estimated by this method. The dissociations of certain acids,

[4] Collinson, Dainton, Smith, Trudel and Tazuké, *Discuss. Faraday Soc.* 1960, **29**, 188. Cf. chapter 7.

often called pseudo-acids,[5a] occur at easily measurable rates, which may be determined by halogenation, deuterium exchange, or conductivity measurements. The equilibrium constants, though small, can be determined by the sensitive methods available, such as emf or conductivity. Equation 2.3 then gives the rate constants for the back reactions, namely the exchange of a proton between a hydrogen ion and an anion:

$$H_3O^+ + A^- \rightarrow H_2O + HA$$

Many of these reactions have rate constants greater than 10^6 l mole^{-1}sec^{-1}; among the fastest are those producing $CH_2(CN)_2$ ($k = 2 \cdot 3 \times 10^9$ l mole^{-1}sec^{-1}) and acetone ($k = 5 \times 10^{10}$ l mole^{-1} sec^{-1}).[5c]

Competition methods

If the rate constant is known for some reaction—for instance a proton-transfer such as those just mentioned—it may be used to obtain rate constants for other reactions if competition can be arranged. Suppose that cations M^{++} are added to the buffer solution (HA, A$^-$) and that they form complexes with the anion A$^-$, so that there are two competing reactions:

$$A^- + H_3O^+ \underset{k_{-1}}{\overset{k_1}{\rightleftharpoons}} HA + H_2O$$

$$A^- + M^{2+} \overset{k_2}{\longrightarrow} MA^+$$

The rate constant k_2 can then be determined, relative to the known rate constant k_1, by finding the proportions of MA^+ and HA in the product.

The rate constants for complex-formation between various metal cations and the anion of thenoyl trifluoroacetone have been determined in this way.[6a] Some of them are greater than 10^8 l mole^{-1} sec^{-1}. The rate constant appears to be greater the smaller the value of z^2/r for the cation (z = charge, r = radius); that is, the smaller the

[5] (a) Bell, *The Proton in Chemistry* (Methuen, 1959), pp. 13 *seq*. (b) For a list see Pearson and Dillon, *J. Amer. Chem. Soc.* 1953, **75**, 2439; reprinted in (c) Bell, *op. cit.*, pp. 161–2. Cf. p. 262.
[6] (a) Taft and Cook. *J. Amer. Chem. Soc.* 1959, **81**, 46; cf. (b) Basolo and Pearson, *Mechanisms of Inorganic Reactions* (Wiley, 1958), p. 112.

Born charging energy of the cation. This may indicate that the important factor is the energy of binding of the hydration sphere to the cation; the solvated ion must be partly freed from its sheath of water molecules before reaction can occur.[6b]

Low-temperature methods

Reactions which are fast at room temperature can often be slowed down by cooling so that the rates can be determined by ordinary physical methods. By adjusting the temperature, reactions whose rates at room temperature cover a wide range may be observed. For example, solutions in ethanol have been studied down to $-114°$; at this temperature the rate will be less than at $25°$ by a factor of more than 10^6, if the energy of activation is 10 kcal mole^{-1} or over. The lower limit of temperature is determined by the solubilities of the reagents and (if the reaction is initiated by mixing) by the increase in the viscosity of the solvent as the temperature falls; the lowest practicable temperature, even when the solvent has as low a viscosity as isopentane, is around $-140°$. Some techniques, however, do not make use of mixing to initiate reaction, and these could be used at lower temperatures (p. 22).

Techniques. These range from the simple to the elaborate. It is possible to dispense with a thermostat for fairly fast reactions; polymerization reactions taking 3 to 300 sec have been measured at temperatures down to $-120°$ by breaking a bulb of monomer under a cooled solution in a Dewar vessel, and following the rise in temperature.[7] More often, some kind of thermostat is desirable. If temperature-control to ± 0.5 degrees or so is adequate, a convenient cryostatic bath is obtained by adding solid carbon dioxide to acetone or ethanol (*ca.* $-78°$), or by cooling methanol with liquid nitrogen until part of it is frozen (*ca.* $-100°$).[8,9] A pioneer study

[7] Biddulph and Plesch, *Chem. & Ind.* 1959, 1482.

[8] As mixtures of organic substances with liquid air or oxygen are very dangerous, only 'oxygen-free' liquid nitrogen should be used; ordinary liquid nitrogen may on occasion contain enough oxygen to give a dangerous concentration after partial evaporation (McCarty and Balis, *Chem. Eng. News*, 1949, **27**, 2612).

[9] For other solid–liquid systems suitable as low-temperature baths see Dodd and Robinson, *Experimental Inorganic Chemistry* (Elsevier, 1954), pp. 53 *seq.*

of the rates of reaction of various metal cations with dithizone, dimethylglyoxime, and other complexing agents made use of such baths, along with approximate photometric methods.[10]

Thermostat baths of the normal type can be run at temperatures down to about $-40°$ by circulating a low-freezing liquid such as ethanol or ethanol-water through a commercial refrigerator system and a coil in the bath. This arrangement has the advantage that it runs continuously without attention. It was used in a study[11a] of a proton-transfer reaction in aqueous solution down to $-21°$, which provided the first instance of a non-linear Arrhenius plot due to quantum-mechanical tunnelling (p. 272). In some earlier work in this field, the rates of several reactions were measured at temperatures down to $-44°$. The thermostat consisted of a double-walled vessel with liquid ammonia or sulphur dioxide boiling in the annular space under controlled pressure. The reaction was started by breaking a thin tube containing one of the reactants, and was followed either by conductivity measurements or by chemical analysis after quenching.[12]

For lower temperatures, a simple thermostat which gives good temperature control (± 0.03 degrees) down to at least $-100°$ has been described.[13a,b] It consists of a lagged metal tank containing ethanol or ethanol-acetone, which is stirred mechanically. The liquid is cooled continuously by solid carbon dioxide and acetone contained in a glass tower, or by liquid nitrogen in a double-walled metal vessel.[8] A regulator of the usual mercury-toluene type, modified so that the mercury is outside the cold bath, controls the current in an electric heater. To keep the reactant solutions apart until they have taken up the thermostat temperature, the reaction cell has a side-tube, as shown in Fig. 2.1. The cell shown is designed

[10] (a) Bjerrum and Poulsen, *Nature*, 1952, **169**, 463; cf. (b) Poulsen, Bjerrum and Poulsen, *Acta chem. Scand.* 1954, **8**, 921.

[11] (a) Hulett, *Proc. Roy. Soc. A*, 1959, **251**, 274; (b) *J. Chem. Soc.* 1960, 468; cf. (c) Bell, Fendley and Hulett, *Proc. Roy. Soc.*, A, 1956, **235**, 453, and (d) ref. 14 *d*.

[12] (a) Bell and Thomas, *J. Chem. Soc.* 1939, 1573; (b) Bell and Norris, *J. Chem. Soc.* 1941, 118; (c) *idem, ibid.*, 854.

[13] (a) Caldin and Trickett, *Trans. Faraday Soc.* 1953, **49**, 772; (b) Ainscough and Caldin, *J. Chem. Soc.* 1956, 2528; (c) Caldin and Jackson, *J. Chem. Soc.* 1960, 2411.

for photometric observation; it could be adapted for conductivity or other physical methods of following reactions. The temperature range can be extended to $-140°$, and the temperature variations reduced to within $\pm 0\cdot01$ degrees, by using a glass Dewar vessel for the thermostat; the temperature is regulated by means of a

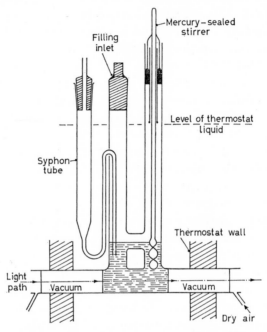

Fig. 2.1. Low-temperature reaction cell.[13]

thermocouple, and measured with a platinum resistance thermometer[13c] Such thermostats have been used in studies of the mechanisms of colour-producing reactions of aromatic nitro-compounds with bases, and in tests of the Arrhenius equation over long ranges of temperature.[13, 14] A larger cryostat bath, with equally good temperature control down to $-130°$, embodies a

[14] (a) Caldin and Long, Proc. Roy. Soc., A, 1955, 228, 263; (b) Ainscough and Caldin, J. Chem. Soc. 1956, 2528, 2540, 2546; 1960, 2407; (c) Caldin and Jackson, idem, 1960, 2411, 2413; (d) Caldin and Harbron, idem, 1962, 3454. Cf. below pp. 273–274.

double-walled vessel surrounded by liquid nitrogen contained in an outer Dewar vessel (Fig. 2.2).[15]

Probably the coldest medium in which a homogeneous chemical reaction has been followed is solid nitrogen at $21°K$.[16] A little

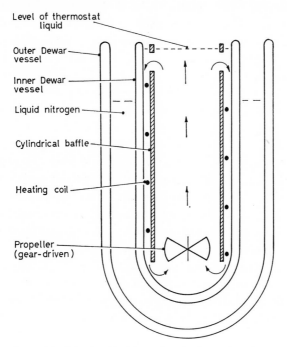

Level of thermostat
liquid

Outer Dewar
vessel

Inner Dewar
vessel

Liquid nitrogen

Cylindrical baffle

Heating coil

Propeller
(gear-driven)

FIG. 2.2. Low-temperature thermostat (after Scott
and Brickwedde).

oxygen and hydrazoic acid were added before cooling, and the mixture was exposed to ultraviolet light for some time. Subsequent

[15] Scott and Brickwedde, *J. Res. Nat. Bur. Stand.* 1931, **6**, 401; cf. ref. 17. The inner vessel should be of metal, because of the danger of breakage of glass Dewar vessels (cf. note 8, p. 18). Temperature control to $\pm 0.001°$ down to $-170°$ is claimed. Non-inflammable bath liquids are described by Kanolt, *Bur. Stand. Sci. Paper* no. 520, 1926; cf. Dodd and Robinson, *Experimental Inorganic Chemistry* (Elsevier, 1954), p. 57.

[16] (a) Pimentel, *J. Amer. Chem. Soc.* 1958, **80**, 62; cf. (b) Pimentel and Brown, *J. Chem. Phys.* 1958, **29**, 883. A method of studying reactions in thin layers at 2–4°K has been described: (c) Thomas, *Trans. Faraday Soc.* 1961, **57**, 1679.

changes in the infra-red spectrum were observed; a line at 868 cm^{-1}, formed during exposure, gradually disappeared, while a line at 818 cm^{-1} increased somewhat in intensity. The reaction was tentatively identified as the cis-trans isomerization of HNO_2, formed by photolysis ($HN_3 + h\nu \rightarrow N_2 + NH$; $NH + O_2 \rightarrow HNO_2$). The apparent energy of activation was $1 \cdot 5 \pm 0 \cdot 1$ kcal mole^{-1}. The method of initiation is not of general application. However, it appears that diffusion of gases into solid argon (for example) is rapid when the temperature is about half the melting-point, so that reactants might be brought together in solid solution by diffusion in a few seconds, and reactions followed spectroscopically.

Many of the techniques of observing fast reactions have been combined with the use of low temperatures. For example, a stopped-flow apparatus (see p. 47) which will work at temperatures down to $-120°$ has been developed[17]; reactions with half-lives of a few milliseconds can be observed. The range of rates accessible to study is thus increased by a factor of the order of 10^4, and a given reaction can be studied over a very long temperature range (p. 54). A quenching method (see p. 24) has been adapted for use down to $-100°$.[18] Flash and fluorescence techniques, nuclear magnetic resonance, electron spin resonance, and ultrasonic relaxation also lend themselves to low-temperature work; these methods have the advantage that the reactions do not have to be initiated by mixing.

Applicability. Low-temperature methods are adaptable, in that they allow the rates of many reactions to be reduced until some temperature is found at which they are convenient to measure. Moreover, as the last paragraph shows, long ranges of temperature may be used. In mechanistic investigations, concurrent or consecutive reactions can be isolated and studied at different temperatures. Much may be done with simple equipment. Physical methods of following reactions are convenient, but chemical methods are

[17] Allen, Brook and Caldin, *Trans. Faraday Soc.* 1960, **56**, 788 (apparatus); for results, see pp. 273–274.

[18] (*a*) Stranks, *Discuss. Faraday Soc.* 1960, **29**, 74 (ferrocene–ferrocinium exchange). (*b*) Cf. Swinehart, Rogers and Taube, *J. Chem. Phys.* 1963, **38**, 398 (exchange of $CH_3^{18}OH$ between solvent and solvated Mg^{++} ions in methanol at $-82 \cdot 5°$ and $-96 \cdot 9°$).

not ruled out.[12] The main limitation is that imposed by the the freezing-point of the solvent; this greatly restricts the application of these methods to aqueous solutions.

The thermal maximum method[19]

The principle of this method is as follows. If an exothermic reaction takes place in an insulated vessel, the temperature will rise to a steady value T_0 (Fig. 2.3). If the reaction takes place in a vessel which is losing heat to its surroundings under controlled conditions, the temperature will rise to a maximum T_m determined by the relative rates of heat production and heat loss. This maximum

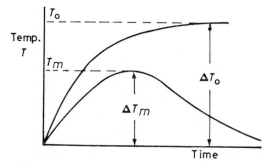

Fig. 2.3. Thermal maximum method. Plots of temperature against time (see text).

value is easier to observe than an instantaneous value. The relation between the observed value of ΔT_m and the rate constant k depends on the order of reaction. For a first-order reaction,

$$\Delta T_m / \Delta T_0 = (k/k_2)^{k_2/(k_2-k)}$$

where k_2 is the cooling constant; if ΔT_0 is not directly known, a useful empirical relation is $\Delta T_m / \Delta T_0 = A - B(k_2/k)^n$, where A, B and n are numerical constants. An accuracy of a few per cent in k is attainable for reactions with half-times down to 0·2 sec; thus the method effects a useful extension of the normal range of rates.

The apparatus is simple in construction and operation.[19a] One of

[19] (a) Bell and Clunie, Proc. Roy. Soc., A, 1952, 212, 16; (b) Bell, Gold, Hilton and Rand, Discuss. Faraday Soc. 1954, 17, 151; (c) Bell, Rand and Wynne-Jones, Trans. Faraday Soc. 1956, 52, 1093.

the reactant solutions (about 100 ml) is contained in a metal vessel, which is surrounded by water maintained thermostatically at a constant temperature and circulated rapidly by a centrifugal pump. The other reactant is contained in a glass bulb which is broken to start the reaction, or in a syringe from which it can be quickly ejected. The reaction mixture is stirred mechanically. The temperature-rise is followed by means of a thermocouple and galvanometer. To ensure that the cooling conditions are reproducible from run to run, the reaction mixture and thermostat bath are stirred at constant speeds, and the position of the stirrer and other parts of the reaction vessel are accurately fixed. The value of ΔT_0 is determined either from separate experiments in an insulated vessel, or by measuring ΔT_m for a series of increasing reaction rates and extrapolating to infinity.

The method can be applied to extend the range of ordinary measurements where the order of reaction is already known. Reactions which have been studied include the hydrolysis of esters, acid anhydrides, and acid chlorides; the neutralization of nitro-paraffins; and the hydration of acetaldehyde.

Quenching methods[20]

The principle is that the reactant solutions are mixed rapidly, and after a short time-interval the reaction is stopped by mixing the solution rapidly with a suitable quenching reagent; analysis may then be done at lesiure. The simplest form of apparatus is represented diagrammatically in Fig. 2.4. The reactant solutions are forced, by gas pressure or from hypodermic syringes, through a mixing-chamber along a tube in which the reaction occurs, then

[20] See also (a) Roughton, in *Investigation of Rates and Mechanisms of Reactions*, ed. Friess, Lewis and Weissberger (*Technique of Organic Chemistry*, vol. VIII, 2nd edn., Interscience, 1963), part II, pp. 779–781. For some applications, see (b) Pinsent, *Discuss. Faraday Soc.* 1954, **17**, 140; (c) Wahl, *Z. Elektrochem.* 1960, **64**, 90; (d) Stranks, ref. 18a; (e) Baldwin and Taube, *J. Chem. Phys.* 1960, **33**, 208. For earlier work on the reactions of hydrogen peroxide with bromine and chlorine in aqueous solution, and that of nitrite ion with aqueous sulphuric acid, see (f) Bray and Livingston, *J. Amer. Chem. Soc.* 1928, **50**, 1654; (g) Makower and Bray, *idem*, 1933, **35**, 4765; (h) Schmidt, *Z. phys. Chem.*, A, 1929, **141**, 41; 1930, **148**, 321.

into the quenching solution; a second mixing-chamber may be used for adding the quencher. The reaction time is determined by measuring the volume rate of flow and the dimensions of the tube, and can be varied by changing either of these. Times from about 2 sec to 0·1 sec can be used with very simple apparatus. Each experiment gives a point on the reaction–time curve. An apparatus in which carefully-designed mixing-chambers were used[20b] gave results reproducible to $\pm 7\%$ when the half-time was 0·4 sec; the

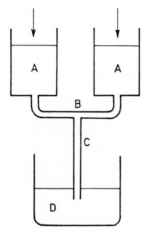

FIG. 2.4. Principle of quenching methods. A, A, reactant solutions; B, mixing chamber; C, reaction tube; D, quenching solution.

determination of the rate constant required about 25 ml. of each reactant solution.

Isotope-exchange reactions involving electron-transfer have been studied by quenching methods.[20c] An example is the exchange between permanganate and manganate ions. Neutron-irradiated permanganate solution (about 10^{-4} M) was mixed with inactive manganate solution in an apparatus resembling that shown in Fig. 2·4; the reaction was quenched after 1–10 sec by mixing with a suitable solution which either precipitated or extracted the permanganate. The rate constant (in 0·16 M NaOH aq.) was found to be 710 l mole^{-1}sec^{-1} at 0°, and the energy of activation 10·5 kcal mole^{-1}. The ferrocene–ferrocinium exchange was studied in the same way; it was too fast at 0°, but a measurable rate was found at −75°.[18a]

A measurable rate of exchange between solvent water and the solvation sheath round a cation has been observed,[20e] by mixing an aqueous solution of an aluminium salt with water containing $H_2^{18}O$, in a simple apparatus such as that shown in Fig. 2.4, and stopping the exchange by running the solution into cooled pentane. The half-time of the exchange was found to be more than 0·02 sec; the energy of activation is probably of the order of 20 kcal mole^{-1} (cf. p. 276). For the corresponding exchange of $CH_3O^{18}H$ between methanol and solvated Mg^{++} ions,[18b] the energy of activation is about 12·5 kcal mole^{-1}.

The quenching method has the advantages that it makes use only of simple apparatus, and that since the reaction is followed chemically it is possible to use standard accurate analytical techniques. On the other hand, it is applicable only when a rapid quenching reaction is available; and a series of experiments is needed to determine a reaction–time curve. If the reaction can be followed by some physical property, the rate may be more accurately measurable by one of the flow methods (chapter 3). For *ad hoc* experiments, however, or measurements where high accuracy is not needed, the simplicity of the quenching method is a strong recommendation.

The capacity-flow method[21]

The principle of this method may be illustrated with reference to Fig. 2.5. The reactant solutions A and B are fed separately at constant rates into the reaction vessel R, where they are mixed and stirred thoroughly, so that the composition of the solution is uniform during virtually the whole time of contact. After partial reaction the solution passes out through C. A steady state is reached, in which the extent of reaction depends on a balance between the rate of reaction and the rate of outflow.

[21] (a) Denbigh and Page, *Discuss. Faraday Soc.* 1954, **17**, 145; (b) Buss and Taylor, *J. Amer. Chem. Soc.* 1960, **82**, 5991; (c) Hammett *et al.*, *J. Amer. Chem. Soc.* 1950, **72**, 280, 283, 287; (d) Page, *Trans. Faraday Soc.* 1953, **49**, 1033.

Consider a second-order reaction, $A + B \xrightarrow{k} C$. Let the concentrations in the reaction vessel be a, b, c. If the rate of outflow in litres per second is u, the number of moles of C leaving the vessel per second is uc. The rate of production of C is kab per litre, or $Vkab$ if the volume of the reaction vessel is V. In the steady state, the concentration of C is stationary, and so $Vkab = uc$, whence

$$k = uc/Vab$$

This equation is in terms of the steady-state concentrations of the

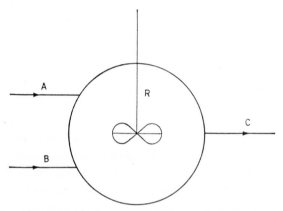

Fig. 2.5. Principle of the capacity-flow method. A, B, entry of reactant solutions; R, reaction vessel; C, exit.

reactants. In terms of their initial concentrations (a_o, b_o) and flow rates (u_a, u_b), the equation turns out to be

$$k = cu^3/V(a_o u_a - uc)(b_o u_b - uc)$$

The rate constant k can thus be found from a knowledge of the steady-state value of c (which may be determined by physical methods such as photometry or emf's, or by quenching followed by analysis) the initial values of a and b, and the flow rates. It is not necessary to analyse a reaction–time curve; this is an advantage in dealing with complex reactions where the differential equations would be intractable. On the other hand, the method is at a certain disadvantage in determining orders of reaction, since each experiment refers only to a single set of concentrations. It is probably most useful in extending the observable range of rates for reactions whose order is already known. The range of reaction times (V/u) that can be conveniently studied is about 1 to 4000 sec; rate constants up to about 10 l mole^{-1}sec^{-1} have been determined. The accuracy depends largely on the constancy of the flow rate. With special care (e.g. if a piston drive is used) the variation may be reduced to $\pm 0.1\%$; the rate constant can then be determined within $\pm 1\%$.[21c]

Reactions that have been studied by the capacity-flow method include the hydrolysis of esters,[21d] the bromination of acetone,[21d] and the iodination of 2,4-dichlorophenol.[21c] A special feature of the method is that reaction intermediates can be conveniently studied, for instance the violet complex $FeS_2O_3^+$ which is formed in the reaction between ferric and thiosulphate ions.[21e]

Electrolytic addition of reagent[22]

The principle here is somewhat similar to that of the capacity-flow method. A reagent is added at a constant rate, without diluting the solution; this may be achieved by electrolytic generation. A steady state is set up. Consider the first-order reaction: A → products. Let the concentration of A at time t be a. If A is added at a constant rate p (moles per second) the rate of disappearance of A is

$$-da/dt = ka - p$$

In the steady state, $da/dt = 0$, and so if the concentration of A is then a_s,

$$k = p/a_s$$

The method may be applied to second-order reactions where one reactant is in large excess, such as the reaction of nitroethane with hydroxide ions. The time of mixing can be reduced to about 0.01 sec by vigorous stirring. The maximum rate that can be observed depends also on the minimum concentration of A that can be measured. If this is of the order of 10^{-6} M, reactions with half-times down to about 0.07 sec can be studied.

[22] Pearson and Piette, J. Amer. Chem. Soc. 1954, 76, 3087; cf. ref. 2c.

CHAPTER 3

Flow Methods

General Introduction

Two reactant solutions can be mixed within about 10^{-3} sec by bringing together rapid streams of the two solutions in a well-designed mixing chamber. The subsequent course of the reaction in the mixed solution may be followed by one of several procedures, depending on how quickly the observations can be made and how much solution is available. There are thus three flow techniques, known as the continuous-flow, accelerated-flow, and stopped-flow methods.[1] These will be described in turn. A fourth, which may be called the baffle method, is included in this chapter because the technical problems it involves are in some ways similar to those of flow methods. The development of these methods since the pioneer work of 1923 has been marked by thorough tests of reliability and careful thought about design.

THE CONTINUOUS-FLOW METHOD

Principles

The principle, first applied to solutions by Hartridge and Roughton,[2] is illustrated in Fig. 3.1. The two reactant solutions are forced into a mixing chamber, and the mixed solution passes down an observation-tube with a velocity (u) of several metres per second. A distance d from the mixing-chamber evidently corresponds to a time d/u. The extent of reaction at various distances along the

[1] For a review see Roughton and Chance, in *Investigation of Rates and Mechanisms of Reactions*, ed. Friess, Lewis and Weissberger (Interscience, 1963), part II, chapter 14.
[2] Hartridge and Roughton, *Proc. Roy. Soc.*, A, 1923, **104**, 376.

observation-tube (corresponding to various times) is found by measuring the optical density, electrical conductivity, or some other physical property of the solution.[3] The flow velocity is found from the bore of the tube and the volume delivered over a measured time interval. With a flow velocity of ten metres per second, which is not difficult to produce, a distance of 1 cm corresponds to 10^{-3} sec, and reactions with half-times of this order can be observed.[4] The

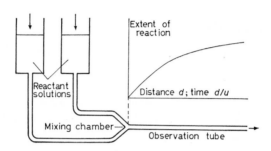

Fig. 3.1. Principle of continuous-flow method.

upper limit is about 0·1 sec (p. 41).[5] The technique is also applicable to reactions that can be initiated photochemically, by passing a stream of solution through an illuminated region.[6]

[3] If there is no convenient physical method of following the reaction, chemical analysis must be used, and the nearest alternative to the flow methods here described is the quenching method (p. 24). This resembles the flow methods insofar as the reaction is initiated by rapid mixing, and short measurable time-intervals are obtained by a streaming technique; but each experiment gives only one point on the reaction-time curve, instead of the whole curve.

[4] As a variant, the observations can all be made at a fixed distance, with a series of different flow velocities. Since, however, these must not be too low for turbulence (see p. 39), the range is restricted. Cf. (a) Millikan, *Proc. Roy. Soc.*, A, 1936, **155**, 277; (b) Bünau, De Maeyer and Matthias, *Z. Elektrochem.* 1960, **64**, 14; and ref. 21.

[5] By interposing dead spaces between the mixing chamber and the point of observation, the time can be extended to several minutes (Hartridge and Roughton, *Proc. Camb. Phil. Soc.* 1926, **23**, 450), but the whole reaction cannot then be followed in a single run: cf. the capacity-flow method (p. 26).

[6] Hartridge and Roughton, *Proc., Roy. Soc.*, B, 1923, **94**, 336.

Mixing must be fast and efficient, and much attention has been given to the design of mixing chambers. [7] An ordinary three-way glass T-tap of capillary bore can be used for reactions with half-times of 10 msec or more. For faster reactions it is desirable to use four or more jets, 0·5 to 1 mm in diameter, arranged semi-tangentially, so that the liquid acquires a rotary motion which accelerates mixing (Fig. 3.2). Such mixing-chambers may be made in glass, plastic, or metal, and cemented to the observation tube. Mixing is effectively complete within one or two milliseconds after leaving such a mixing chamber (see below, p. 37).[8]

The method of observation need not be rapid; it is enough

FIG. 3.2. Four-jet mixing chamber.

if an observation can be made in a few seconds. This is the special advantage of the continuous-flow over other flow techniques. Besides photometry,[9] much use has been made of thermal measurements[10]; electrical conductivity[11] and emf

[7] Roughton, in *Investigation of Rates and Mechanisms of Reactions*, ed. Friess, Lewis and Weissberger (Interscience, 1963), Part II, pp. 709–711.

[8] For a more elaborate 24-jet mixer, see ref. 52.

[9] See below, pp. 35, 41.

[10] See below, p. 34.

[11] Platinum wires may be sealed into the observation tube. (a) Prince, *Trans. Faraday Soc.* 1958, **54**, 838, and (b) *Z. Elektrochem.* 1960, **64**, 13; (c) Pearson, Meeker and Basolo, *J. Amer. Chem. Soc.* 1956, **78**, 709 (see p. 36); (d) Saal, *Rec. Trav. Chim.* 1928, **47**, 73, 264; (e) Schudusikov and Shilov, *J. Phys. Chem. U.R.S.S.* 1945, **19**, 405, and (f) *Acta Phys. Chem. U.R.S.S.* **20**, 667. Cf. also Sirs, ref. 59.

measurements[12] have also been employed, and the use of e.s.r. has been suggested.[13]

The more time the observations require, however, the more liquid is needed. If the reagents are available only in small quantities, or if the solvent has to be specially purified, the volume of liquid consumed is an important factor. In the development of continuous-flow apparatus, mainly by Roughton and his associates, the volume has been progressively reduced, by using faster methods of observation and narrower observation-tubes. The performances of several types of apparatus are given in Table 3.1. In the early work,[2] the diameter of the tube was 5 mm and the observations were made visually with a reversion spectroscope; the volume of each reagent solution for a single experiment was 3–4 litres, and gas pressure was used to force the solutions out of the reservoirs. This volume can be reduced to 300–500 ml if the diameter of the tube is reduced to 2 mm and observations are made by means of a thermocouple[14] or a commercial spectrophotometer.[15] By use of a photocell as detector, and a 1-mm observation tube, the volume has been further reduced to 20–30 ml[16]; and by adding automatic scanning and recording, it can be brought down to about 6 ml.[17] With these smaller volumes, mechanically-operated hypodermic syringes can be used to produce the flow. However, when such rapid and sensitive techniques of observation as photoelectric photometry are available, the stopped-flow method has decided advantages (p. 43).

The continuous-flow method now has its most useful applications where each observation takes a few seconds, either because the response of the detector is relatively slow or because it cannot

[12] Silver, platinum, and silver–silver iodide electrodes were used by Saal, (a) Rec. Trav. Chim. 1928, 47, 73, 264, 385. A glass electrode has been used by (b) Meier and Schwarzenbach, Helv. chim. Acta, 1957, 40, 907; cf. Sirs, ref. 58.
[13] Chance, ref. 43; cf. Piette, in N.m.r. and E.s.r. Spectroscopy, ed. Varian Associates (Pergamon Press, 1960), p. 210.
[14] Roughton, ref. 1, p. 760. Cf. below, p. 34.
[15] Dalziel, ref. 20a. Cf. Roughton, Proc. Roy. Soc., A, 1936, 155, 269.
[16] Millikan, Proc. Roy. Soc. A, 1936, 155, 277.
[17] (a) Caldin and Trowse, Discuss. Faraday Soc. 1954, 17, 133; (b) Trowse and Lindley, unpublished work.

TABLE 3.1

Performance of some types of flow apparatus

Type of apparatus	Authors	Date	Detector	Temp. range	Volume per curve (ml)	Least $t_{1/2}$ (msec)	Max. 2nd-order k (1 mole^{-1} sec^{-1})	Precision ($\pm$%)	Ref.
Continuous flow	Hartridge and Roughton	1923	Reversion spectroscope		3000	0·3			2
	Millikan	1936	Selenium cell		20				16
	Dalziel	1953	Spectro-photometer	10°–30°	500	5	5×10^6	3	20
	Trowse	1954	Photomultiplier	10°–50°	6	0·5	3×10^4	2	17
	Roughton et al.	1956	Thermocouple	0°–40°	500	2	2×10^4	7	19
	Pearson et al.	1956	Conductivity		100	10	10^5	5	11c
Accelerated flow	Chance	1951	Photocell		0·1	1	2×10^7		46, 47
Stopped flow	Chance	1951	Photocell		0·1	4			50
	Gibson	1954	Photomultiplier	7°–43°	0·15	3	7×10^7	2	51b
	Gibson	1962	Photomultiplier	0°–40°	0·6	2	7×10^7	2	59
	Sirs	1958	Conductivity	0°–25°	0·5	ca.5	ca. 10^4	5	58
	Sirs	1958	Emf	0°–50°	0·5	50			
	Prince	1960	Conductivity		0·6	5	3×10^5	2	11a, b
	Allen, Brook and Caldin	1960	Photomultiplier	–120°–+25°	1·7	3	8×10^4	2	60
Baffle	Below, Connick and Coppel	1958	Photomultiplier	14°–30°	30	ca.15	$1·4 \times 10^3$		61

conveniently be recorded automatically. Three particular types of apparatus, out of the many that have been developed, may be of general interest, since they are not difficult to construct or operate, and should be quite widely applicable.

Some types of continuous-flow apparatus

Thermal method: Roughton's apparatus

In this technique,[18, 19] the small temperature-changes along the observation tube are measured. The apparatus is illustrated in Fig. 3.3. The reactant solutions are forced by gas pressure through a four-jet mixing chamber (p. 31) along a 2-mm glass observation tube, 10 cm long. The temperature-change at any point in this tube can be observed by means of a thermo-junction whose position is adjusted by a rack and pinion. The reference junction is immersed in the thermostat bath which surrounds the reservoirs and obser-vation tube and is maintained to about ± 0.002 degrees. A wider tube is attached to the top of the observation tube so that the temperature rise of the completed reaction can be found if necessary. Less than four seconds is required to take a reading, with the help of a short-period galvanometer and optical amplifier. About twelve readings are taken in an experiment. For this about 300 ml of each solution is needed; further development may reduce this amount to 5–15 ml. The time-range within which readings can be obtained is 0.5 to 35 msec after mixing; reactions with half-times down to 2 msec can be studied. Readings are reproducible to $\pm 0.001°$. Rate constants are reproducible to $\pm 7\%$, provided that the total temperature rise is greater than about 0.03 degrees (the maximum for the apparatus described is 0.22 degrees). Thus even if the heat of reaction is as low as 1 kcal mole^{-1}, the concentration of the solutions need only be about 0.03 M.

[18] For fuller descriptions see (a) Roughton, in *Investigation of Rates and Mechanisms of Reactions*, ref. 1, pp. 758–776; (b) Pearson, Pinsent and Roughton, *Discuss. Faraday Soc.* 1954, **17**, 141. Results are given by the same authors in (c) *Trans. Faraday Soc.* 1956, **52**, 1512 ($CO_2 + OH^-$); (d) *ibid.*, p. 1594 ($CO_2 + NH_3$).

[19] On the thermal method see also (a) Roughton, *J. Amer. Chem. Soc.* 1941, **63**, 2930; (b) LaMer and Read, *idem*, 1930, **52**, 3098; (c) Lifshitz and Perlmutter-Hayman, *J. Phys. Chem.* 1960, **64**, 1663.

This method, though not of the highest accuracy, has the great advantages that it is applicable to many reactions (if reagents and solvent are available in sufficient quantity) and that good thermostat control is easy to arrange. The only specialized part of the equipment, apart from the mixing-chamber, is the short-period galvanometer.

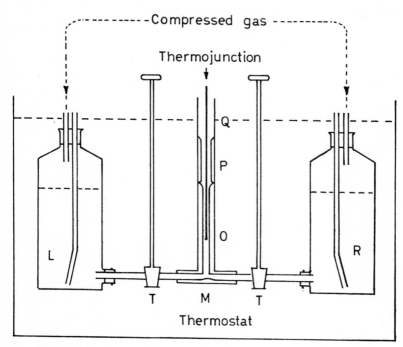

Fig. 3.3. Thermal continuous-flow apparatus of Roughton. L, R, containers; T, taps; M, mixing chamber; O, observation tube. From *Investigation of Rates and Mechanisms of Reactions* (ref. 1) by permission.

Spectrophotometric method: Dalziel's apparatus

An apparatus that uses a standard Beckmann spectrophotometer as detector has been described by Dalziel.[20] A horizontal glass

[20] (a) Dalziel, *Biochem. J.* 1953, **55**, 79, 90; (b) *Discuss. Faraday Soc.* 1954, **17**, 128; (c) Roughton, ref. 7, pp. 745–748. A similar apparatus is described by (d) Davis and MacF. Smith, *Canad. J. Chem.* 1962, **40**, 1836; cf. also refs. 68a, 68c.

observation tube, 30 cm long and 2 mm in internal diameter, is held in a rectangular metal block, which can be moved across the cell compartment of the spectrophotometer; readings of optical density are taken in the usual way at a series of positions. The mixing chamber is made by drilling two holes near the end of the observation tube. The reactant solutions are forced into the mixing chamber from reservoirs by gas pressure (2–3 atm). Each run requires about 500 ml of each reactant. Reactions with half-times down to about 5 msec can be studied. Rate constants are reproducible to 2–3%, if the temperature is constant to 0·1°. This degree of thermostatting is not difficult to achieve in the temperature range 10–30°; it is enough to have a constant-temperature bath surrounding the reservoirs, and heating elements in the metal block. Such an apparatus has the considerable merit of simplicity in operation, and does not require a knowledge of electronics. It may be used for any reaction that leads to a change of absorption in the visible or ultraviolet, provided that sufficient quantities of reagents and solvent are available.

Conductivity method: simple apparatus

Ionic reactions with half-times from 10 msec to a few seconds can be studied with a very simple conductivity apparatus.[21]. It consists of a two-jet plastic mixing chamber, and a 1-mm observation tube with a single pair of platinum electrodes set in its walls at some distance from the mixing-chamber. Solutions are delivered from aspirator bottles under pressure at a series of different rates, and for each flow rate the conductivity is determined. About 100 ml of each solution is used in obtaining five observations, enough for a determination of the rate constant to within ±5%. The temperature is controlled by immersing the reservoirs in a thermostat, from which water is pumped to a jacket surrounding the observation tube.

Tests of the continuous-flow method

It was already realized by Hartridge and Roughton in their early work that the reliability of the continuous-flow method depends

[21] Pearson, Meeker and Basolo, ref. 11c.

upon two conditions: the mixing must be efficient and the character of the flow must be such that the composition of the liquid is effectively uniform at any cross-section of the observation tube. Careful attention has been given to these two points.[22]

Efficiency of mixing

The time required for effectively complete mixing must be small in comparison with the half-time of the reaction under investigation. (This applies to all flow methods.) Tests on the rate of mixing have been of two types. In the 'chemical' tests, the extent of a very fast reaction, such as that between hydrogen and hydroxyl ions or iodine and thiosulphate, is determined at points close to the mixing chamber; this may be done by the thermal method[23] or by photometry.[24] In the 'physical' tests, two liquids of different refractive index (such as water and aqueous ammonium sulphate) are mixed, and the approach to optical homogeneity is observed, either by a 'schlieren' technique[25] or by photometry.[26] The results show that, with the apparatus and flow rates commonly used, mixing (as measured by either type of test) is completed to the extent of 97–98% within a millisecond after leaving the mixing-chamber.[27] This is about the shortest time at which observations are reliable with most mixing-chambers.

The apparent rate constant of a reaction must be affected by incomplete mixing, because the concentrations are not the same as they would be if mixing were complete, and it is of interest to make a numerical estimate of the error introduced in this way. To do this we need a more detailed model of the mixing process. This is envisaged by Trowse[26] as taking place in two stages. The first, which takes place in the mixing chamber, is pictured as a macroscopic process of mechanical mixing, giving a uniform dispersion of

[22] Roughton, ref. 1, pp. 711–725.
[23] (a) Roughton and Millikan, *Proc. Roy. Soc.*, A, 1936, **155**, 258; (b) Millikan, *ibid.*, 277; (c) Dalziel, ref. 20a.
[24] (a) Hartridge and Roughton, ref. 2; (b) Chance, *J. Franklin Inst.* 1940, **229**, 737; and other workers.
[25] Dubois, *J. Biol. Chem.* 1941, **137**, 123.
[26] (a) Trowse, Ph.D. Thesis, Leeds, 1952; cf. Caldin and Trowse, ref. 17a.
[27] A table of detailed results is given by Roughton in ref. 1, p. 713.

4

minute blocks of the two solutions; the second is a microscopic process in the observation tube, in which diffusion produces a homogeneous solution. A precise definition of 'extent of mixing' can then be given; the product on mixing solutions A and B may be said to be '$x\%$ mixed' if $x\%$ of it consists of a homogeneous solution, and the rest consists of A and B dispersed in this solution. From his experiments on the optical density near the mixing-chamber when liquids of different refractive index were mixed, Trowse obtained linear plots of log (% unmixed) against time, the slope and position depending on the mixing-chamber. From this logarithmic relation it is possible to calculate how the concentrations of reagents and products in the solution vary with time when a reaction occurs with a given rate law; this calculation was carried through for first-order reactions, and an explicit equation derived.[28] The error decreases as the time of reaction increases. For half-times greater than 1 msec, it was found to be less than 1%. This applies to a particular apparatus, but can probably be regarded as typical of the 4-jet mixing chambers listed by Roughton.[27] The upshot is that as far as mixing is concerned, rate constants determined by means of the usual types of flow apparatus (including stopped-flow) may be taken as reliable for half-times down to about a millisecond.

Character of flow in the observation tube

If the time elapsed is to be linearly related to the distance along the observation tube, a necessary condition is that the composition of the liquid shall be effectively uniform at any cross-section of the tube. Ideally this would require 'mass' flow, with velocity uniform at all points across the tube. This cannot occur, because of retardation of the flow at the wall; there will always be a maximum velocity

[28] The true rate constant k is related to the apparent rate constant k_a by the equation:

$$k_a/k = 1 + (\beta - k)(1 - \alpha) \exp(-\beta t)/[k(1 - \alpha) \exp(-\beta t) + (\alpha k - \beta) \exp(-kt)]$$

where α and β are derived from the linear plots of log(% unmixed) against time, and are defined by the equation:

$$V/V_0 = 1 - (1 - \alpha) \exp(-\beta t)$$

Here V is the volume of homogeneous solution contained in a total volume V_0.

at the centre of the tube. If the flow is 'laminar' ('stream-line'), the velocity profile across a diameter is parabolic, and the ratio of the maximum velocity at the centre to the mean velocity is 2. A closer approach to mass flow is 'turbulent' flow, in which the distribution of velocity across the tube is more uniform, the ratio of maximum to mean velocity being about 1·25 for high rates of flow.[29] Moreover, turbulent flow is accompanied by eddying, which will lead to improved mixing of the solution.

The condition for turbulence is that the velocity must be above a critical value u_c(cm/sec), which has been empirically found to be related to the diameter d of the tube (cm) and the density ρ(g/ml) and viscosity η (poise) of the liquid, by the equation[29] $u_c = N_R\eta/\rho d$. The numerical factor N_R, known as Reynolds' number, is about 2000 for fairly short tubes with a stream-line entry. According to this equation, the critical velocity for water at 20° in a tube of 1 mm diameter is about 2 metres per second. Since the liquid at entry is already in violent motion, the true critical velocity will be less than this. It will be proportionately smaller for wider tubes.

The velocity of flow in most continuous-flow experiments is well above the critical values given by Reynolds' formula, and we can assume that the flow is turbulent. Confirmation of this is provided by the experiments of Chance on the pressure-drop in tubes of various lengths and bores; he found that the pressure-drop is nearly proportional to the square of the velocity, and independent of the bore, as predicted for turbulent flow.[30] Near the mixing-chamber, the flow probably approximates still more closely to mass flow.

Numerical calculations of the error in the rate constant k due to deviations from mass flow have been made by several authors, by taking into account the different velocities at different distances from the centre of the tube.[31, 32, 33] The calculated error in k for

[29] Dodge and Thompson, *Fluid Mechanics* (McGraw Hill, New York, 1937), chapters 8 and 9.
[30] Chance, *J. Franklin Inst.* 1940, **229**, 455. The results enable one to estimate the pressure required for a given design of apparatus.
[31] Roughton and Millikan, *Proc. Roy. Soc.*, A, 1936, **155**, 258.
[32] Dalziel, ref. 20a, b.
[33] Trowse, ref. 26.

turbulent flow (which is considerably less than for laminar flow) is in the region of -5%, both for first-order and second-order reactions.[34] The actual error will be smaller than this, because of the favourable conditions near the mixing-chamber and the effect of eddying during turbulent flow. If we take the observed value of k as 2% less than the true value, we are unlikely to be in error by more than $\pm 2\%$. This uncertainty, incidentally, lies within the standard deviation of most of the experimental results, which is about $\pm 5\%$.

Empirical tests

Errors due to deviations from mass flow and to imperfect mixing would both be expected to increase with decrease of flow velocity, and if the errors were appreciable we should expect a variation of the apparent rate constant; this has not been observed.[35] The rate constant determined by the continuous-flow method for the reaction $CO_2 + OH^- \rightarrow HCO_3^-$ can be compared with the value found by a conventional method, or by stopped-flow methods (in which mass flow is much more nearly realized); the results agree within about $\pm 5\%$.[36] Similar agreement between continuous-flow and stopped-flow methods is found for other reactions.[37, 38] The 'slit-length' error due to the finite length of tube observed has been found[39] to be negligible, in agreement with calculations.[40]

The scope of the continuous-flow method

The continuous-flow method is most useful when a reaction has to be followed by a detector whose response is slow (p. 31), otherwise the stopped-flow method (p. 43) is usually preferable. The shortest half-time that can be determined by the continuous-flow method is

[34] Roughton, in ref. 1, p. 718.
[35] Roughton, ref. 1, pp. 720–722.
[36] See the Arrhenius plot derived from measurements by five different methods given by Sirs, *Trans. Faraday Soc.* 1958, **54**, p. 206.
[37] Sirs, ref. 58 ($H^+ + HCO_3^-$).
[38] Caldin and Long, *Proc. Roy. Soc. A*, 1955, **228**, 263.
[39] Dalziel, ref. 20*b*.
[40] Cf. Roughton, ref. 1, pp. 722–724; Chance, ref. 46*b*.

in the region of one millisecond.[41] The longest half-time is fixed by the minimum velocity for turbulent flow (p. 39) and is in the region of 0·1 sec. The maximum and minimum rate constants that can be determined depend also on the magnitude of the change in optical density or other property, and the sensitivity of the detector (see Table 3.1); an explicit equation for the maximum value has been derived by Chance.[42] The most sensitive photometric and fluorimetric techniques now permit the use of solutions as dilute as 10^{-9} M, and this should allow the measurement of second-order rate constants as high as 10^8 l mole^{-1}sec^{-1}.[43]

The uncertainty in the rate constant is generally put at about $\pm 5\%$, though with automatic scanning and recording the standard deviation can be reduced to $\pm 2\%$ or less.[44] Thermostatic control can be made adequate from about $0°$ to about $50°$. The volume of solution used depends on the time required for taking a reading (Table 3.1). The method can be adapted to special studies of inter-mediates, in enzyme reactions for example, by recirculation techniques[45]; besides the usual properties, magnetic susceptibility and electron-spin resonance may then be studied.[43]

THE ACCELERATED-FLOW METHOD

In this method, the general arrangement resembles that of the continuous-flow method (Fig. 3.1), except that observations are made at a fixed point close to the mixing chamber, while the velocity of the liquid is varied continuously. The method of observation must be a rapid one such as photometry. In Chance's apparatus (Fig. 3.4), the reactant solutions are contained in hypodermic syringes, whose plungers are driven manually, by pressing on a sliding block: a short sharp push produces accelerated flow for about 0·1 sec. The time elapsing before observation is proportional to the reciprocal of the rate of flow, and therefore decreases steadily.

[41] To reduce this by a factor of 10 would need driving pressures of the order of 100 atm, which would raise considerable difficulties.
[42] (a) Chance, *Disc. Faraday Soc.* 1954, **17**, 120; cf. (b) Millikan, *Proc. Roy. Soc.*, A, 1936, **155**, 277.
[43] Chance, *Z. Elektrochem.* 1960, **64**, 7.
[44] Trowse, ref. 26.
[45] Chance, *Disc. Faraday Soc.* 1954, **17**, 123.

A voltage proportional to the rate of flow can be generated by link-ing the sliding block by a chain and pulley to a rotary potentiometer connected to appropriate differentiating circuits. This voltage is applied to the X-plates of a cathode-ray oscillograph, while to the Y-plates is applied a voltage controlled by the photometer response. The curve traced on a the screen is photographed, and can be

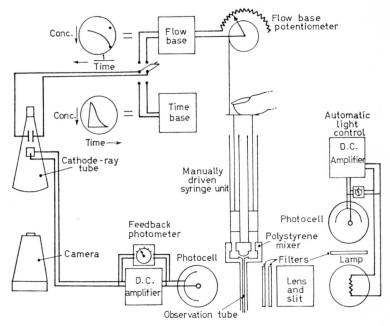

Fig. 3.4. Accelerated-flow apparatus of Chance (from ref. 46a).

measured at leisure, and the reaction–time curve deduced. The run can easily be repeated, and requires only 0·1 ml of each solution.

The shortest half-time that can be measured by the accelerated-flow method is about one millisecond, and is thus comparable with that for the continuous-flow method. However, the small volume of solution required constitutes a great advantage when reagents are available only in small quantities. It was for this reason that the method was developed by Chance,[46, 47] who combined it with

[46] (a) Chance, J. Franklin Inst. 1940, 229, 455; (b) ibid., 613; (c) ibid., 737.
[47] (a) Chance, Rev. Sci. Instr. 1951, 22, 619; (b) ref. 7, pp. 728 seq.

sensitive photometric techniques, and evolved a versatile apparatus which was used with great success during the years 1946–50 in studying reactions of catalase and peroxidase (p. 55).

With Chance's apparatus the stopped-flow technique (below) could also be used, but the stoppage of the fluid took several milliseconds, and the fastest reactions could not be investigated in this way. The introduction of a better stopping device has, however, reduced the minimum half-time that can be observed to a few milliseconds. The great advantages of the accelerated-flow method are therefore possessed also by the current versions of the stopped-flow method, which moreover, use simpler electronic circuits.[49]

THE STOPPED-FLOW METHOD

Principles

In this technique, two reactant solutions are rapidly mixed by being forced through a mixing chamber, and the mixed solution flows down a tube, as in Fig. 3.1 (p. 30). The flow is suddenly stopped so that the solution comes to rest within a millisecond or two. The element of solution that comes to rest at (say) 1 cm from the mixing-chamber will have been mixed for a few milliseconds. The reaction in this fixed element of solution is followed by making observations at this point, by some rapid method such as photoelectric photometry. The response may be applied to a cathode-ray oscillograph; with the help of a time-base, a curve representing the extent of reaction against time may be displayed on the screen. If the reaction is slow enough, a pen recorder may be used, or even visual readings of a meter. The time-scale thus extends from a millisecond up to several minutes, and is continuous with that available to conventional techniques.[50]

[49] Errors due to deviations from ideal mass flow (p. 38) will be greater for the accelerated-flow than for the continuous-flow method, but less for the stopped-flow method.

[50] The stopped-flow method was first used by (a) Roughton, *Proc. Roy. Soc.,B*, 1934, **115**, 473, for reaction times of *ca.* 10 sec. It was developed for reaction times of a few milliseconds by (b) Chance, *J. Franklin Inst.* 1940, **229**, 455, 613, 737, along with the accelerated-flow method; for a description of the combined apparatus, see (c) Chance, ref. 1, pp. 733 *seq.*; (d) Chance, ref. 47; cf. fig. 3.4. The wider use of the stopped-flow method dates from Gibson's modification (below).

The efficient operation of a stopped-flow apparatus depends on several factors. The reactant solutions must be thoroughly mixed; the mixing-chamber must therefore be properly designed, in the light of the investigations made on continuous-flow methods (p. 37), and the flow velocity must be adequate. The observation point must be some millimetres from the mixing-chamber, to ensure that mixing is complete; but not too far away, since the lost time between mixing and observation must be minimized. Finally, the flow must be stopped very quickly, for the following reason. The efficiency of mixing falls if the flow is too slow; consequently if the rate of flow were to be decreased gradually, the liquid which ultimately came to rest at the observation point might be incompletely mixed, and the apparent reaction rate would initially be too low. Moreover, the more sudden the stoppage, the faster the reactions that can be observed.

Practical designs for stopped-flow apparatus

The stopped-flow method owes its wide adoption to the stopping device due to Gibson.[51] A small piston at the end of the observation tube (Fig. 3.5) is pushed along by the reaction mixture, and

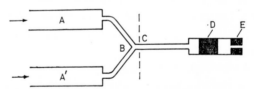

FIG. 3.5. Stopped-flow method: Gibson's stopping device (schematic). A, A′, reactant solutions; B, mixing chamber; C, point of observation; D, stopping-piston.

is suddenly stopped by coming up against a seating, or an external stop. This simple arrangement is extremely effective; the flow is stopped in 1–2 msec.

The apparatus used by Gibson has been the prototype of most of

[51] (a) Gibson, J. Physiol. 1952, 117, 49P; (b) Discuss. Faraday Soc. 1954,; 17, 137; (c) Gibson and Roughton, Proc. Roy. Soc., B, 1955, 143, 310; (d) Gibson and Antonini, Biochem. J., 1960, 77, 328; (e) Gibson and Greenwood, Biochem. J. 1963, 86, 541.

the stopped-flow machines now in existence. It is shown diagram-matically in Fig. 3.6a. The reactant solutions are contained in hypo-dermic syringes (2 ml) whose plungers are driven manually by means of a block sliding between guides. The mixing chamber is of perspex and has two sets of four tangentially-arranged jets.[52] The observation tube is 2 mm in diameter. It leads to a cylinder with a light perspex piston, which comes up against a seating and so stops the flow.[53] The liquid is observed at a point 8 mm from the mixing chamber; the time between mixing and observation, with a flow velocity of about 5 metres per second, is about 3 msec. Observations are made photometrically. The light-source is a lamp with filters, or a monochromator, and the detector is a photomultiplier, whose output is applied to an oscillograph with a time-base; the trace on the screen is photographed (Fig. 3.6b). Optical densities recorded are reproducible to about $\pm 1\%$. Each run requires about 0·15 ml of each reactant solution. Reactions with half-times down to a few milliseconds can be studied. The temperature is controlled by enclosing the driving syringes in steel blocks through which water is circulated; or the whole apparatus may be immersed in a thermostat.[54] The flow velocity and stopping-time can be deter-mined with the aid of a triangular vane attached to the stopping-piston; the movement of the piston causes the vane to move across the path of a beam of light falling on a photocell, whose response can be displayed on the oscillograph screen.[55]

Methods of observation must be adapted to the reaction under investigation. The simple spectrophotometric system described

[52] Cf. p. 31. In some later work a more elaborate mixing arrangement has been used: (a) Gibson, Fanelli and Antonini, Z. Elektrochem. 1960, 64, 4. Cf. (b) Chance, ref. 45.

[53] Alternatively the observation tube may lead to a 1-ml hypodermic syringe whose plunger comes up against an external stop (Sirs, Trans. Faraday Soc. 1958, 54, 201). It has been found equally effective to arrest (by means of a rigid stop) the block which drives the plungers of the syringes containing the reactant solutions (Prince, Z. Elektrochem. 1960, 64, 13).

[54] Prince, ref. 53; Sirs, ref. 58.

[55] Instead of the vane, one may use a magnet moving inside a solenoid (cf. ref. 60a below); or Chance's device of a rotary potentiometer attached by a chain to the sliding block (ref. 50b).

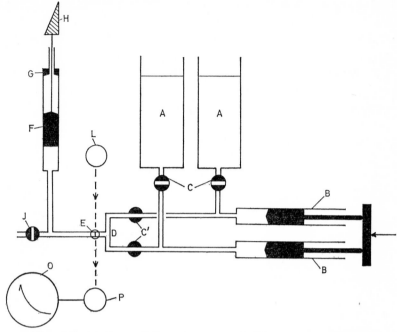

FIG. 3.6. (*a*) Stopped-flow apparatus of Gibson. A, reservoirs; B, hypodermic syringes; C, C′, valves; D, mixing chamber; E, observation window; F, stopping-piston; G, seating; H, vane attached to piston; J, exhaust valve; L, light source; P, photo-multiplier (the light-path is actually at right angles to the page); O, oscilloscope.

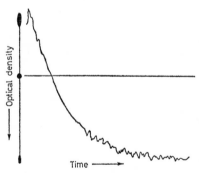

(*b*) Stopped-flow method: oscillographic record showing variation of optical density (proportional to concentration) with time, and horizontal reference line.

above is adequate for many reactions. If it is essential to use light of a narrow band of wavelengths variable at will, the lamp and filters may be replaced by a monochromator,[52] or a spectrophotometer.[56] If reactions lasting more than a few seconds are to be investigated, the light-source must be stabilized; and if the highest sensitivity is needed, it may be necessary to provide high-gain amplification.[47a] The stopped-flow method is not limited to reactions involving colour-changes; besides spectrophotometry, it has been adapted to emf measurements with a glass electrode[58] and to conductivity measurements.[59]

To increase the range of reactions that may be studied, the method has been adapted to low temperatures.[60] The reactant reservoirs, mixing-chamber, observation tube, stopping-piston and optical system are all within a stainless-steel block which is enclosed in a cryostat bath. Reaction rates may be studied down to $-120°$, provided the liquid is not so viscous that mixing is inefficient.

Reliability. It will be clear from the preceding description that the development of the stopped-flow method has benefited greatly from the experience gained from continuous-flow methods, particularly on mixing-chambers and observation techniques. The evidence that the method is reliable also depends largely on the careful tests applied to the continuous-flow methods (pp. 36 *seq*.). These tests have shown that mixing is effectively complete, with the flow velocities and mixing-chambers in practical use. The character of the flow near the mixing-chamber approximates to mass flow, and the velocity-profile for the subsequent flow does not matter; so the small systematic error which may arise from turbulent flow in the continuous flow method need not be expected in the stopped-flow method. The slit-width error is again negligible; light-beams several millimetres wide have sometimes been used when extra sensitivity was required. The path-length is normally around 2 mm, but can be extended to 2 cm, taking advantage of the fact that

[56] Gibson, ref. 51e; Wilkins, ref. 67.
[58] Sirs, *Trans. Faraday Soc.* 1958, **54**, 207.
[59] Sirs, *ibid*., 201; Prince, *ibid*., 838 and ref. 53.
[60] (a) Allen, Brook and Caldin, *Trans. Faraday Soc.* 1960, **56**, 788 (apparatus); (b) *J. Chem. Soc.* 1961, 2171 (results); cf. also (c) ref. 70; (d) Weaver, *J. Amer. Chem. Soc.* 1962, **84**, 2289.

for first-order reactions no error arises if the light-beam passes along the tube instead of across it.[51d, 11b]

The scope of the stopped-flow method

The stopped-flow method requires a rapid method of observation; this is the only important limitation on its applicability. Given a detector with a suitably short response time, it can be used for half-times as low as a few milliseconds (Table 3.1), up to seconds or even minutes at the other end of the scale. It is thus more elastic than the continuous-flow method, though its minimum half-time is a little larger. It uses much less liquid (0·1–0·2 ml); this is a great advantage when reagents or solvents are hard to make or purify. The apparatus in its normal form can be thermostatted from about 0° to 50°. It produces a photographic record of each run: replication is quick and easy. The precision of the rate constants so determined is comparable with that of conventional kinetic measurements (the standard deviation is ± 1–2%; cf. Table 3.1), and the method is free from systematic errors. In ease of construction, the apparatus is comparable with the simpler forms of continuous-flow apparatus (pp. 34, 35), but it requires in addition a photomultiplier and an oscillograph with camera, or some other rapid detecting and recording system. For accurate kinetic investigations, not involving a special study of intermediates, it is probably the best of the flow methods, except when a relatively slow method of following the reaction must be used (p. 40).

The Baffle Method[61]

In this, as in the stopped-flow method, the reactant solutions are rapidly mixed and the reaction is followed by a technique with a fast response; but the method of mixing is radically different. The reactant solutions are initially separated by a baffle, which is suddenly removed by a strong spring. The solutions are mixed to the extent of about 90% in 15 msec or so.[62] The reaction may then

---

[61] (a) Below, Connick and Coppel, *J. Amer. Chem. Soc.* 1958, **80**, 2961; (b) Connick and Coppel, *idem*, 1959, **81**, 6389.

[62] Mixing by ejection of one reactant from a hypodermic syringe is reported to take about 40 msec: Stern and Dubois, *J. Biol. Chem.* 1936, **116**, 575.

be followed photometrically with the aid of a photomultiplier and oscillograph as usual. The optical path may be made longer than in flow methods (about 6 cm); this allows more dilute solutions to be used, and compensates for the slower mixing. The method appears to have possibilities for reactions with half-times of the order of 0·1 sec and upwards, near room temperature.

REACTIONS INVESTIGATED BY FLOW METHODS

For many years these methods were exploited chiefly by workers with physiological or biochemical interests, notably by Roughton and later Gibson and others working on reactions of haemoglobin, and by Chance on enzyme reactions. Latterly, however, the range of reactions studied has begun to extend. It is illustrated in Table 3.5 (p. 56) and includes proton transfers, redox reactions, hydrolyses, the formation and dissociation of complexes, and the reactions of carbon dioxide with water, ammonia and hydroxyl ion. Some of these reactions may be briefly noticed.

The reactions of simple anions with ferric and other cations[63]

Reactions of thiocyanate ion. The reaction with ferric ion is easily followed photometrically, by reason of the intense red colour of the product; it has been studied by the baffle method.[63a] In aqueous solution at 25°, the rate law is

$$d(\text{FeSCN}^{++})/dt = k_1(\text{Fe}^{3+})(\text{SCN}^-) + k_2(\text{Fe}^{3+})(\text{SCN}^-)/(\text{H}^+)$$

This indicates that simultaneous reactions of SCN^- with Fe^{3+} and FeOH^{2+} occur. The two rate constants were determined over a range of temperatures; the enthalpies of activation are

$$\Delta H_1^* = 13\cdot0 \pm 1\cdot4 \quad \text{and} \quad \Delta H_2^* = 20\cdot2 \pm 1\cdot4\,\text{kcal mole}^{-1}$$

respectively, and the corresponding entropies of activation are -5 ± 5 and $+15 \pm 5\,\text{cal deg}^{-1}\text{mole}^{-1}$.[64] The reaction with Ni^{2+}

---

[63] (a) Connick *et al.* ref. 61 (baffle method); (b) Wendt and Strehlow, *Z. Elektrochem.* 1962, **66**, 228 (pressure-jump); (c) Matthies and Wendt, *Z. phys. Chem. (Frankfurt)*, 1961, **30**, 137 (continuous flow).

[64] The values of ΔH_1^* and ΔS_1^* in methanol, obtained from low-temperature work (p. 19, ref. 10), are about 13 kcal mole^{-1} and $+5$ cal deg^{-1} mole^{-1} respectively.

has been studied by the continuous-flow and stopped-flow methods[65]; the rate constant at 25° is in the region of 10^3 l mole^{-1}sec^{-1}. With Co^{2+} the reaction is faster ($k > 7 \times 10^3$ l mole^{-1}sec^{-1}), as predicted by ligand-field theory.

Reactions of halide and sulphate ions with ferric ions. The rate law is the same as for SCN$^-$. Results on k_1 obtained by various methods are collected in Table 3.2. The values obtained by the flow[63c] and

TABLE 3.2

Reactions of ferric ions with anions in aqueous solution

The reactions are between (1) $Fe^{+++} + X^-$ (k_1, etc.) and (2) $FeOH^{++} + X^-$ (k_2, etc.). k_1 in l mole^{-1}sec^{-1}, k_2 in sec^{-1}, at 25° (except ‡). ΔH_1^* and ΔH_2^* in kcal mole^{-1}. ΔS_1^* and ΔS_2^* in cal deg^{-1}mole^{-1}.

Anion X$^-$	$Fe^{+++} + X^-$			$FeOH^{++} + X^-$			Method	Ref.
	k_1	ΔH_1^*	ΔS_1^*	k_2	ΔH_2^*	ΔS_2^*		
F$^-$	1×10^4†	23 ± 2.5	35 ± 9	—	—	—	Low concs.	ch. 2, ref. 31
SO$_4^{--}$	6.4×10^3	18 ± 2	19 ± 7	—	—	—	Cont. flow	20d
	—	—	—	720 ± 40	—	—	Pressure-jump	63b
SCN$^-$	127 ± 10	13.0 ± 1.4	-5 ± 5	20 ± 2	20.2 ± 1.4	15 ± 5	Baffle	61
	150 ± 50	—	—	45 ± 4	—	—	Pressure-jump	63b
Cl$^-$	9.4 ± 1	16.6 ± 2	2 ± 6	18 ± 2	23.3 ± 2	25 ± 6	Baffle	61
	—	—	—	21 ± 2	—	—	Pressure-jump	63b
Br$^-$	20 ± 6‡	—	—	31 ± 8‡	—	—	Cont. flow	63c

† Extrapolated from values at 0·11°, 7·16° and 11·1°.
‡ At 22° ± 2.

baffle[63a] methods have been confirmed and extended by the pressure-jump method[63b] (p. 69). The rate constant shows some parallelism with the basicity of the anion, which decreases from top to bottom of the table. It has been suggested[66] that the first step

[65] Davies and MacFarlane Smith, *Proc. Chem. Soc.* 1961, 380.
[66] Eigen in *Advances in the Chemistry of Coordination Compounds*, ed. Kirschner (Macmillan, 1961), p. 371. For some relevant n.m.r. work, see p. 257, below.

in the reaction is the loss of a proton from the hydrated ferric ion to the anion, followed by substitution:

$$(Fe^{+++}H_2O) + F^- \rightarrow FeOH^{++} + HF \rightarrow FeF^{++} + H_2O$$

This mechanism, involving the hydrolysis of Fe^{+++}, contrasts with that suggested for the reactions of sulphate ions with less hydrolysable cations (p. 96), in which desolvation is the rate-determining step. The matter is further discussed in Chapter 12, p. 275 *seq.*

The dissociation of nickel complexes[67]

The complexes of nickel ion with ethylenediamine (en) or butylenediamine (bn) dissociate stepwise in presence of strong acid, according to equations such as:

$$[Ni(en)_3]^{2+} + 2H_3O^+ \rightarrow [Ni(en)_2(H_2O)_2]^{2+} + (en)H_2^{2+}$$

The complexes have different colours and so the reactions may be followed photometrically, with the help of a monochromator. Rates at several temperatures have been determined by the

TABLE 3.3

Dissociation of nickel (II) complexes in aqueous acid.
k in sec^{-1} at $25°$; E in $kcal\ mole^{-1}$; A in sec^{-1}.

Dissociating species	k at $25°$	E	A
$[Ni(en)_3]^{++}$	86·6	18·0	15·2
$[Ni(en)_2(H_2O)_2]^{++}$	5·2	19·8	15·3
$[Ni(en)(H_2O)_4]^{++}$	0·145	20·5	14·3
$[Ni(bn)_3]^{++}$	8·25	14·6	11·6
$[Ni(bn)_2(H_2O)_2]^{++}$	0·257	16·1	11·2
$[Ni(bn)(H_2O)_4]^{++}$	0·020	18·4	11·8
$[Ni(NH_3)(H_2O)_5]^{++}$	5·8	14·3	11·2
$[Ni(C_5H_5N)(H_2O)_5]^{++}$	38·5	16·3	13·6
$[Ni(C_2H_4NH)(H_2O)_5]^{++}$	5·0	17·2	13·3
$[Ni(NH_2CH_2CH_2NMe_2)(H_2O)_5]^{++}$	40·0	16·0	13·3
$[Ni(N_2H_4)(H_2O)_5]^{++}$	3·6	18·9	14·5

[67] (a) Ahmed and Wilkins, *J. Chem. Soc.* 1960, 2901; (b) Melson and Wilkins, *J. Chem. Soc.* 1962, 4208; cf. (c) Wilkins, *Quart. Rev. Chem. Soc.* 1962, **16**, 4.

stopped-flow method.[67a] The differences in rate between successive stages ($\mathrm{Ni(en)_3^{++}} \to \mathrm{Ni(en)_2^{++}} \to \mathrm{Ni(en)^{++}} \to \mathrm{Ni^{++}}$) appear to be due to differences in the energies of activation, which are of the order of 20 kcal mole^{-1}, comparable with that given by Taube (p. 26) for the exchange of a water molecule in $\mathrm{Al(H_2O)^{3+}}$. Both E and A are markedly lower for the butylenediamine dissociations. The rates of dissociation of the mono-complexes with a series of unidentate ligands such as ammonia have also been measured[67b]; E and A both vary along the series. Comparison with the dissociation constants shows that differences in the thermodynamic stability of the complexes are due mainly to differences in the rate of dissociation rather than that of association. The results are collected in Table 3.3.

Electron-transfer reactions[68]

The reactions of ferrous ion in water with a considerable series of ferric and other complexes have been studied by Sutin and his collaborators,[68b,c] by means of the stopped-flow and continuous-flow techniques.[68a,d] The reactions were followed spectrophotometrically; micromolar concentrations could be used. The second-order rate constants range from about 10^3 to nearly 10^7 l mole^{-1}sec^{-1} (Table 3.4). There is a general tendency for the rate to increase with the free energy change ΔG^0 in the reaction, as measured by the difference of the standard redox potentials of the reactants. For the series of reactions between $\mathrm{Fe^{++}}$ and ferric complexes, there is a nearly linear relation between ΔG^* and ΔG^0, as would be expected from the theory of these reactions due to R. A. Marcus.

An exception to this regularity is the reaction of $\mathrm{Fe^{++}}$ with $\mathrm{IrCl_6^{--}}$, the only negative ion examined, which gives a rate ten times higher than that with $\mathrm{Fe(phen)_3^{+++}}$ which has the same value of ΔE^0. Determination of the temperature-coefficients for the two reactions shows that their energies of activation are comparable (1·9 and 0·8 kcal mole^{-1}), but that the entropy of activation ΔS^* is much less

[68] (a) Sutin and Gordon, *J. Amer. Chem. Soc.* 1961, **83**, 70; (b) Ford-Smith and Sutin, *ibid.*, p. 1830; (c) Gordon, Williams and Sutin, *ibid.*, p. 2061. For a review of electron-transfer reactions see (d) Halpern, *Quart. Rev. Chem. Soc.* 1960, **15**, 207. See also p. 259 below.

for $IrCl_6^{--}$ than for $Fe(phen)_3^{+++}$ (-25 as against -37 caldeg^{-1} mole^{-1}).

The rates of some oxidation-reduction reactions between complex ions were also measured, though many were found to be too fast, with $k > 10^8$ 1 mole^{-1}sec^{-1} (Table 3.4). The observed rates gave

TABLE 3.4

Rate constants for electron-transfer reactions of complex ions

Second-order rate constant k in 1 mole^{-1}sec^{-1} at 25° in water. Concentrations are formal.

ΔE^0 = difference of standard oxidation potentials of reactions, in volts.

phen = 1,10-phenanthrolene; dipy = 2,2'-dipyridine; tripy = 2,2'2''-tripyridine. The original tables should be consulted for complete results.[68b, c]

Oxidizing agent	Reducing agent	Medium, concn.	ΔE°	k
$Fe(phen)_3^{+++}$	Fe^{++}	H_2SO_4, 0·5 M	0·37	$3\cdot0 \times 10^5$
$Fe(5\text{-methyl-phen})_3^{+++}$	Fe^{++}	H_2SO_4, 0·5 M	0·33	$1\cdot5 \times 10^5$
$Fe(5\text{-nitro-phen})_3^{+++}$	Fe^{++}	$HClO_4$, 0·5 M	0·56	$1\cdot1 \times 10^6$
$Fe(5\text{-chloro-phen})_3^{+++}$	Fe^{++}	H_2SO_4, 0·5 M	0·43	$1\cdot5 \times 10^6$
$Fe(5\text{-phenyl-phen})_3^{+++}$	Fe^{++}	H_2SO_4, 0·5 M	0·39	$3\cdot2 \times 10^5$
$Fe(5,6\text{-dimethyl-phen})_3^{+++}$	Fe^{++}	H_2SO_4, 0·5 M	0·28	$6\cdot9 \times 10^4$
$Fe(4,7\text{-diphenyl-phen})_3^{+++}$	Fe^{++}	H_2SO_4, 0·5 M	0·55	$(3\cdot3 \times 10^4)$
$Fe(3,4,7,8\text{-tetramethyl-phen})_3^{+++}$	Fe^{++}	H_2SO_4, 0·5 M	0·12	$1\cdot9 \times 10^3$
$Fe(dipy)_3^{+++}$	Fe^{++}	H_2SO_4, 0·5 M	0·28	$2\cdot2 \times 10^5$
$Fe(4,4'\text{-dimethyl-dipy})_3^{+++}$	Fe^{++}	H_2SO_4, 0·5 M	0·26	$5\cdot9 \times 10^3$
$Fe(tripy)_2^{+++}$	Fe^{++}	H_2SO_4, 0·5 M	0·24	$7\cdot4 \times 10^5$
$Ag(phen)_2^{++}$	Fe^{++}	H_2SO_4, 0·5 M	—	$1\cdot7 \times 10^6$
$Ag(dipy)_2^{++}$	Fe^{++}	H_2SO_4, 0·5 M	0·74	$1\cdot4 \times 10^6$
$Ru(dipy)_3^{+++}$	Fe^{++}	$HClO_4$, 0·5 M	0·58	$7\cdot2 \times 10^5$
$IrCl_6^{--}$	Fe^{++}	$HClO_4$, 0·5 M	0·37	$3\cdot2 \times 10^6$
$Os(dipy)_3^{+++}$	Fe^{++}	H_2SO_4, 0·5 M	0·14	$1\cdot35 \times 10^4$
$IrCl_6^{--}$	$Fe(CN)_6^{4-}$	H_2O	0·66	$1\cdot30 \times 10^6$
$IrCl_6^{--}$	$Fe(CN)_6^{4-}$	$HClO_4$, 0·5 M	0·34	$4\cdot1 \times 10^5$
MnO_4^-	$Fe(CN)_6^{4-}$	NaOH, 0·1 M	0·10	$1\cdot34 \times 10^4$
$OsCl_6^{--}$	$Fe(CN)_6^{4-}$	H_2O	0·07	$1\cdot79 \times 10^{-1}$
$IrCl_6^{--}$	$Os(dipy)_3^{++}$	$HClO_4$, 0·5 M	0·23	$> 10^8$
$Fe(phen)_3^{+++}$	$Fe(CN)_6^{4-}$	$HClO_4$, 0·5 M	0·23	$> 10^8$
$Os(dipy)_3^{+++}$	$Fe(CN)_6^{4-}$	$HClO_4$, 0·5 M	0·11	$> 10^8$
$Ru(dipy)_3^{+++}$	$Fe(t\text{-phen})_3^{++}$	H_2SO_4, 0·5 M	0·46	$> 10^8$
$Fe(dipy)_3^{+++}$	$Os(dipy)_3^{++}$	$HClO_4$, 0·5 M	0·44	$> 10^8$
$Fe(phen)_3^{+++}$	$Os(dipy)_3^{++}$	$HClO_4$, 0·5 M	0·23	$> 10^8$
$Ru(dipy)_3^{+++}$	$Fe(p\text{-phen})_3^{++}$	H_2SO_4, 0·5 M	0·19	$> 10^8$
$Fe(d\text{-dipy})_3^{+++}$	$Fe(t\text{-phen})_3^{++}$	H_2SO_4, 0·5 M	0·14	$> 10^8$
$Fe(phen)_3^{+++}$	$Fe(d\text{-dipy})_3^{++}$	$HClO_4$, 0·5 M	0·11	$> 10^8$

values of ΔG^* considerably greater than would be expected from the Marcus theory. The high rate constants even for reactions between ions of similar charge are noteworthy; they indicate that electrostatic repulsion contributes relatively little to the free energy of activation. The theory of electron-transfer reactions[68e] suggests that several factors are important, and the results here reported must be correlated with the large body of work on slower reactions.

Proton-transfer reactions

Most proton-transfer reactions involving O—H or N—H bonds are too fast for flow techniques (p. 262), and many involving C—H bonds are too slow. Some, however, fall within the range, notably the colour-reactions of aromatic nitro-compounds with bases, and the reversal of these with acids[69]; these have also been investigated at low temperatures, so that Arrhenius plots over a range of 100 degrees or more are available (p. 273). In the case of *p*-nitrobenzylcyanide the reactions have been studied by the stopped-flow technique at low temperatures.[70] The reaction of indene with the sodium derivative of triphenylmethane ($Na^+CPh_3^-$) has been studied, under anaerobic conditions, by the continuous-flow method.[17] The rate of the reaction $H^+ + HCO_3^- \rightarrow H_2CO_3$ has been measured many times, since it is convenient for testing the performance of flow apparatus[71]; it is also of interest because the results give a value for the dissociation constant of H_2CO_3 as an acid.[72]

Reactions of haemoglobin

Haemoglobin in aqueous solution combines reversibly with various dissolved gases, especially oxygen and carbon monoxide. It is thought that addition occurs in four stages (which perhaps correspond to the four iron atoms in mammalian haemoglobin):

$$Hb_4 + X \rightarrow Hb_4X \rightarrow Hb_4X_2 \rightarrow Hb_4X_3 \rightarrow Hb_4X_4.$$

[69] See chapter 2, refs. 13 and 14.
[70] (*a*) Caldin and Harbron, *J. Chem. Soc.* 1962, 2314; (*b*) Caldin and Kasparian, unpublished work.
[71] See, e.g., refs. 19*a*, 20*a*, 12*a*, 12*b*.
[72] Cf. Bell, *The Proton in Chemistry* (Methuen, 1959), pp. 29–31.

The rate constants for several of these stages have been determined, largely by flow methods, by Roughton and Gibson.[73] Physiological problems connected with reactions in the lungs have been illuminated by these results.[74]

Enzyme catalysis[75]

For the decomposition of a substrate S, catalysed by an enzyme E, the mechanism put forward by Michaelis involves a preliminary complex-formation:

$$E + S \underset{k_2}{\overset{k_1}{\rightleftarrows}} ES \xrightarrow{k_3} \text{product}$$

For the decomposition of hydrogen peroxide in presence of catalase, Chance measured the rate constants k_1, k_2 and k_3 by accelerated-flow and stopped-flow methods, of specially high spectrophotometric sensitivity. His results confirmed the Michaelis mechanism.

In presence of a donor such as an alcohol, the complex ES may undergo another reaction:

$$ES + AH_2 \xrightarrow{k_4} E + SH_2 + A$$

For instance, ethanol is oxidized to acetaldehyde in presence of catalase and ethyl hydrogen peroxide. The kinetics of these reactions have been elucidated by the work of Chance. The rate constants k_4 vary greatly with the donor; the highest approach 10^8 l mole^{-1} sec^{-1}.

[73] For a full review of this important subject see Gibson, in (a) *Progress in Biophysics* (Pergamon Press, 1959) **9**, 1–53. Some of the original papers are:(b) Gibson and Roughton, *Proc. Roy. Soc.*, B, 1955, **143**, 310 (O₂); (c) Gibson, *J. Physiol.* 1956; **134**, 112, 123 (CO; flash method (p. 110); (d) Gibson and Roughton, *Proc. Roy. Soc.*, B, 1957, **146**, 206 (CO); (e) Ainsworth and Gibson,*J. Physiol.* 1958, **137**, 26P (CO); (f) Antonini and Gibson, *Biochem. J.*, 1960, **76**, 534.
[74] For a review, see Roughton in ref. 73a, pp. 55–104. The problem which led to the first flow experiments in 1923 has been solved; the rate of uptake of oxygen by the blood depends both upon the rate of reaction in solution and upon the rate of passage of oxygen through the red cell membranes (*ibid.*, p. 99).
[75] For reviews see (a) Chance, ref. 1, chap. 22; (b) *The Enzymes*, ed. Boyer, Lardy, and Myrbach (2nd edn., Academic Press, 6 vols., 1959–62), esp. vol. 1; see also ref. 12 on p. 68 below.

TABLE 3.5

Reactions studied by flow methods

This table is intended to illustrate the range of reactions that have been studied and the range of second-order rate constants (k) that have been determined. Some of the reactions have been the objects of systematic investigation, others of a single experiment; these differences are shown in the columns headed 'Concentration varied' and 'Temperature varied'. The solvent is water unless otherwise stated. For ionic strengths the original paper should be consulted. The values of k given under 'Results' are illustrative, not exhaustive; they are expressed in $1 \text{ mole}^{-1} \text{sec}^{-1}$. Temperatures are in degrees C. The following abbreviations are used: cf = continuous flow; af = accelerated flow; sf = stopped flow; cond. = conductivity; phot. = photometry.

Reaction type	Reaction	Method, detector	Conc. varied	Temp. varied	Results		Ref.
					Temp. (°C)	k ($1 \text{ mole}^{-1}\text{sec}^{-1}$)	
Redox reactions	$Fe^{++} + Fe(phem)_3^{+++}$ (see also Table 3.4)	sf, cf, phot.	yes	yes	25	3×10^5	68
	$Fe^{++} + S_2O_8^{--}$	cf; emf	yes				12a
	$I_2 + Fe(CN)_6^{4-}$	cf; emf	yes				12a
	$Ce^{3+} + I^-$	sf; phot.	yes		18	3×10^4	46c
	$H_2O_2 + Cr_2O_7^{--}$	sf; phot.			18	1.9×10^3	46c
	$H_2O_2 + Ti^{3+}$	sf; phot.	yes		18	500	46c
	$H_2O_2 + Ce^{3+}$	af; phot.			18	9×10^5	46c
	$H_2O_2 + MnO_4^-$	sf; phot.			18	3×10^3	46c
Proton transfer	$(C_6H_4NO_2)_3CH + OEt^-$ in EtOH	cf; phot.	yes		25	70	69
	$C_6H_2(NO_2)_3CH_3 + OEt^-$ in EtOH	cf; phot.	yes		19	63	38
	$C_6H_2(NO_2)_3CH_2^- + $ acids in EtOH	cf; sf; phot.	yes		20	360 to 10^4	38
	Indene $+ Na^+OPh_3$ in Et_2O	cf; phot.	yes	yes	20	140	17b
	$NO_2 \cdot C_6H_4CH_2CN + OEt^-$ in EtOH·Et_2O	sf; phot.	yes	yes	−77	5.5×10^2	70a, b
	$(NO_2 \cdot C_6H_4CHCN)^- + $ phenols in EtOH·Et_2O	sf; phot.	yes		−77	ca. 10^2 to 10^3	70a

Complexes, etc.	$Fe^{+++} + SCN^-$	baffle; phot.	yes		25	127	63a
	$(Ni\ en_3)^{+++} + H^+$ (see also Table 3.2)	sf; phot.	yes	yes	25	87	67
	(see also Table 3.3)						
	$C_6H_3(NO_2)_3 + OEt^-$ in ethanol	cf; phot.	yes		20	3×10^4	38
	$C_6H_3(NO_2)_3 + NHEt_2$ in acetone–ether	sf; phot.	yes		-59 to -86	(3rd order)	60b
Hydrolysis of halides	$Ph_3SiCl + H_2O$ in acetone	sf; cond.	yes		25	1 to 10^5	77
	$Co(NH_3)_5Cl^{++}$, etc. $+ OH^-$	cf; cond.	yes		25		11c
Haemoglobin	$Haemoglobin + O_2$	sf; phot.	yes			$1 \cdot 1 \times 10^7$	73b
	$Haemoglobin + CO$	sf; phot.	yes			10^6 to 10^7	73d
	(4 steps)						
	$Globin + carboxyhaem$	sf; phot.	yes			7×10^7	52a
Enzymes	$Catalase + H_2O_2$	af, sf; phot.	yes			ca. 5×10^7	75a
	$Catalase + H_2O_2 + ethanol$	af, sf; phot.	yes			10^3	75a
	$Peroxidase + H_2O_2 + ascorbic\ acid$	af, sf; phot.	yes			$2 \cdot 8 \times 10^3$	75a
Miscellaneous	$CO_2 + OH^- \rightarrow HCO_3^-$	cf; thermal	yes	yes	0	$1 \cdot 1 \times 10^3$	18c
		sf; cond.	yes	yes	20	5×10^3	53
		sf; phot.	yes	yes	30	$1 \cdot 3 \times 10^4$	53
	$CO_2 + NH_3$	cf; thermal	yes	yes	0	74	18a
	$H^+ + HCO_3^- \rightarrow H_2CO_3 \leftrightarrows H_2O + CO_2$	cf; thermal, phot., cond.	yes	yes	0	$2 \cdot 0$	19a, 20a, 12a, 12b
		sf; e.m.f., phot.	yes	yes			58, 51c
	$Cr_2O_7^{--} + H_2O$	cf; thermal	yes	yes	0	$2 \cdot 0$	19b
		sf; thermal	yes				46c
	$Cl_2 + H_2O$	cf; cond.	yes	yes	0	$1 \cdot 8$	11e, 19c
	$I_2 + HSO_3^-$	cf; phot.	yes	yes	22	$2 \cdot 3 \times 10^9$	76

The reactions of iodine in sulphite solutions[76]

The reactions of iodine in sulphite solutions containing iodide ion and acid have been investigated by the continuous-flow method. In the pH range 0–5, sulphite reacts as HSO_3^-, and the rate constants for the reactions of this ion with I_2, I_3^- and I_2Cl^- were determined; they are respectively 2.3×10^9, 2.2×10^7 and 1.1×10^9 l mole^{-1}sec^{-1}, at 22° and ionic strength 1.0.

The hydrolysis of halides

Silicon and germanium halides. The hydrolysis of chlorotriphenyl silane Ph_3SiCl by water in acetone solution has been studied.[77, 11a,b] The mechanism appears to involve several molecules of water. With Ph_3GeCl the reaction is considerably slower, possibly because the transition state is more stabilized by d-orbital participation at Si than at Ge.

Cobalt complex chlorides. The hydrolysis by water and hydroxyl ions of a series of complex ions such as $Co(NH_3)_5Cl^+$ has been investigated.[11c] The second-order rate constants for the reaction with hydroxyl ions vary from 1 to 10^5 l mole^{-1}sec^{-1}; they show the effects of increased chelation in increasing the rate, and of substitution on the carbon and nitrogen atoms of the ligand.

[76] Bünau and Eigen, *Z. phys. Chem. (Frankfurt)*, 1962, **32**, 27; for apparatus see ref. 4b.
[77] Chipperfield and Prince, *Proc. Chem. Soc.* 1960, 385.

CHAPTER 4

Relaxation Methods (I):
Temperature-jump, Pressure-jump, and Electric-impulse Methods

Introduction

The principle of relaxation methods is as follows.[1] Suppose that the reaction whose rate we wish to measure comes to an equilibrium, which can be disturbed by a change of some external parameter such as temperature. If such a change of conditions is made suddenly, there is a time-lag while the system approaches the new position of equilibrium. This time-lag is related to the rate constants of the forward and back reactions. The range of half-times accessible to one or other of the relaxation methods is about 10^{-9} to over 1 sec.

Some relaxation methods make use of a single displacement of temperature, pressure, or electric field; the reaction is then followed as it moves towards the new equilibrium. These techniques are dealt with in this chapter. Other methods make use of a periodic disturbance, set up by ultrasonic waves, or by a high-frequency alternating field; the power absorbed by reason of the time-lag is measured. Such methods are discussed in the next chapter. These two chapters together cover methods that make use of small displacements of the system, unlike (for example) the flash method (chapter 6).

The time-lag is expressed as a 'relaxation time', and we must now

[1] General reviews include (a) Eigen, *Discuss. Faraday Soc.* 1954, **17**, 194; (b) De Maeyer, *Z. Elektrochem.* 1960, **64** 65; (c) Eigen, *ibid.*, 115; (d) Eigen and De Maeyer, in *Investigation of Rates and Mechanisms of Reactions*, ed. Friess, Lewis and Weissberger (Interscience, 1963), part II, chapter 18.

derive the equations by which this is related to the kinetics and rate constants of reactions.

Relaxation time and its relation to rate constants

First-order reactions. The relaxation time is an inverse measure of the rate constant. To begin with, let us consider the simple case of a reversible change of the first order in each direction, represented

by:
$$A \underset{k_b}{\overset{k_f}{\rightleftharpoons}} C \qquad (4.1)$$

The molecularity of the reactions does not matter for our present purpose. Both forward and back reactions may be unimolecular,

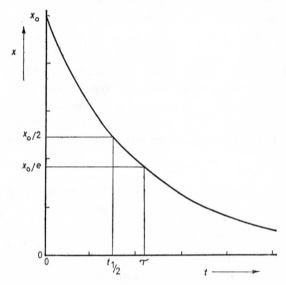

FIG. 4.1. Relaxation after single displacement (see text)

as in an inversion of configuration; but they may also be bimolecular changes in which one reactant is at constant concentration, as in a catalysed reaction or an exchange reaction.

Let the concentrations of A and C at any time t be a and c respectively. Suppose the system is initially at equilibrium, with concentrations a_0 and c_0, and that the conditions are then suddenly disturbed, by an instantaneous jump of temperature for example.

Let the equilibrium concentrations corresponding to the new conditions be $\bar{a}(< a_0)$ and $\bar{c}(> c_0)$. The actual concentrations will start to move towards these values. Suppose that at time t from the disturbance the actual values still differ from the equilibrium values by an amount x, so that:

$$x = a - \bar{a} = \bar{c} - c \qquad (4.2)$$

The net forward rate at time t is:

$$-dx/dt = k_f a - k_b c \qquad (4.3)$$

where k_f and k_b are the rate constants for the forward and back reactions. At equilibrium, this rate would become zero, so that by equation 4.3,

$$0 = k_f \bar{a} - k_b \bar{c} \qquad (4.4)$$

The net forward rate at time t can be expressed in terms of x by substituting $a = \bar{a} + x$ and $a = \bar{c} - x$ from equation 4.2 into equation 4.3, and making use of equation 4.4. The result is:

$$-dx/dt = (k_f + k_b)x \qquad (4.5)$$

This is the well-known equation for a reversible reaction of the first order in each direction. The rate of equilibration evidently depends on the overall first-order constant k defined by:

$$k = (k_f + k_b) \qquad (4.6)$$

Integration of equation 4.5, after substitution from 4.6, gives:

$$x/x_0 = e^{-kt} \qquad (4.8)$$

where x_0 is the value of x immediately after the disturbance. Equation 4.8 describes the course of equilibration, which is illustrated in Fig. 4.1. It implies that after a time-interval such that $kt = 1$, $x/x_0 = 1/e$; that is, the difference between the actual and equilibrium concentrations has been reduced to $1/e$ of the original difference. It is convenient to define this time-interval as the *relaxation time*, commonly denoted by τ. Thus:

$$\tau^{-1} = k \qquad (4.9)$$

Hence for the reaction scheme 4.1, we obtain by equation 4.6:

$$\tau^{-1} = k_f + k_b \qquad (4.9a)$$

The relaxation time is thus the reciprocal of the overall first-order rate constant. It is of the same order of magnitude as the half-time $t_{1/2}$ for the reaction; from equations 4.8 and 4.9,

$$t_{1/2}/\tau = kt_{1/2} = \ln 2 \approx 0\cdot7 \qquad (4.10)$$

When the reactants and products are effectively identical, as in isotope-exchange reactions, k_f and k_b must be equal, so that:

$$k = k_f + k_b = 2k_f = 2k_b \qquad (4.11)$$

It is sometimes convenient to define $\tau_A = 1/k_f$ and $\tau_C = 1/k_b$ as the *mean lifetimes* of A and C, since the mean lifetime is the concentration divided by the rate of reaction; then by equation 4.9a,

$$\tau_A^{-1} + \tau_C^{-1} = \tau^{-1} \qquad (4.11a)$$

If τ_A and τ_C are equal, therefore,

$$\tau_A = \tau_C = 2\tau \qquad (4.11b)$$

If A and C can be interconverted by two different mechanisms, so that there are two concurrent first-order processes, with relaxation times τ_1 and τ_2 respectively, the effective relaxation time for the two processes combined is given by:

$$\tau^{-1} = \tau_1^{-1} + \tau_2^{-1} \qquad (4.11c)$$

just as the composite first-order rate constant is the sum of the two separate rate constants.

Reaction $A + B = C$. Suppose next that we are dealing with an equilibrium such as complex-formation, or ion-association, which we can write:

$$A + B \underset{k_b}{\overset{k_f}{\rightleftharpoons}} C \qquad (4.12)$$

Let the concentrations at any time be a, b, c. Suppose as before that the system is initially at equilibrium, and that the conditions are suddenly disturbed. Let the equilibrium concentrations corresponding to the new conditions be $\bar{a}$, $\bar{b}$, $\bar{c}$. Suppose that at time t the actual concentrations differ from these by an amount x, so that:

$$x = a - \bar{a} = b - \bar{b} = \bar{c} - c \qquad (4.13)$$

The net forward rate at time t, in the simplest case, is:

$$-dx/dt = k_f ab - k_b c \qquad (4.14)$$

At equilibrium this would become zero, so that:

$$k_f \bar{a}\bar{b} - k_b \bar{c} = 0 \qquad (4.15)$$

The net forward rate is obtained in terms of x by using equation 4.13 and substituting $a = \bar{a}+x$, etc., in equation 4.14, making use of equation 4.15. If we confine ourselves to small displacements by neglecting a term in x^2, we obtain, in place of equation 4.5,

$$-dx/dt = x[k_f(\bar{a}+\bar{b}) + k_b] \qquad (4.16)$$

The quantity in square brackets is a constant, independent of time; the equation therefore respresents a first-order approach to equilibrium, with this quantity as rate constant (k). For reactions represented by equation 4.12, the process is first-order only for small displacements. The relaxation time may be defined as before as $1/k$, and is therefore related to k_f and k_b as follows (compare equation 4.9a):

$$\tau^{-1} = k = k_f(\bar{a}+\bar{b}) + k_b \qquad (4.17)$$

To determine the rate constants k_f and k_b, therefore, we may find τ experimentally at a series of concentrations, and plot τ against $(\bar{a}+\bar{b})$; the slope gives k_f and the intercept k_b.[2] If the equilibrium lies far to the right, so that k_b is negligible, equation 4.17 reduces to

$$\tau^{-1} \approx k_f(\bar{a}+\bar{b}) \qquad (4.17a)$$

Consecutive reactions. The relation between the relation time and the rate constants may actually be more complex, if activity coefficients have to be considered, or if more than one relaxation is concerned. When the system exhibits several consecutive relaxation processes, each with its characteristic relaxation time, the mathematics is more complicated, since linear combinations of the various x's must be used; but the rate constants can still be determined if measurements are made over a sufficient range of concentrations[3].

[2] See, e.g., refs. 7c and 12a.
[3] Eigen, (a) Z. phys. Chem. (Frankfurt), 1954, **1**, 176; (b) Discuss. Faraday Soc. 1957, **24**, 25; (c) ref. 1c, 1d; cf. refs. 1f and 16f of chapter 5 (pp. 81, 94). For other references on the mathematics of relaxation see (d) Bewick and Fleischmann, Ann. Rep. Chem. Soc. 1960, 92.

Temperature-jump method

General

The principle of this method is to alter suddenly the temperature of a system in equilibrium and use some fast-recording detector to follow the course of the resulting change towards the new position of equilibrium. From the reaction–time curve can be found the relaxation time and the rate constant. The method can be applied to any reaction whose equilibrium position is sufficiently shifted by a change of temperature. The shift depends on the value of ΔH for the reaction, according to the familiar thermodynamic equation $d\ln K/dT = \Delta H/RT^2$.

Techniques

In the technique developed for ionic solutions by Eigen and his co-workers,[4a, 4b] a temperature-jump of the order of 2 to 10 degrees is effected in about 10^{-6} sec. by a discharge from a high-voltage condenser at a potential difference of the order of 100 kV. The ensuing reaction may be followed by the change in conductivity with the help of a Wheatstone bridge; the alteration of the bridge balance is followed by means of a cathode-ray oscillograph with a fast time-base. If there is a colour change in the reaction, photo-electric spectrophotometry can be used, with the advantage that different species can be identified and their concentrations followed. The apparatus for this is shown diagrammatically in Fig. 4.2. It is convenient to use twin cells, one for the reaction and one as reference, and to display the difference between the responses of two photo-multipliers on the screen of the oscillograph. If there is no colour change, an indicator may be introduced; similarly if ΔH is too small, the reaction may be combined with some fast equilibrium of greater ΔH. It is not necessary that the reaction should involve ions, only that some ions should be present to carry the current.

[4] (a) Czerlinski and Eigen, *Z. Elektrochem.* 1959, **63**, 652; (b) Czerlinski, *Rev. Sci. Instr.* 1962, **33**, 1184; (c) Halpern, Legare and Lumry, *J. Amer. Chem. Soc.* 1963, **85**, 680. It is planned to reduce the time to 10^{-7} sec: (d) Czerlinski, *idem*, 1960, **64**, 78. A similar apparatus, giving a larger temperature-rise, has been built by Bewick and Fleischmann (personal communication).

An alternative method of raising the temperature suddenly is to use a pulse of microwaves. By applying about 15 kV to a magnetron for a few microseconds, a pulse of 3-cm waves can be produced sufficient to raise the temperature of a sample of water in a capillary tube by 0·7 degrees.[5] This technique has the advantage that it is applicable to non-conducting solutions; a polar solvent absorbs microwaves, and no ions need be present.

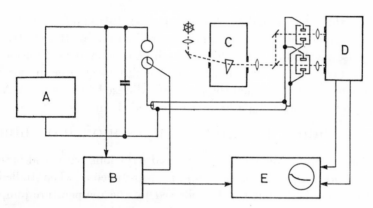

FIG. 4.2. Temperature-jump apparatus. A, H.T. generator; B, H.T. measurement and triggering; C, monochromator; D, photo-multipliers and pre-amplifiers; E, differential amplifier and oscillo-scope. (From De Maeyer, ref. 1b.)

The temperature-jump method might also be adapted to non-reversible reactions, by starting at a temperature low enough for the reaction to be slow, and suddenly raising it by, say, 100 degrees.

Applications

Proton-transfer reactions. An important reaction that has been studied by the temperature-jump method is the dissociation of water and recombination of hydrogen and hydroxyl ions[5]:

$$2H_2O \underset{k_a}{\overset{k_d}{\rightleftarrows}} H_3O^+ + OH^-$$

[5] Ertl and Gerischer, (a) *Z. Elektrochem.* 1961, **65**, 629; (b) *idem*, 1962, **66**, 560 (comparison of H_2O and D_2O).

After a sudden rise in temperature, the conductivity of water increases measurably with time; the relaxation time τ at $23°$ is 37×10^{-6} sec ($\pm 5\%$). The rate of the dissociation is negligible compared with that of the recombination of the ions, so that the rate constant k_a for recombination is given in terms of the known ionic concentrations by equation 4.17a:

$$k_a = 1/\tau[(\mathrm{OH}^-) + (\mathrm{H}^+)]$$

The value of k_a found in this way is $1\cdot3 \times 10^{11}$ l mole^{-1}sec^{-1}, in good agreement with an earlier determination by the electric-impulse method (p. 72). This is a high value even for a diffusion-controlled reaction. Its interpretation is discussed later (p. 268); it is suggested that when the ions have diffused to within 6–8 Å, the protons shift along a hydrogen-bonded chain:

$$\mathrm{H_3O^+ \ldots HOH \ldots HOH \ldots OH^- \longrightarrow H_2O \ldots H_2O \ldots H_2O \ldots HOH}$$

The reactions of hydrogen and hydroxyl ions with acid-base indicators in aqueous solution appear 'instantaneous' when studied by flow methods, but can be followed by the temperature-jump technique.[6] Relaxation times are determined at various concentrations, and the rate constants for the forward and back reactions

TABLE 4.1

Reactions of hydrogen and hydroxyl ions studied by the temperature-jump method

Second-order rate constant k in l mole^{-1}sec^{-1}, in water.

Reagents		Temp. (°C)	k	Ref.
H$^+$	OH$^-$	23	$(1\cdot3 \pm 0\cdot1)\,10^{11}$	5
	Phenol red	13	3×10^{11}	6a
	Chlorphenol red	13	$2\cdot3 \times 10^{11}$	6a
OH$^-$	Cresol red		4×10^9	6c
	Phenolphthalein		$ca.\ 1 \times 10^9$	4a
	Imidazole	25	$(1\cdot5 \pm 0\cdot5)\,10^{10}$	6b

are thence determined with the aid of equation 4.17. Phenol red,[6a] chlorphenol red,[6a,b] phenolphthalein,[4a] and cresol red [6c] have been studied in this way; imidazole also has been investigated, with an added indicator. The reactions with hydrogen ion have rate constants in the region of 10^{11} l mole^{-1}sec^{-1}; those with hydroxyl ion are slower by about an order of magnitude (Table 4.1). These very high values suggest that the reactions occur at effectively every collision and are diffusion-controlled; they are further discussed later (chapter 12, p. 262).

Metal complexes.[7] Kinetic studies have been made on the formation of complexes between certain cations and ions derived from phthaleincomplexone,[7a,b] adenosine-5'-diphosphate,[6a] and adenosine-5'-triphosphate.[7c] The rate constants range from about 10^6 to over 10^9 l mole^{-1}sec^{-1}. The variations for a given metal with different ligands are less than might be expected from the stabilities of the various complexes if attack by the ligand were the rate-determining step. This evidence supports the view that the rate is controlled by loss of a water molecule from the coordination shell of the metal ion, so that the mechanism is analogous to an S_N1 process rather than S_N2.[7f] These results may be compared with those of ultrasonic-absorption measurements on aqueous solutions of divalent metallic sulphates (p. 94); see also chapter 12, p. 276.[8]

Redox reactions. The rate constant for the electron-transfer reaction between ferrocyanide and ferricyanide ions has been

[6] (a) Eigen and Hammes, *J. Amer. Chem. Soc.* 1960, **82**, 5951; (b) Eigen, Hammes, and Kustin, *ibid.*, p. 3482; (c) Eigen and Kruse (personal communication from Dr. Kruse).

[7] (a) Czerlinski and Eigen, ref. 4a; (b) Czerlinski, Diebler and Eigen, *Z. phys. Chem. (Frankfurt)*, 1959, **19**, 246; (c) Diebler, Eigen and Hammes, *Z. Naturforsch.* 1960, **15B**, 554; for reviews see Eigen, (d) *Z. Elektrochem.* 1960, **64**, 120; (e) *Suom. Kem.*, *A*, 1961, **34**, 25; (f) *Advances in the Chemistry of Coordination Compounds*, ed. Kirschner (Macmillan, 1961), p. 371; (g) Eigen, *Pure and Appl. Chem.* 1963, **6**, 97. See also (h) Hammes and Steinfeld, *J. Amer. Chem. Soc.* 1962, **84**, 4639.

[8] The temperature-jump method has been used in the investigation of aqueous beryllium sulphate, which is a special case by reason of hydrolysis (p. 98): Diebler and Eigen, *Z. phys. Chem. (Frankfurt)*, 1959, **20**, 299.

measured, with the aid of a redox indicator, as $1 \cdot 5 \times 10^5$ l mole^{-1} sec^{-1}.[9] The reaction between quinone and quinol, $Q + Q^{--} \rightleftharpoons 2Q^{\cdot-}$, has rate constants in the region of 10^8 l mole^{-1}sec^{-1} in both directions.[10]

Hydrolysis of halogens. The reactions of chlorine, bromine and iodine with water have been studied by the temperature-jump method.[11] The overall reaction is:

$$X_2 + H_2O \rightleftharpoons X^- + H^+ + XOH$$

The kinetic scheme suggested as an interpretation of measurements at various concentrations and pH's is considerably more complex:

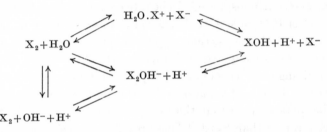

Some of the reactions are very fast; thus for the association $I_2 + OH^- \rightarrow I_2OH^-$ the rate constant is greater than 5×10^9 l mole^{-1}sec^{-1}.

Reactions of proteins, enzymes, etc. Kinetic studies of the interactions of proteins with dyestuffs and of antibodies with haptens have shown[12a] that these are simple association reactions, with rate constants in the region of 10^6–10^7 l mole^{-1}sec^{-1}. It seems likely that useful results will be obtained for enzyme reactions.[12b–12e] The biochemical applications of the temperature-jump method will probably become an important field.

[9] Diebler, *Z. Elektrochem.* 1960, **64**, 128.
[10] Diebler, Eigen and Matthies, *idem*, 1961, **65**, 634.
[11] Eigen and Kustin, *J. Amer. Chem. Soc.* 1962, **84**, 1355. Cf. chapter 3, refs. 11e and 19c.
[12] (a) Froese, Sehon and Eigen, *Canad. J. Chem.* 1962, **40**, 1786; (b) Alberty and Hammes, *Z. Elektrochem.* 1960, **64**, 124; (c) *J. Amer. Chem. Soc.* 1960, **82**, 1564; (d) Hammes and Fasella, *J. Amer. Chem. Soc.* 1962, **84**, 4644; (e) Eigen and Hammes, in *Advances in Enzymology*, 1963.

Pressure-jump method

General

A sudden change of pressure can be used in the same way as a temperature-jump. The sensitivity of an equilibrium to pressure depends on the change of volume ΔV associated with the reaction, according to the relation $d\ln K/dP = -\Delta V/RT$. The method has been used in investigations of some ionic reactions in water, where ΔV is favourable and the reaction can be conveniently followed by the conductivity. It is best to compare the effects of pressure on the conductivities of two cells, one of which contains the reaction solution and the other a solution of a non-reacting electrolyte in the same solvent; this is because when the pressure is changed the conductivity alters by reason of the changes in volume and viscosity, as well as by reason of the reaction, whose effect may be relatively small.

Technique[13]

In the apparatus of Strehlow and Becker[13a,f] (Fig. 4.3), the two conductivity cells form two of the arms of a Wheatstone bridge, and any change in the bridge balance is displayed on the screen of a cathode-ray oscillograph. The cells are enclosed under an inert liquid (xylene or kerosene) in a pressure-vessel which is closed by a thin metal disc. A pressure of about 50 atmospheres is set up in the vessel by means of compressed air. The pressure can be reduced to one atmosphere within about 10^{-4} sec, by puncturing the metal disc with a blow from a needle. Electrical circuits are arranged so that this operation also triggers the time-base of the cathode-ray oscillograph, whose response is photographed.

The range of times accessible is about 10^{-4} sec to 50 sec. Any fast method of following the reaction might be used, subject to the need for enclosing the apparatus in a pressure-vessel; for instance, emf methods have been investigated.[13c] To shorten the time, and increase the pressure-change, the use of shock-waves is being

[13] (a) Strehlow and Becker, Z. Elektrochem. 1959, 63, 457; (b) Ljunggren and Lamm, Acta chem. Scand. 1958, 12, 1834, and (c) Z. Elektrochem. 1960, 64, 79; (d) Yeager, ibid., 86; (e) De Maeyer, ibid., 72; (f) Strehlow and Wendt, Inorganic Chemistry, 1963, 2, 6.

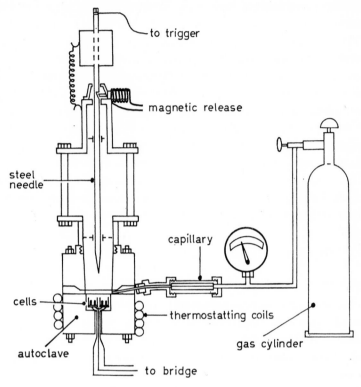

FIG. 4.3. Pressure-jump apparatus. (From Strehlow and Wendt, ref. 13*f*.)

investigated; it may be possible to produce changes of the order of 10^4 atmospheres in 10^{-6} sec.[13e]

Applications

Reactions of ferric ion with anions. The formation of complexes between ferric ions and various anions (Cl^-, SCN^-, SO_4^{--}) has been investigated by the pressure-jump method.[14a] The half-times are in the region of milliseconds. The results with Cl^- and SCN^- can be compared with those obtained by the baffle method; they are in fair

[14] (*a*) Wendt and Strehlow, *Z. Elektrochem.* 1962, **66**, 228 (Cl^-, SCN^-, SO_4^{--}); (*b*) Wendt, *Z. Elektrochem.* 1962, **66**, 235.

agreement, as may be seen from the table on p. 50. A slower change observed with the same solutions was attributed to the dimerization of $FeOH^{++}$.[14b]

Metal sulphates. Solutions of aluminium sulphate showed a relatively slow reaction; the rate-determining step is thought to be the replacement of a water molecule in the coordination sphere of the aluminium ion (cf. pp. 26, 96).[15a] Vanadyl sulphate showed a relaxation time of the order of a millisecond, attributed to the same type of process.[13f] With beryllium sulphate, a process with a relaxation time of about 4×10^{-4} sec was detected (cf. p. 98).[15b]

Hydration of pyruvic acid.[15c, d] The rates of hydration of pyruvic and some related acids have been determined. The reactions are acid-base catalysed, and the relaxation times are of the order of a second.

Electric-impulse method

General

For solutions of weak electrolytes, a third method of suddenly changing the position of equilibrium is available, namely the application of a strong electric field, which increases the degree of dissociation of the electrolyte. This phenomenon is called the 'dissociation field effect' or 'second Wien effect', and is well understood.[16] For the change ($\Delta\alpha$) in the degree of dissociation in a field of strength E, the following equation is a first approximation for a weak electrolyte giving two univalent ions:

$$d\alpha/dE \simeq [\alpha(1-\alpha)/(2-\alpha)][9\cdot64/\epsilon T^2]\,\mathrm{cm/volt}$$

For example, acetic acid shows an increase of 12% in degree of dissociation under a field of 200 kV/cm. Thus very strong fields are required, and because of their heating effect it is convenient to apply them only for a very short time. The change in degree of dissociation of the electrolyte may be followed by the change of

[15] (a) Behr and Wendt, Z. Elektrochem. 1962, 66, 223; (b) Strehlow and Becker, idem, 1959, 63, 457; (c) Strehlow, idem, 1962, 66, 392; (d) Eigen, Kustin and Strehlow, Z. phys. Chem. (Frankfurt), 1962, 31, 140.
[16] Theory: (a) Onsager, J. Chem. Phys. 1933, 2, 599. Experimental: (b) Wien and Schiele, Physik. Zeit. 1931, 32, 545; (c) Bailey and Patterson, J. Amer. Chem. Soc. 1952, 74, 4756.

conductivity. To eliminate all other influences, such as that of temperature, it is best to measure the difference in resistance of two identical conductivity cells, containing respectively a solution of the weak electrolyte and a solution of some strong electrolyte. The cells form two arms of a Wheatstone bridge, and the electric field is applied to the liquid in each cell by means of coaxial electrodes. There are two ways of using the electric impulse, differing in the form of the impulse, the time-intervals attainable, and the concentrations that can be used; these will now be considered in turn.[17]

Rectangular impulse

Technique.[17] This is analogous to the temperature-jump method. A nearly rectangular impulse (Fig. 4.4a) is applied to the electrodes; after the initial rise, which occupies less than 10^{-8} sec, there is a period of practically constant field strength, lasting up to 2×10^{-4} sec. During this period the conductivity change due to the dissociation reaction is followed by means of an oscillograph with a specially fast time-base, and a photographic record of the reaction is thus obtained (Fig. 4.4b). The impulse is produced by charging a condenser to 20 kV and discharging it through the electrodes with a spark-gap in parallel. The product of resistance and capacity must be made high in order to keep the field strength nearly constant over an interval. The resistance must also be high because otherwise too much heat would be generated. The method is therefore suitable only for dilute solutions, or pure solvents. It has the advantage that the relaxation time can be obtained from a single experiment. Only small quantities of liquid are needed. The range of relaxation times that can be measured is roughly 10^{-6} to 10^{-4} sec.

Application. A striking early application of this technique was the determination by Eigen and De Maeyer[18] of the rate of recombination of hydrogen and hydroxyl ions in water: (cf. p. 65):

[17] For general accounts see: (a) Eigen, *Discuss. Faraday Soc.* 1954, **17**, 194; (b) De Maeyer, *Z. Elektrochem.* 1960, **64**, 65; (c) Eigen, ref. 1d.

[18] Eigen and De Maeyer, (a) *Z. Elektrochem.* 1955, **59**, 986; (b) *Proc. Roy. Soc., A,* 1958, **247**, 505; (c) *The Structure of Electrolytic Solutions*, ed. Hamer (Chapman & Hall, 1959), p. 64.

$H_3O^+ + OH^- \rightarrow 2H_2O$. An oscillogram is shown in Fig. 4.4. The rate constant at $25°$ is $(1·4 \pm 0·2) \times 10^{11}$ l mole^{-1}sec^{-1}, with an apparent activation energy of 2–3 kcal mole^{-1}. The interpretation of this very high rate is discussed later (p. 268).

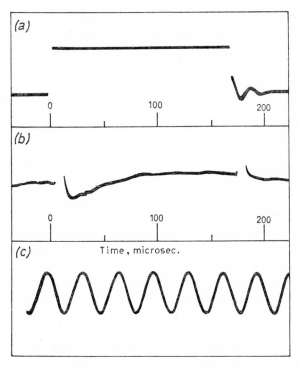

FIG. 4.4. Electric impulse method: rectangular impulse. Oscillographic records: (a) Voltage-time record. (b) Conductivity-time record for dissociation of water during rectangular impulse. (c) Time standard; oscillations at 3×10^7 c/sec. (Records b and c are from Eigen and De Maeyer, ref. 18a; record a was kindly supplied by Dr. De Maeyer.)

Damped harmonic impulses

Technique[19] For solutions which have appreciable conductivities it is necessary to use shorter times, in the range 10^{-7} to 10^{-5} sec, if the heat evolved is not to be excessive. A damped harmonic

[19] Eigen and Schoen, *Z. Elektrochem.* 1955, **59**, 483; cf. also ref. 17.

impulse may be applied, by adjusting the inductance and capacity of the circuit; the damping resistance is made so large (by including spark-gaps) that only one oscillation occurs. The duration is controlled by varying the capacity of the condenser or the resistance.

If the dissociation equilibrium were set up immediately ($\tau = 0$), the degree of dissociation would follow the changes in field strength without a time-lag, and the difference $\Delta\alpha$ between the value at time t and the initial value would follow the curve shown as a full line in Fig. 4.5. This is represented by the equation $\Delta\alpha = Ae^{-bt}\sin\omega t$, where A is the undamped amplitude, $\omega/2\pi$ is the frequency of oscillation of the field, and b is the damping constant. When τ is

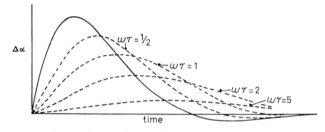

FIG. 4.5 Electric impulse method: damped harmonic impulse. Curves of $\Delta\alpha$ against time for various values of relaxation time.

finite, the maximum value of $\Delta\alpha$ is smaller than the maximum value for $\tau = 0$, and lags behind it, by amounts depending on $\omega\tau$. This is shown by the dashed lines in Fig. 4.5, which represent $\Delta\alpha$ when τ is comparable with the period of oscillation of the field ($\omega\tau = \frac{1}{2}$, 1, 2, 5). The mathematical treatment (p. 78) shows that the maximum value of $\Delta\alpha$ is reduced below A by a factor $[(1 - b\tau)^2 + \omega^2\tau^2]^{1/2}$. Thus by a series of experiments in which the period of the impulses (and so ω) is varied, and the maximum conductivity measured, it is possible to determine τ. The lower limit is about 10^{-7} sec. Low concentrations (ca. 10^{-4} M) can be used, with a sensitive conductivity bridge. Consequently very high second-order rate constants can be determined.

Applications. The method has been extensively applied by Eigen and his group to aqueous solutions of weak acids and bases, in order to study reactions of hydrogen and hydroxyl ions.[19, 20] For example, the relaxation times for acetic acid solutions of various concentrations give (with the help of equation 4.17) the rate constants for the reaction $H^+ + Ac^- \rightleftarrows HAc$; those for ammonia solutions give the rate constants for $NH_4^+ + OH^- \rightleftarrows NH_3 + H_2O$. Some results for the forward reactions are collected in Table 4.2.

TABLE 4.2

Reactions of hydrogen and hydroxyl ions studied by the electric-impulse methods

Second-order rate constant k in $l\,mole^{-1}sec^{-1}$, in water.

	Reagents	Temp. (°C)	k	Ref.
H+	OH−	25	$(1\cdot3 \pm 0\cdot2)10^{11}$	18a
	SH−	25	$(7\cdot5 \pm 1)10^{10}$	20a
	F−	25	1×10^{11}	20c
	HOCO−		$4\cdot7 \times 10^{10}$	7e
	CH_3CO^-	20	$5\cdot1 \times 10^{10}$	20b
	$C_2H_5CO_2^-$		$4\cdot3 \times 10^{10}$	7e
	Benzoate	25	$3\cdot7 \times 10^{10}$	20b
	o-Aminobenzoate	25	$5\cdot8 \times 10^{10}$	20b
	m-Aminobenzoate	25	$4\cdot6 \times 10^{10}$	20b
	p-Aminobenzoate	25	$3\cdot7 \times 10^{10}$	20b
	N,N-dimethyl-o-aminobenzoate	25	$ca.2\cdot5 \times 10^{10}$	20b
	N-methyl-o-aminobenzoate	25	$ca.5 \times 10^{10}$	20b
	m-Nitrophenolate	25	$4\cdot2 \times 10^{10}$	20a
	p-Nitrophenolate	25	$3\cdot6 \times 10^{10}$	20a
OH−	NH_4^+	20	$(3\cdot3 \pm 0\cdot3)10^{10}$	19
	$CH_3NH_3^+$		$3\cdot7 \times 10^{10}$	7e
	$(CH_3)_2NH_2^+$		$3\cdot1 \times 10^{10}$	7e
	$(CH_3)_3NH^+$		$2\cdot1 \times 10^{10}$	7e
	RNH_3^+ (glycine)		$1\cdot4 \times 10^{10}$	7e
	$RN(CH_3)H_2^+$ (sarcosine)		$1\cdot1 \times 10^{10}$	7e
	$R = NH_3^+$ (imidazole)	25	$(2\cdot3 \pm 0\cdot4)10^{10}$	6b

[20] (a) Eigen and Kustin, *J. Amer. Chem. Soc.* 1960, **82**, 5952; (b) Eigen and Eyring, *idem*, 1962, **84**, 3254; (c) Eigen, Hammes and Kustin, ref. 6b. For discussions, including otherwise unpublished values, see Eigen, refs. 1d, 7e and 7g.

The rate constants lie in the range 10^{10} to 10^{11} l mole^{-1}sec^{-1}, and are among the highest known. Some of the relatively small variations among them may be due to steric effects; this could account for the difference between F$^-$ and SH$^-$, for example. Others may be ascribed to differences in the localizations of charge. The results are discussed further in chapter 12 (p. 262).

Comparison of single-displacement relaxation methods

The temperature-jump method has the considerable advantage that it can be combined with spectrophotometric detection, which enables chemical species and reactions to be specifically identified. It has so far been used only for solutions containing ions, but the use of micro-wave absorption may remove this limitation, and the method is fairly widely applicable. The minimum time observable is at present about 10^{-6} sec and may soon be reduced to 10^{-7} sec; low concentration of reagents may be used, and rate constants up to 10^{10} l mole^{-1}sec^{-1} may be determined. The method is not confined to very high rates. It does not require large volumes of solution. It does, however, need special electrical equipment.

The pressure-jump method uses somewhat simpler apparatus. It has so far been used only for rather slower reactions, with relatively large values of ΔV. The application of shock-waves may remove these limitations, at the expense of a more complex experimental arrangement.

The electric-impulse methods require only low concentrations of ions and small quantities of solution; thus in the range 10^{-4} to 10^{-6} sec they have some advantages over the ultrasonics method, for example. The measurement of half-times down to 10^{-7} sec is possible, and new developments may improve on this. Difficulties arise at relatively long times (about 10^{-5} sec for the damped-oscillation method and about 2×10^{-4} sec for the rectangular-impulse method) on account of the heat produced. Electric-impulse methods are limited to weak electrolytes, and require elaborate electrical apparatus.

Table 4.3 summarizes for each method the time-intervals accessible, and the largest observed bimolecular rate constants (which depend also on the sensitivity of the method). Figures for

TABLE 4.3

Relaxation methods

'Min. time' = minimum time measured, in sec.
'Max. k' = maximum observed second-order rate constant,
in $l\,mole^{-1}sec^{-1}$

Method	Min. time (sec.)	Max. time (sec.)	Max. k ($l\ m^{-1}s^{-1}$)
Temperature-jump	$ca.\ 10^{-6}$	1	1×10^{11}
Pressure-jump	5×10^{-5}	50	$ca.\ 10^3$
Rectangular electric impulse	10^{-6}	2×10^{-4}	1×10^{11}
Damped oscillatory impulse	10^{-7}	10^{-5}	4×10^{10}
Ultrasonic absorption	4×10^{-9}	$ca.\ 10^{-4}$	1×10^{11}
Dielectric absorption	10^{-12}	—	—

the other relaxation methods, to be considered in chapter 5, are
added for comparison.

Some general characteristics of relaxation methods

Compared with flow methods (chapter 3), the great advantage of
relaxation methods is that reaction is not initiated by mixing, so
that measurements are possible on much faster reactions. The half-
times that can be measured by one or other of the methods range
from over 1 sec to about 10^{-9} sec, and the sensitivity of several of
the methods is such that even reactions that take place at every
encounter can be studied (Table 4.3). The main limitation is that
only reversible reactions can be investigated.

The relaxation methods described in this chapter and the next
(unlike flash methods) do not produce any radical change in the
system, only a displacement of the equilibrium. Even this must be
kept small, so that the mathematical treatment in terms of linear
differential equations may be applicable. It is of interest that the
rate measured is the rate near equilibrium, whereas flow and conventional methods measure rates when the system is far from
equilibrium. It would be expected that the rate constant would be

unaffected by the difference in conditions; but there is little direct evidence on this point.[21]

Identification of the reaction whose relaxation time is being determined may present difficulties, except when spectrophotometric detection can be used; conductivity changes and sound absorption may be susceptible of more than one interpretation, in terms of (for example) hydration changes, hydrolysis, or incomplete dissociation (cf. p. 96). The difficulty is felt especially when several different relaxation times are observed. Single-step relaxations with a single relaxation time are the ideal for theoretical treatment, but in practice the effects of different relaxation processes may overlap. The experiments must then be designed to elucidate the spectrum of relaxation times, by variation of concentrations and use of a wide range of reaction-times.[2] An extreme example is beryllium sulphate in aqueous solution, which has six relaxation times between 1 and 10^{-9} sec.[8]

Mathematical theory of damped oscillatory impulses[1]

The determination of rate constants by means of damped harmonic impulses (p. 73) requires an extension of the treatment of relaxation time given on pp. 60–63. We there took account of the difference between the actual and the steady equilibrium values of the concentrations; we must now consider what happens when the equilibrium values themselves vary with time. We again consider the reaction $A + B \rightleftarrows C$. As reference values we take the initial equilibrium values (which are the same as the final values); call these a^*, b^*, c^*. We now define (in place of x, defined by equation 4.13) two variables: y, the difference at time t of the actual concentrations (a, b, c) from these reference values; and $\bar{y}$, the difference at time t of the equilibrium concentrations $(\bar{a}, \bar{b}, \bar{c})$ from the reference values:

$$y = a - a^* = b - b^* = c^* - c \qquad (4.19)$$

$$\bar{y} = \bar{a} - a^* = \bar{b} - b^* = c^* - \bar{c} \qquad (4.20)$$

[21] The two rates have been found to agree within experimental error for the reaction between arsenious acid and iodine, followed by isotope-exchange and conventional methods: Wilson and Dickenson, J. Amer. Chem. Soc. 1937, 59, 1358.

For the net forward rate, we have from equation 4.14:

$$-dy/dt = k_f(y+a^*)(y+b^*) - k_b(c^*-y) \qquad (4.21)$$

At equilibrium this is zero, so that

$$k_f(\bar{y}+a^*)(\bar{y}+b^*) - k_b(c^*-\bar{y}) = 0 \qquad (4.22)$$

Combining the last two equations, and imposing the restriction that the displacements are small, by neglecting terms in y^2 and $\bar{y}^2$, we obtain (in place of the former equation 4.16):

$$-dy/dt = (y-\bar{y})[k_f(a^*+b^*)+k_b] \qquad (4.23)$$

This important relation may be written in the following form:

$$\tau(dy/dt)+y = \bar{y} \qquad (4.24)$$

where

$$\tau^{-1} = k_f(a^*+b^*)+k_b \qquad (4.25)$$

Equation 4.24 is the fundamental equation in what follows, and also in the theory of ultrasonic absorption (p. 84). It determines the response of the concentration variable y to variations in the equilibrium value $\bar{y}$ due to changes in temperature, pressure or electric field.[22] When $\bar{y} = 0$, that is, when the equilibrium value is independent of time, equation 4.24 reduces to $dy/dt = -y/\tau$, which is a form of the usual first-order rate equation.

The parameter τ defined by equation 4.25 is the relaxation time of the system, as in equation 4.17. It is not completely independent of time, since k_f and k_b must change slightly as the equilibrium constant is altered; however, all displacements must be kept small, and to a sufficient approximation τ may be assumed constant during the impulse.[23] We consider only systems with a single relaxation time; if there are several, linear combinations of the various y's must be used.[3]

[22] An alternative form of equation 4.24 is

$$\tau(dz/dt)+z = K$$

where $z = c/ab$. This again shows the dependence of concentration changes on variations in K. Cf. Freedman, *J. Chem. Phys.* 1953, **21**, 1784.

[23] Strictly speaking, the conditions should also be specified, e.g. constant pressure and temperature, or constant pressure and entropy, etc. Cf. Davies and Lamb, *Proc. Phys. Soc.*, B, 1956, **69**, 293.

The solution of the general differential equation 4.24 depends upon the way in which $\bar{y}$ is made to vary with time. A damped harmonic oscillation is represented by the equation:

$$\bar{y} = Ae^{-bt}\sin \omega t \qquad (4.26)$$

Here b is the damping constant, $\omega/2\pi$ is the frequency in cycles per second (determining the duration of the impulse), and A is the undamped amplitude. Combining equations 4.26 and 4.24, we obtain:

$$\tau(dy/dt) + y = Ae^{-bt}\sin \omega t \qquad (4.27)$$

The solution of this is:

$$y = Ae^{-bt}[(1-b\tau)^2 + \omega^2\tau^2]^{-1/2}[\sin(\omega t - \delta) + e^{-t(1-b\tau)/\tau}\sin \delta] \qquad (4.28)$$

where

$$\tan \delta = \omega\tau/(1-b\tau) \qquad (4.29)$$

This equation, when compared with equation 4.26, implies that y follows the damped oscillation of $\bar{y}$ but with an amplitude reduced by a factor of $[(1-b\tau)^2 + \omega^2\tau^2]^{1/2}$, as well as a phase difference depending on δ. The amplitude thus depends on τ (cf. Fig. 4.5), and τ may be determined from measurements of the amplitude (i.e. the maximum value) of some property related to y, such as conductivity, along with an independent determination of the damping constant b.

CHAPTER 5

Relaxation methods (II): Ultrasonic absorption and related methods

GENERAL PRINCIPLES

The general principle of relaxation methods is (p. 59) that some parameter affecting a chemical equilibrium is changed so rapidly that the reaction lags behind. We have seen in Chapter 4 how this principle is applied to single displacements of temperature, pressure or electric field, and have noticed some of the general characteristics of relaxation methods (p. 77). In this chapter we turn to methods based on periodic displacements. The effect of such a disturbance will depend on the relation of the relaxation time of the reaction to the periodic time or frequency of the disturbance.[1] We can approach the matter by considering first the effect of an alternating field on a weak electrolyte, although this has not been successfully applied to the measurement of reaction rates in practice.

Periodic variation of electric field

Suppose we apply a high-frequency alternating field to a solution of a weak electrolyte, so that the dissociation field effect (p. 71) is

[1] For short accounts, see Eigen, (a) *Discuss. Faraday Soc.* 1954, **17**, 194; (b) *Discuss. Faraday Soc.* 1957, **24**, 25; (c) *Z. Elektrochem.* 1960, **64**, 115. For a fuller account see (d) Eigen and De Maeyer, in *Investigation of Rates and Mechanisms of Reactions*, Part II, ed. Friess, Lewis and Weissberger (Interscience, 1963), chap. 18). The fundamental theory is fully treated by (e) Sette, *Dispersion and Absorption of Sound Waves in Liquids and Mixtures of Liquids*, in *Handbuch der Physik*, vol. xi, part 2 (Springer Verlag, 1961), pp. 202–274; and (f) Tamm, *Schallabsorption und Dispersion in Wassrigen Elektrolytlösungen, ibid.*, pp. 275–360; also by (g) Herzfeld and Litovitz, *Absorption and Dispersion of Ultrasonic Waves* (Academic Press, 1959).

made to occur periodically with frequency $f = \omega/2\pi$ cycles per second. The results are illustrated in Fig. 5.1, in which the upper curve represents the variation with time of the external parameter (the field strength), and the lower curves represent the corresponding variations of some parameter representing the extent of reaction (such as the degree of dissociation) for different relaxation times τ. If the equilibrium is set up relatively slowly, so that τ is much

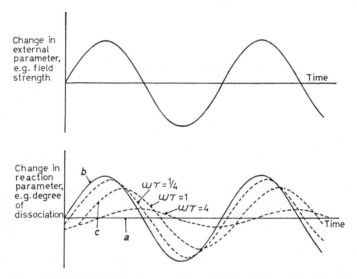

FIG. 5.1. Periodic disturbance of chemical equilibrium by external parameter (electric field, temperature, pressure).

longer than the period of oscillation of the field, the degree of dissociation is little affected and remains practically at the value corresponding to zero field (line a in Fig. 5.1). If the equilibrium is set up relatively very fast, the dissociation follows closely the variations of the field strength, and so alters in phase with it (curve b). If, however, the relaxation-time of the equilibrium is comparable with the periodic time of the field, the dissociation lags behind the field, and therefore varies according to one of the dashed curves such as c. This has a smaller amplitude than curve b, and is out of phase with the variations of the field. This phase difference leads to dissipation of electrical energy as heat, and so to absorption of power from the field. As we increase the frequency of the field from zero, the lag at first increases, and with it the absorption per cycle; later the effect of the decreasing amplitude begins to dominate, and the absorption falls again. Thus at a certain frequency there is a maximum in the absorption per cycle. The mathematical treatment shows that this maximum occurs at a frequency given by $\omega\tau = 1$, where ω is the angular frequency in radians per second, equal to $2\pi f$ where f is the frequency in cycles per second. It would therefore be possible in principle to determine τ for the dissociation equilibrium of a weak acid by applying an alternating field, determining the energy absorption as a function of frequency, and finding the value of ω for maximum absorption, which we may write ω_c; then $\tau = 1/\omega_c$. In practice there are difficulties (p. 102).

Periodic variation of temperature and pressure

The temperature and pressure of a solution can be varied periodically by means of ultrasonic waves. Sound-waves are propagated adiabatically, giving rise to small periodic fluctuations of temperature and pressure in the medium.[2] A reaction whose equilibrium is sensitive to temperature or pressure (cf. pp. 64, 69), and whose relaxation time is comparable with the periodic time, will lag behind the ultrasonic vibrations, and energy will be absorbed. The absorption will be a maximum at a certain frequency, for reasons similar to those given above in connection with electric fields. The treatment outlined below (pp. 84–90) shows that for a single relaxation process the absorption coefficient per wavelength (μ) varies with frequency as shown by curve a in Fig. 5.2; it is proportional to $\omega\tau/(1+\omega^2\tau^2)$. This function has a maximum value ($\frac{1}{2}$) when $\omega\tau = 1$. Thus the curve has the following equation, in which μ_{max} is the maximum value of μ:

$$\mu = 2\mu_{max}\,\omega\tau/(1+\omega^2\tau^2) \tag{5.1}$$

Correspondingly the values of μ/ω are given by:

$$\mu/\omega = 2\mu_{max}\,\tau/(/1+\omega^2\tau^2) \tag{5.2}$$

[2] The temperature fluctuations are of the order of $\pm\,0\cdot001°$ or less. Their magnitude depends on that of $(C_p - C_v)$. In water they are exceptionally small and become zero at about 4°C.

and in the critical region μ/ω declines rapidly with increase of frequency, as shown in curve b of Fig. 5.2. If the frequency for the maximum in curve a, or the point of inflection in curve b, is designated f_c or $\omega_c/2\pi$, then τ is given by $1/\omega_c$, and can be found from the experimental plots. The rate constant can be determined as usual from τ and the equilibrium concentrations (p. 60). This method can be used over a wide range of frequencies, from about 10^4 to

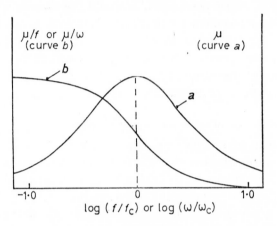

FIG. 5.2. Sound absorption coefficient per wavelength (μ) for a single relaxation, as a function of frequency (f or $\omega/2\pi$).

nearly 10^9 c/sec, and rate constants up to 10^{11} l mole^{-1} sec^{-1} have been determined by its aid.

We must now consider these methods in greater detail.

ULTRASONIC-ABSORPTION OR ACOUSTIC METHODS

Principles

The fundamental equations

We must first define the absorption coefficients.[3] The attenuation of a sound wave passing through a fluid is related exponentially to

[3] See, for example, (a) Hueter and Bolt, *Sonics* (Chapman & Hall, 1955), chapter 8 and Appendix; (b) Bergmann, *Der Ultraschall* (Hirzel Verlag, Stuttgart, 1954; Eng. trans. of 1st edn., Wiley, 1938); (c) refs. 1e, 1f.

the distance travelled by the wave; if P_0 is the initial amplitude, and P the amplitude after a distance d cm, then

$$P = P_0\,e^{-\alpha d} \tag{5.3}$$

Here α is the coefficient of absorption per centimetre. Another useful quantity is the dimensionless coefficient of absorption per wavelength, or per cycle, μ; this is defined by the following equations, in which λ is the wavelength, f is the frequency $(f = \omega/2\pi)$, and c is the velocity of the wave $(c = \lambda f)$:

$$\mu = \alpha\lambda = \alpha c/f = 2\pi\alpha c/\omega \tag{5.4}$$

It is this quantity μ which, for a single relaxation process, shows a maximum when $\omega\tau = 1$, according to equation 5.1 and Fig. 5.2. A brief outline of the derivation of equation 5.1 is as follows. We use the symbols and results of the treatment in chapter 4, and start from the fundamental equation 4.24 (p. 79):

$$\tau(dy/dt) + y = \bar{y}$$

where

$$y = a - a^*, \quad \bar{y} = \bar{a} - a^*, \quad \tau^{-1} = k_f(a^* + b^*) + k_b$$

This differential equation controls the response of the system, indicated by the changes in the term y representing the actual concentrations, to variations in the term $\bar{y}$ representing the (unattained) equilibrium concentrations. The variations in $\bar{y}$ correspond to the changes in equilibrium constant, imposed by the periodic changes of temperature and pressure in the ultrasonic wave; thus $\bar{y}$ varies sinusoidally with time, following the full line in Fig. 5.1. The reference values of the concentrations, a^*, etc., are those at the mean position of the fluctuations. Suppose $\bar{y}$ oscillates with frequency $\omega/2\pi$ and amplitude p, so that:

$$\bar{y} = p \sin \omega t \tag{5.5}$$

This expression for $\bar{y}$ may be substituted in the fundamental differential equation above, to give the following expression for the variation with time of the actual concentration term y:

$$\tau(dy/dt) + y = p \sin \omega t \tag{5.6}$$

Since the displacements are small, τ is effectively constant. The solution of equation 5.6 in the steady state is:

$$y = \left(\frac{1}{1+\omega^2\tau^2}\right) p \sin \omega t - \left(\frac{\omega\tau}{1+\omega^2\tau^2}\right) p \cos \omega t \qquad (5.7)$$

Equation 5.7 is the mathematical representation of the dashed curves in Fig. 5.1. On comparing it with equation 5.5, we see that its first term represents a harmonic variation of y in phase with $\bar{y}$, and its second term a harmonic variation out of phase with $\bar{y}$. It is this out-of-phase term which leads to absorption of power. The absorption per cycle is proportional to the amplitude of this out-of-phase variation of concentrations, which is evidently proportional to $\omega\tau/(1+\omega^2\tau^2)$. Thus we obtain:

$$\mu \propto \omega\tau/(1+\omega^2\tau^2)$$

as was stated earlier without proof (equation 5.1).

The magnitude of μ_{max}

The value of μ_{max} depends on the liquid and the temperature; if the relaxation is due to a reaction between dissolved substances, it depends also on their mole fractions. The full mathematical treatment[4] shows that μ_{max} depends on the relaxational contribution to the adiabatic compressibility β. If β has the value β_0 at zero frequency, and $(\beta_0 - \Delta\beta)$ at infinite frequency, then, if ρ is the density,

$$2\mu_{max} = \pi\rho c^2 \Delta\beta \qquad (5.8)$$

Since the velocity c is nearly constant, and $c^2 \approx 1/\rho\beta_0$, we may also write

$$2\mu_{max} \simeq \pi\Delta\beta/\beta_0 \qquad (5.8a)$$

This $\Delta\beta$ is in turn related to the difference between the heat capacities of the system at zero and at infinite frequency, $C_{p_0} - C_{p_\infty}$, written $\Delta'C_p'$ (this must not be confused with the

[4] (a) Manes, J. Chem. Phys., 1954, 21, 1791; (b) Freedman, ibid., p. 1784; (c) Andreae and Lamb, Proc. Phys. Soc., B, 1956, 69, 814; (d) Davies and Lamb, Quart. Rev. Chem. Soc. 1957, 11, 134; (e) Davies and Lamb, Proc. Phys. Soc. 1959, 73, 767; (f) Herzfeld and Litovitz, ref. 1g, sections 12–18; (g) Andreae, unpublished work; (h) refs. 1e, 1f and 16f.

difference in C_p between products and reactants). In terms of $\Delta'C_p$, the equation for $\mu_{\max}$ is as follows, where θ_0 is the coefficient of thermal expansion at zero frequency and γ_0 is the ratio of specific heats at zero frequency, while ΔH and ΔV are the enthalpy and volume changes associated with the reaction:

$$2\mu_{\max} = \frac{\pi(\gamma_0 - 1)}{C_{p\infty}} \left(1 - \frac{\Delta V}{\Delta H}\frac{C_{p_0}}{V\theta_0}\right)^2 \Delta'C_p \qquad (5.9)$$

If pressure has no appreciable effect on the equilibrium, as with isomerization reactions in pure liquids, equation 5.9 simplifies to:

$$2\mu_{\max} = \pi(\gamma_0 - 1)\,\Delta'C_p/C_{p\infty} \qquad (5.9a)$$

If there is no appreciable temperature-effect, as in water, the following equation may be derived from equation 5.8a:

$$2\mu_{\max} = (\pi T/V\beta_0)(\Delta V/\Delta H)^2\,\Delta'C_p \qquad (5.9b)$$

The relation between absorption coefficient, frequency and relaxation time: determination of relaxation times

We can re-write equation 5.1 in terms of the frequency $f(=\omega/2\pi)$ and the frequency for maximum absorption $f_c(=\omega_c/2\pi = 1/2\pi\tau)$ as follows:

$$\mu = 2\mu_{\max}(f/f_c)\,/\,[1 + (f/f_c)^2] \qquad (5.10)$$

In practice the quantity measured is not μ but the coefficient of absorption per centimetre α, equal to μ/λ or $\mu f/c$. For the variation of α with frequency, substitution in equation 5.10 gives:

$$\alpha/f^2 = \mu/cf = (2\mu_{\max}/cf_c)\,/\,[1 + (f/f_c)^2] \qquad (5.11)$$

The velocity c is not usually measured, since precise determinations are difficult; however, calculation shows that it will vary only slightly with frequency, and this has been confirmed by observation for some liquids.[5] We may therefore take the numerator

[5] The velocity of sound, like μ, depends on the adiabatic compressibility, and will exhibit a change-over from a low-frequency value to a high-frequency value at f_c. The velocity dispersion is given approximately by $\Delta c/c = \mu_{\max}/\pi$. The change is small; with acetic acid, for example, it is less than 2% (see ref. 7a).

on the right of equation 5.11 as independent of frequency, and write
it as A:

$$\alpha/f^2 = A / [1 + (f/f_c)^2] \qquad (5.12)$$

The variation of α/f^2 with frequency will, according to this equation,
follow a curve like curve b in Fig. 5.2, with a point of inflection at f_c.

This equation 5.12 describes the absorption due to a single
relaxation process. Besides this absorption, however, there is
always a considerable background absorption due to viscosity and
heat conduction, and possibly also to other relaxation processes

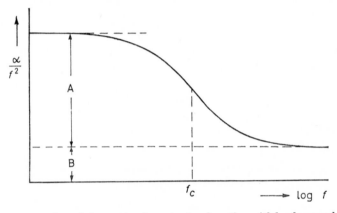

FIG. 5.3. Sound absorption for a single relaxation with background.
Plot of α/f^2 against $\log f$.

having shorter relaxation times, such as dipole orientation or
translation-vibration energy-exchange. This background absorption makes a contribution to α which is proportional to f^2. The
observed relation between α and frequency is thus obtained by
adding a constant B to equation 5.12:

$$\alpha/f^2 = A / [1 + (f/f_c)^2] + B \qquad (5.13)$$

With increase of frequency, α/f^2 falls off not to zero as in Fig. 5.2,
but to a finite limiting value, as shown in Fig. 5.3. By fitting equation 5.13 to the experimental points, it is possible to find f_c and
hence the relaxation time $\tau (= 1/2\pi f_c)$.

The possibility of detecting relaxation for a reaction in solution
depends on the sensitivity of the technique and the relative values

of A and B in equation 5.13. The value of B is generally close to that for the pure solvent, and is especially low for water.[6] The value of A depends on the concentrations and the thermodynamic properties of the reaction (equation 5.9). The concentrations at which relaxation can be observed therefore vary considerably from system to system. For strong electrolytes in water (p. 94), concentrations of 0·01 M are often enough; for acetic acid in toluene (p. 99), about 0·1 M; for trinitrobenzene plus diethylamine in acetone[10c], about 1 M. Pure liquids are exceptionally convenient to work with (pp. 100 seq.).

To find the relaxation time for a reaction in a given solution from measurements of the absorption coefficient α, we can proceed as follows. We first determine α/f^2 at the highest and lowest frequencies available. If there is no appreciable difference, we compare the value of α/f^2 with that for the pure solvent; if the former is larger, a decrease at some higher frequency cannot be ruled out; if the two values are indistinguishable, there may be a decrease at some lower frequency, or the solution may be too dilute to show sufficient relaxation absorption. If, however, the absorption coefficients at the two ends of the frequency range show an appreciable difference, it is probably due to relaxation, and by making measurements at intermediate frequencies we can find the changeover region shown in Fig. 5.3. We then assume that the data will fit equation 5.13, corresponding to a single relaxation, and find the best values for A, B and f_c.[7] If these reproduce the experimental values adequately over a sufficient range of frequencies, we conclude that only a single relaxation is taking place, and evaluate τ as $1/2\pi f_c$. From the variation of τ with the concentrations, we deduce the rate constants, with the help of the relations given on pp. 60 seq., taking activity coefficients into account if necessary. If equation 5.13 does not represent the data satisfactorily, it is probable that more than one relaxation is occurring. (This is often the case for solutions containing ions.) The procedure is then more

[6] Values of A and B for various liquids are listed by (a) Heasell and Lamb, Proc. Phys. Soc., B, 1956, **69**, 869; (b) Andreae et al., refs. 10c, 10d.

[7] (a) Lamb and Pinkerton, Proc. Roy. Soc., A, 1949, **199**, 114; (b) Heasell and Lamb, idem, 1956, **237**, 233; (c) Andreae, Joyce and Oliver, Proc. Phys. Soc. 1960, **75**, 82; (d) Andreae and Joyce, ref. 6b.

complex, but if the measurements cover sufficient ranges of frequency and concentration it is possible to determine the several relaxation times.[1d,16f] An alternative method of determining rate constants from measurements at several temperatures at a single frequency has been developed by Maier.[8]

Identification of the relaxation process. It remains to identify the process or processes responsible for relaxation. The value of τ and its concentration-dependence usually enable us to distinguish relaxation due to chemical equilibrium from that due to such processes as internal rotation and energy-transfer in the solvent (pp. 100, 101). It is also useful to compare A with the value expected for such processes, and B with the value for the pure solvent. Solvent–solute interactions may also be important; they are especially prominent in aqueous solutions of ions, where hydration and hydrolysis may occur, as well as ion-pair formation (p. 94). Separate measurements of the absorption for solutions of the various reactants are therefore desirable, and it is useful to have some independent knowledge of the system from other sources.

Techniques of measuring ultrasonic absorption

General

To determine the frequency f_c at which the absorption coefficient μ is a maximum, measurements of absorption must be made over a frequency range of at least a decade, as may be seen from Figs. 5.2

TABLE 5.1

Ultrasonic-absorption techniques

Method	Frequency range (approx.) (c/sec)	Volume of liquid (litres)	Error in α
Pulse	2×10^8 to $1 \cdot 5 \times 10^6$	$0 \cdot 01$–$0 \cdot 5$	± 2–5%
Optical	1×10^8 to $1 \cdot 5 \times 10^6$		$\pm 5\%$
Streaming	2×10^6 to $1 \cdot 5 \times 10^5$	< 1	± 5–10%
Reverberation	1×10^6 to 5×10^4	*ca.* 100	$\pm 15\%$
Resonant sphere	$1 \cdot 5 \times 10^6$ to 5×10^3	1 to 50	$\lessgtr \pm 5\%$

[8] Maier and Rudolph, *Z. phys. Chem. (Frankfurt)*, 1957, **10**, 83.

and 5.3; the range must be wider if more than one relaxation is involved, as Fig. 5.6 shows. There are several techniques (Table 5.1); each has a limited range, because the background absorption increases steeply, with the square of the frequency. Between them they cover fairly continuously the range from about 10^4 to nearly 10^9 c/sec.[9]

Experimental

Pulse technique.[10] The method adapted to the shortest times is the pulse technique. This is illustrated in Fig. 5.4 which refers to the

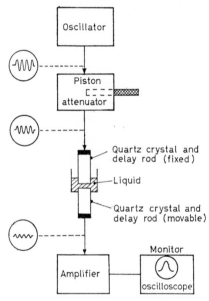

FIG. 5.4. Ultrasonic absorption: pulse technique (schematic).

apparatus described by Andreae and Joyce[10c]. A piezo-electric transducer (a quartz crystal) is subjected to a train of radiofrequency pulses generated by an oscillator, whose frequency can be

[9] For a survey see (a) Tamm, ref. 1e, or Z. *Elektrochem.* 1960, **64**, 73; or (b) Kurtze and Tamm, *Acustica*, 1953, **3**, 33; and ref. 10a; (c) Eigen, ref. 1d.

[10] See, for example, (a) Tamm, Kurtze and Kaiser, *Acustica*, 1954, **4**, 380; (b) Andreae, Bass, Heasell and Lamb, *idem*, 1958, **8**, 133; (c) Andreae and Joyce, *Brit. J. Appl. Physics* 1962, **13**, 462; (d) Edmonds, Pearce and Andreae, *ibid.*, p. 551.

controlled and measured. The resulting ultrasonic pulses pass through the liquid under investigation to another transducer acting as detector. The pulses are kept short, and the path length is increased by silica delay rods, so that the electrical disturbance radiated directly by the oscillator to the detector may be separated from the signal received through the transducers. The absorption is measured at a series of path-lengths, to eliminate end-effects. This may be done by interposing between the oscillator and the transducer a piston attenuator, which gives an accurately-known variable attenuation, and adjusting it so that the changes in absorption are compensated and the transmitted signal maintained constant, while the path-length is changed at a steady rate. This compensation can be effected by servo-motors, and the movement of the piston made to trace automatically a linear plot corresponding to the logarithm of the amplitude against path-length; the slope of this plot gives the absorption coefficient α. This is the most accurate way of measuring absorption. The upper limit of frequency, set by attenuation in the delay rods, is about $2\cdot5 \times 10^8$ c/sec; the lower limit is about 10^6 c/sec, below which the absorption coefficient has decreased so much that long path lengths, large transducers and large quantities of liquid would be needed.

Optical technique.[11] Another method which is applicable in the high-frequency range (1×10^8 to $1\cdot5 \times 10^6$ c/sec) makes use of the Debye-Sears effect. The passage of plane ultrasonic waves through a liquid sets up periodic variations of density, which act like the lines of an optical grating and diffract a light beam crossing the ultrasonic beam at right angles. The light intensity in the first-order diffraction beam is proportional to the sound intensity, so long as this is low. The light intensity is measured photoelectrically at a series of distances (up to a metre) from the ultrasonic transducer.

Streaming technique.[12] When a plane ultrasonic wave passes along a column of liquid, the absorption produces a small difference of pressure between the two ends; the liquid in a narrow tube

[11] (a) Kurtze and Tamm, ref. 9b; (b) Maier, Z. Naturforschung. 1955, **10A**, 997.

[12] (a) Piercy and Lamb, Proc. Roy. Soc., A, 1954, **226**, 43; (b) Piercy, J. Phys. Rad. 1956, **17**, 405; (c) Hall and Lamb, Proc, Phys. Soc. 1959, **78**, 354.

connecting the ends will therefore move, with a velocity that can be determined in various ways. This method can be used down to slightly lower frequencies (about $1\cdot3 \times 10^5$ c/sec) but the technique is difficult.

Damped-oscillation methods. In the *resonant-sphere method*[13] the liquid is contained in a spherical vessel (Fig. 5.5), and a train of ultrasonic pulses is applied radially by a piezo-electric transducer; the frequency is chosen so that the vibrations are almost entirely in the radial modes. A second transducer picks up the signal, which is

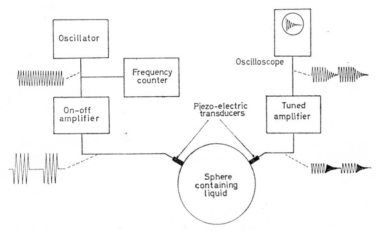

FIG. 5.5. Ultrasonic absorption: resonant-sphere method (after Andreae).

displayed on a cathode-ray oscillograph screen, and shows how the vibration dies away as each pulse comes to an end. The time-constant of the exponential decay is equal to $1/\alpha c$. Wall effects are reduced by supporting the sphere by thin wires in an evacuated chamber; but they cannot be eliminated, and the apparatus must be calibrated with a liquid of known absorption. The frequency range is about 5×10^3 to $1\cdot5 \times 10^6$ c/sec; the volume used ranges from 1 to 50 l. The principle is the same in the *reverberation method*,[13b] except that a cylindrical vessel is used, so that the

[13] (a) Moen, *J. Acoust. Soc. Amer.* 1951, **23**, 62; (b) Kurtze and Tamm, *Acustica*, 1953, **3**, 33; (c) Karpovitch, *J. Acoust. Soc. Amer.* 1954, **26**, 819; (d) Lawley and Reed, *Acustica*, 1955, **5**, 316; (e) Andreae, *Proc. Third Intern. Congr. Acoustics*, ed. Cremer (Elsevier, 1961), p. 556.

symmetry is low and a range of vibrational modes is excited. The *hollow tuning-fork method*[14, 13e] makes use of the fact that compression of an enclosed liquid alters the damping of the oscillations of the fork; its frequency range is in the region of 10^2 c/sec, but it has not yet been developed into a reliable method.

Some general features of the ultrasonic method

The great advantages of the ultrasonic method are that there are no restrictions on the type of equilibrium to which it is applicable, and that a range of relaxation times from about 10^{-4} sec down to nearly 10^{-9} sec can be measured,[15] though the accuracy is good only at the lower end. Several of the techniques are adaptable to low temperatures; the pulse method has been used down to $-80°$. Since relaxation may be due to a variety of causes, it is well to have some independent knowledge of the chemical equilibrium which is to be studied. The equilibrium must be sufficiently sensitive to either pressure or temperature; that is, the reaction must contribute appreciably to the heat capacity (and hence the compressibility) of the liquid. In consequence considerable concentrations may be needed to bring about a measurable effect (p. 89). The volume of liquid required is quite small for the high-frequency pulse technique, but for most of the lower-frequency techniques it is considerable. All the techniques require special electronic equipment.

Applications of ultrasonics measurements

Ion-pair formation and desolvation of ions in aqueous solutions of electrolytes.[16]

The absorption coefficients μ of a number of electrolytes in aqueous solutions have been measured over a wide range of frequencies,

[14] Andreae, Jupp and Vincent, *J. Acoust. Soc. Amer.* 1960, **32**, 406.

[15] At its upper end the range overlaps that of the temperature-jump and similar methods (chapter 4) and approaches that of the flow methods (chapter 3).

[16] Experimental: see especially (*a*) Kurtze and Tamm, ref. 9*b*, and (*b*) Tamm, Kurtze and Kaiser, ref. 10*a*; summarized by Tamm, ref. 1*f*. Discussions: see also (*c*) Eigen, Kurtze and Tamm, *Z. Elektrochem.* 1953, **57**, 103; (*d*) Eigen, ref. 1*d*, 1*c*; (*e*) Suryanarayana, *J. Phys. Chem.* 1962, **66**, 360; (*f*) Eigen and Tamm, *Z. Elektrochem.* 1962, **66**, 93; (*g*) *ibid.*, 107.

from 10^4 to 3×10^8 c/sec, by means of the pulse, optical, resonant-sphere and reverberation techniques. The values of the ratio (μ/concentration) are nearly independent of concentration over

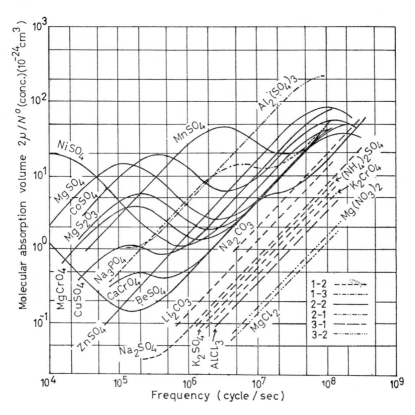

FIG. 5.6. Ultrasonic absorption of electrolytes in aqueous solution (10^{-2} to 10^{-1} M) at $20°$, after correction for background absorption by water. Plots of (μ/conc.) against logarithm of frequency. (From Eigen, ref. 1*b*.)

the range 0·01 to 0·1 M. Some of the results are shown in Fig. 5.6.

The curves for the 2:2 electrolytes, such as the sulphates of divalent cations, are the most interesting; they mostly show two distinct maxima, which usually have the shape characteristic of a

single relaxation (like curve a in Fig. 5.2), so that the two critical
frequencies and relaxation times can readily be determined.
When the temperature is varied, linear plots of $\ln(f_c/T)$ against
$1/T$ are obtained, from which energies of activation may be
derived.

The next step is to identify the relaxation processes. The following is the interpretation given by Eigen and his co-workers.[16]
Solvent–solvent, ion-solvent, and intramolecular relaxations can
be excluded in this frequency range. Both maxima are attributed to
specific interactions, rather than to long-range coulombic interactions, after detailed consideration of the absolute magnitudes of
the absorption coefficients and relaxation times, and their dependence on concentration and temperature. It is known that these
electrolytes are associated to ion-pairs, to the extent of about 10%
at these concentrations. However, the rate constant for the meeting
of the ions by diffusion is around 10^{10} to 10^{11} l mole^{-1}sec^{-1} (p. 12),
which corresponds to a relaxation time too short to be observed.
The occurrence of two maxima therefore suggests that, after the
ions have approached close enough by a diffusion process (1 in the
scheme below) for specific interactions to become important, two
subsequent processes (2 and 3) with longer relaxation times occur
within the complex:

$$M^{++} + X^{--} \underset{1}{\rightleftarrows} (M, X) \underset{2}{\rightleftarrows} (M, X)' \underset{3}{\rightleftarrows} (M, X)''$$

These processes 2 and 3 are identified by Eigen as the removal
of solvent molecules from the anion and cation of the ion-pair,
according to the scheme below. The higher-frequency maximum
(corresponding to process 2) has a frequency almost independent
of the cation; it is therefore attributed to removal of water from
the anion, which remains separated from the cation by a solvation
shell of water molecules. The rate constants for this process 2 are
all of the order of 10^9 sec^{-1}. The lower-frequency maximum (corresponding to process 3) is much the same for different anions, but
very specifically influenced by the cation; the values of f_c for
Be^{++}, Mg^{++} and Mn^{++} are respectively about 10^3, 10^5, and 3×10^6
c/sec. This maximum is attributed to removal of water from the

coordination shell of the cation and its replacement by SO_4^{--} to form the inner ion-pair. Thus the complete scheme is:

$$M^{++} + X^{--} \; \underset{k_{1b}}{\overset{k_{1f}}{\rightleftharpoons}} \; \left[M^{++} O \overset{H}{\underset{H}{\diagdown}} O \overset{H}{\underset{H}{\diagdown}} B^{--} \right] aq. \; \underset{k_{2b}}{\overset{k_{2f}}{\rightleftharpoons}}$$

$$\left[M^{++} O \overset{H}{\underset{H}{\diagdown}} B^{--} \right] aq. \; \underset{k_{3b}}{\overset{k_{3f}}{\rightleftharpoons}} \; M^{++} B^{--} \; aq.$$

The rate constants for the lower-frequency process $3(k_{3f}$ and $k_{3b})$ are given in Table 5.2. In the series Be^{++}, Mg^{++}, Ca^{++}, both rate

TABLE 5.2

Rate constants for relaxation in aqueous 2:2 electrolyte solutions at 20°.

For meanings of symbols see text. The data are taken from refs. 1c and 16g. Values of k_{3b} are determined from f_c. Those of k_{3f} are obtained by combining k_{3b} with an equilibrium constant estimated from the absolute values of μ_{max}, and are less exact.

M^{++}	X^{--}	k_{3f} (sec^{-1})	k_{3b} (sec^{-1})	r_M (Å)
Be^{++}	SO_4^{--}	1×10^2	$1 \cdot 3 \times 10^3$	$0 \cdot 35$
Mg^{++}	SO_4^{--}	1×10^5	8×10^5	$0 \cdot 78$
Ca^{++}	SO_4^{--}	$ca.\ 10^7$	$ca.\ 10^8$	$0 \cdot 99$
Mg^{++}	$S_2O_3^{--}$	1×10^5	$1 \cdot 5 \times 10^6$	$0 \cdot 78$
Mg^{++}	CrO_4^{--}	1×10^5	$1 \cdot 5 \times 10^6$	$0 \cdot 78$
Zn^{++}	SO_4^{--}	$> 10^7$	$> 10^8$	$0 \cdot 83$
Cu^{++}	SO_4^{--}	$> 10^7$	2×10^8	$0 \cdot 72$
Ni^{++}	SO_4^{--}	1×10^4	1×10^5	$0 \cdot 78$
Co^{++}	SO_4^{--}	2×10^5	$2 \cdot 5 \times 10^6$	$0 \cdot 82$
Fe^{++}	SO_4^{--}	1×10^6	6×10^6	$0 \cdot 83$
Mn^{++}	SO_4^{--}	4×10^6	2×10^7	$0 \cdot 91$

constants increase greatly with increase of ionic radius r_M, that is with decrease of the field of the cation, as would be expected.[17] In the transition-metal series Mn^{++}, Fe^{++}, Co^{++}, Ni^{++}, Cu^{++}, the variations of k_f are not accounted for by the changes in ionic radius;

they have been attributed to the effects of crystal field stabilization.[1c,16g] Energies of activation are in the region of 6–9 kcal mole^{-1} for Mg^{++}, Ni^{++} and Co^{++}. For Mg^{++} and Co^{++}, the rate constants are very similar to those for the association of these ions with other complexing agents.[17]

These reactions of sulphate ion with metal cations are markedly slower than its reaction with hydrogen ion (below). The reason is no doubt that, while the formation of the ion pair $M^{++}SO_4^{--}$ requires the removal of solvating water molecules, that of HSO_4^- requires only the transfer of a proton from one of them (p. 267).

Beryllium sulphate is a special case.[18] At pH 3·5 it shows not less than six relaxation-times between 1 and 10^{-9} sec, the fastest having been found by ultrasonic absorption and others by the temperature-jump method (p. 67n). Three of these are attributed to hydrolysis and three to the stepwise formation of the ion-pair.

The important general conclusion emerges that encounters between unsolvated ions (at least of the higher charge-types) are much less frequent than those between hydrated ions, and require activation energy. This presumably applies to ionic reactions as well as to ion-pair formation. These results are further discussed in chapter 12 (pp. 275–279).

Proton-transfer reactions

Sulphuric acid.[19] The critical frequency for aqueous sulphuric acid is too high to observe, but a relaxation process is indicated by the displacement with increasing concentration of the nearly linear plots of μ against frequency. From the concentration dependence and the absolute value of μ, it is possible to attribute the relaxation to the proton-transfer reaction:

$$H_3O^+ + SO_4^{--} \rightleftarrows HSO_4^- + H_2O$$

[17] Cf. Eigen (a) in *Advances in the Chemistry of Coordination Compounds*, ed. Kirschner (Macmillan, 1961), p. 371; (b) Eigen, *Pure and Appl. Chem.* 1963, **6**, 97; and the discussions below in chapter 12 (pp. 276, 288). For other results see also pp. 50, 67, 257.

[18] Diebler and Eigen, *Z. phys. Chem.* (*Frankfurt*), 1959, **20**, 299.

[19] Experimental: refs. 9b, 10a. Interpretation: (a) Eigen, Kurtze and Tamm, ref 16c; (b) Eigen, *Z. phys. Chem.* (*Frankfurt*), 1954, **1**, 176.

with a rate constant of $(1 \pm 0.5) \times 10^{11}$ l mole^{-1}sec^{-1}. This is comparable with the values obtained for similar reactions by other methods. The significance of the results is discussed later (p. 262).

Aqueous ammonia.[10a, 19b] Here the critical frequency can be determined; it is concentration-dependent, as expected for the reaction

$$NH_4^+ + OH^- \rightleftarrows NH_4OH$$

and agrees with the rate constant found for this reaction by the electric-impulse method, 3×10^{10} l mole^{-1}sec ^{1} (p. 75).

Aqueous sulphurous acid.[20] From the critical frequency, the forward and reverse rate constants at $20°$ for the overall reaction

$$H_3O^+ + HSO_3^- \rightleftarrows SO_2 + 2H_2O$$

are found to be 2×10^8 l mole^{-1}sec^{-1} and 3.4×10^6 sec^{-1} respectively. These are several powers of ten faster than for the corresponding reaction involving carbon dioxide (p. 57).

Association of carboxylic acids by hydrogen bonding

Ultrasonic relaxation has been observed in solutions of benzoic acid, and attributed to the dimerization equilibrium $2A \rightleftarrows A_2$, which had already been studied from the thermodynamic point of view and ascribed to hydrogen bonding. Relaxation times have been measured[21] for solutions in toluene and carbon tetrachloride, from $10°$ to $50°$. Some of the results are given in Table 5.3.

The results may perhaps be interpreted as follows. The value of ΔH in carbon tetrachloride has about the value to be expected for the rupture of the two hydrogen bonds, and suggests that there is little difference of solvation between dimer and monomer in this solvent. The lower value in toluene suggests that the monomer is here more solvated than the dimer. The fact that ΔH_a^* is nearly unaffected by the change in solvent, while ΔH_d^* is reduced by 4.6 kcal mole^{-1}, indicates that for the dissociation in toluene the extra solvation has occurred already in the transition state. This is an

[20] Eigen, Kustin and Maass, *Z. phys. Chem. (Frankfurt)*, 1961, **30**, 130.
[21] Maier, (a) *Z. phys. Chem. (Frankfurt)*, 1960, **14**, 133; (b) *Z. Elektrochem.* 1960, **64**, 132. For a review of the thermodynamic data see (c) Allen and Caldin, *Quart. Rev. Chem. Soc.* 1953, **7**, 255.

TABLE 5.3

Dimerization of benzoic acid in solution

ΔH_a^* and k_a refer to association, ΔH_d^* and k_d to dissociation. ΔH's in kcal mole^{-1}; k_a in l mole^{-1}sec^{-1}, k_d in sec^{-1}, at 25°.

Solvent	k_a	k_d	ΔH_a^*	ΔH_d^*	ΔH
CCl_4	$4 \cdot 7 \times 10^9$	$7 \cdot 4 \times 10^5$	$2 \cdot 9 (\pm 20\%)$	$13 \cdot 3 (\pm 20\%)$	$10 \cdot 4 (\pm 15\%)$
$C_6H_5CH_3$	$1 \cdot 6 \times 10^9$	$3 \cdot 7 \times 10^6$	$3 \cdot 0 (\pm 5\%)$	$8 \cdot 7 (\pm 8\%)$	$5 \cdot 7 (\pm 15\%)$

instance where the change of solvation makes a considerable difference to the energy of activation.

The results on acetic acid, which historically was one of the first liquids in which ultrasonic relaxation was observed, are more complex.[22] Two relaxation times, differing by an order of magnitude, are observed in solution, though only one is found in the pure liquid. It has been suggested that in solution the two hydrogen bonds in the dimer are broken stepwise, each with its characteristic relaxation time. The velocity constants are in the region of 10^5 l mole^{-1}sec^{-1}.

The dimerization of phenol in carbon tetrachloride is another reaction that has been studied by ultrasonics.[23] Other hydrogen-bonding reactions have been investigated by fluorescence methods (pp. 161, 163). They are further discussed on p. 275.

Rotational isomerism

Certain pure liquids exhibit ultrasonic absorption, with a single relaxation time. This is attributed to rotational isomerisms of various types.[24, 25] Hindered rotation about a C—C single bond is

[22] (a) Davies and Lamb, *Quart. Rev. Chem. Soc.* 1957, **11**, 134 (pp. 157–158); (b) Tabuchi, *Z. Elektrochem.* 1960, **64**, 141; see also (c) Sette, ref. 1e, p. 316, and (d) Herzfeld and Litovitz, ref. 1g, section 116.

[23] (a) Maier and Mez, *Z. Naturforsch.*, 1952, **7A**, 300; (b) idem, 1955, **10A**, 997; (c) Eppler, *ibid.*, 744.

[24] (a) Davies and Lamb, ref. 22a, pp. 147 *seq.*; (b) Sette, ref. 1e, p. 313.

[25] Lamb, *Z. Elektrochem.* 1960, **64**, 135 (table, p. 139).

presumed to be responsible for the relaxation in esters (I), unsatura-
ted aldehydes and ketones (II), and methylbutanes:

I

$$\underset{O}{\overset{R}{>}}C\text{—}O\overset{R'}{} \rightleftharpoons \underset{O}{\overset{R}{>}}C\text{—}O\underset{R'}{}$$

II

$$\underset{R}{\overset{R'}{>}}C\text{—}C\underset{R''}{\overset{O}{}} \rightleftharpoons \underset{R}{\overset{R'}{>}}C\text{—}C\underset{O}{\overset{R''}{}}$$

From the variation of relaxation time with temperature, it is possible to determine ΔH for these reactions, and also the enthalpies
of activation for the forward and back reactions, ΔH_f^* and ΔH_b^*.
As a way of studying hindered rotation, the ultrasonics method has
the advantage that it is applicable when fewer than 1% of the
molecules are in the state of higher energy, compared with 10% for
other methods[26] such as the study of Raman and infra-red spectra,
heat capacities, dielectric constants, and electron diffraction. The
values for ΔH_f^* are mostly in the region 5–8 kcal mole^{-1}; those for
ΔH are mostly between 1 and 2 kcal mole^{-1}. Steric and electrostatic
influences may be distinguished.

Cyclohexane derivatives exhibit a relaxation, with τ about 10^{-5}
sec, which is attributed to equilibrium between the alternative
chair conformations.[24] Such equilibria have also been studied by
n.m.r. methods (p. 251).

Triethylamine shows a relaxation, with τ about 10^{-8} sec, attributed to equilibrium between various configurations differing in
the arrangement of the bent —CH_2—CH_3 chains;[27] the value of
ΔH is 3·4 kcal mole^{-1} and the enthalpies of activation for the forward and back reactions are 10·2 and 6·8 kcal mole^{-1}.

Energy exchange; vibrational relaxation

Carbon disulphide, which cannot exhibit rotational isomerism,
none the less exhibits ultrasonic absorption, with a single relaxation
time of about 10^{-8} sec. Analysis of the results at 25° and $-63°$
shows that the relaxation involves the whole of the vibrational

[26] E. B. Wilson, *Adv. Chem. Physics*, 1959, **2**, 367.
[27] (a) Ref. 24; (b) Padmanabhan and Heasell, *Proc. Phys. Soc.* 1960, **76**,
321. For an interpretation in terms of inversion see (c) Andreae,
Edmonds and Joyce, ref. 13e, p. 542.

8

specific heat.[28] This behaviour is similar to that of gases,[28, 29] which is attributed to transfer between vibrational and translational modes. Similar effects would be expected in all liquids at high frequencies, but in polar liquids they are obscured by dipole interactions. Benzene appears to behave similarly to carbon disulphide.[28a] Methylene chloride, on the other hand, exhibits an absorption associated with only part of the vibrational specific heat, in the region of 1.7×10^8 c/sec; it appears that the lowest vibrational level must be associated with a second relaxation at some higher frequency.[30]

HIGH-FREQUENCY ALTERNATING-FIELD METHODS

Dissociation field effect at high frequencies

The basis of this method has been outlined on pp. 81–83. Consider the dissociation of a weak acid in aqueous solution, in a radio-frequency field:

$$HA + H_2O \underset{k_2}{\overset{k_1}{\rightleftharpoons}} H_3O^+ + A^- \qquad (5.14)$$

The mathematical treatment[31] shows that, just as for ultrasonic absorption (p. 83), the degree of dissociation will change over from the high-field to the low-field value in the frequency region around $\omega\tau = 1$, and the power absorbed will show a maximum at the point of inflection where the critical frequency $\omega_c = 1/\tau$. Since $k_2 \gg k_1$, the general equation for τ (p. 63) becomes $1/\tau = k_2(\bar{a}+\bar{b})$ where $\bar{a}$ and $\bar{b}$ are the equilibrium concentrations of the ions. Hence if the dissociation constant is K_a and the concentration of the acid is c,

$$k_2 = \omega_c/(\bar{a}+\bar{b}) \approx \omega_c/2(cK_a)^{1/2} \qquad (5.15)$$

In principle it is therefore possible to determine τ by varying the frequency and measuring the conductivity or the dielectric loss.

[28] For reviews see (a) Davies and Lamb, ref. 22a, pp. 155 *seq.*; (b) Herzfeld and Litovitz, ref. 1g, p. 412; (c) Sette, ref. 1e, p. 308.
[29] McCoubrey and McGrath, *Quart. Rev. Chem. Soc.* 1957, **11**, 87.
[30] Andreae, Joyce and Oliver, *Proc. Physical Soc.* 1960, **75**, 82.
[31] Pearson, *Discuss. Faraday Soc.* 1954, **17**, 187.

The expected effects are small, however, and neither method has been successfully applied in practice. The precision required for such conductivity measurements may be attainable [31]; but the expected dielectric absorption is too small, in comparison with the ohmic loss in the conducting solution, to be measured by present techniques.[32]

Dielectric absorption and molecular rotation

The measurement of dielectric absorption at high frequencies is practicable for non-electrolytes, and gives information on the rotation of molecules and of groups within molecules.[33] Measurements on water and heavy water in the microwave region show a relaxation time in the region of 10^{-11} sec, with an energy of activation of 4·5 kcal mole^{-1}; these results are attributed to rotation of water molecules, involving the breaking of two hydrogen bonds.[34] Hydroxy-compounds such as alcohols and phenols in benzene solution have also been examined in this way.[35a] At microwave frequencies (wavelengths 0·7 to 60 cm), typical absorption curves show two overlapping maxima, indicating processes with relaxation times of the order of 10^{-11} and 10^{-12} sec. These are attributed respectively to rotation of the molecule as a whole and to rotation of the OH group in the molecule. Glycine in water has been similarly studied, and shows a relaxation with an energy of activation of 3·9 ± 0·4 kcal mole^{-1}; this is interpreted in terms of rotation of the molecule with breaking of hydrogen bonds.[35c] It is proposed to apply an analogous method to dimerization reactions of polar molecules, with relaxation times of the order of 10^{-7} to 10^{-8} sec. [35b]

[32] (a) Bell and Robinson, *Trans. Faraday Soc.* 1962, **58**, 2358. These authors were unable to confirm a claim made by (b) Gilkerson, *J. Chem. Phys.* 1957, **27**, 914. On the measurement of dielectric loss, see, e.g. (c) Powles and Smyth, in *Physical Methods of Organic Chemistry*, ed. Weissberger (3rd edn., Interscience, 1959), part 3, chapter 38.

[33] For a review see (a) Brot, Magat and Reinisch, *Kolloid Z.* 1953, **134**, 101; (b) Davies, *Quart. Rev. Chem. Soc.* 1954, **8**, 250.

[34] (a) Collis, Hasted and Ritson, *Proc. Phys. Soc.* 1948, **60**, 145; (b) Haggis, Hasted and Buchanan, *J. Chem. Phys.* 1952, **20**, 1452; (c) Lane and Saxton, *Proc. Roy. Soc.*, A, 1952, **213**, 400.

[35] (a) Hanna and Klages, *Z. Elektrochem.* 1961, **65**, 620; (b) Eigen, *Suom. Kem.*, A, 1961, **34**, 25; (c) Aaron and Grant, *Trans. Faraday Soc.* 1963, **59**, 85.

CHAPTER 6

Flash and related methods

FLASH METHODS

General principles

The flash method was originally developed for gases, but has increasingly been applied to solutions.[1, 2] An intense flash of light, lasting some microseconds (10^{-6} to 10^{-4} sec), is used to initiate a disturbance photochemically. The course of the resulting change is observed by fast photometric methods. Reactions with half-times down to 10^{-5} sec can be observed without difficulty. The following are the main types of change that can be studied.

(i) The absorption of light may photolyse a molecule, producing a non-equilibrium state in the solution; reaction proceeds so that equilibrium is re-established. For instance, iodine in hexane solution is partly dissociated, and the recombination of the iodine atoms can be followed. It seems possible that many equilibria might be displaced in this way, but only a few have been investigated (pp. 108 *seq.*). The principle is the same as that of the relaxation methods discussed in chapter 4, in that a disturbance is initiated by physical means and the return to equilibrium is observed. The difference from these methods is that there is a drastic alteration of the system, not merely a small shift of equilibrium.

[1] For reviews on flash methods applied to solutions see (a) Porter, *Z. Elektrochem.* 1960, **64**, 59 (methods); (b) Porter, in *Investigation of Rates and Mechanisms of Reactions*, ed. Friess, Lewis and Weissberger (2nd edn., Interscience, 1963), part II, chapter 19; (c) Porter, *Radiation Research*, Supplement 1, 1959, p. 479. For reviews on applications to gases see (d) Norrish and Porter, *Discuss. Faraday Soc.* 1954, **17**, 40 (methods); (e) Norrish and Thrush, *Quart. Rev. Chem. Soc.* 1956, **10**, 149 (applications).
[2] The earliest paper is that of Porter and Windsor, *Discuss. Faraday Soc.* 1954, **17**, 178.

(ii) The absorption of light may produce an electronically-excited molecule, which in time is deactivated and returns to its original state. The decay of triplet states, in particular, can be studied (p. 111), since their lifetimes in solution are usually greater than 10^{-5} sec. Here again the principle is that of relaxation.

(iii) The excited molecules may react with some other molecules, producing permanent changes. The principle here is not relaxation but photochemical initiation of an irreversible reaction. The main differences from ordinary photochemistry (chapter 7) are that the energy absorption occurs in a very short time and the subsequent fast changes are directly followed. The applications here are numerous, since in many reactions the excited molecule will be a free radical and will undergo irreversible changes.

An advantage of the flash methods is that the absorption spectrum of the reaction solution can be photographed at a known time after initiation of the reaction. This is done by passing a second flash from another lamp through the solution to a spectrograph; the time-interval between the two flashes is controlled electronically. A series of experiments with different intervals shows the changes in the spectrum over the whole reaction period. These absorption spectra, though less characteristic than those of gases, provide very useful information about the species taking part in the reaction. Intermediates may be detected and identified. This greatly reduces the difficulties of interpretation of the kinetic data. Moreover, in the kinetic experiments it is possible to follow changes in the concentrations of two species separately, by following the absorption of light at different wavelengths.

Experimental arrangement

The general arrangement is represented in Fig. 6.1, which shows the apparatus of Bridge and Porter.[3] The flash is generated by a discharge through a gas, from condensers which are typically of capacity 4—10 μF and charged to 4–20 kV. The reaction vessel, made of silica, is 10–20 cm long and 2–4 cm in diameter. The flash-lamp and the reaction vessel are parallel, and are enclosed in a

[3] Bridge and Porter, *Proc. Roy. Soc.*, *A*, 1958, **244**, 276.

reflector, to increase the amount of light absorbed by the solution. For the same reason, and also to ensure uniformity, two or more flash-lamps may be used.

To determine the rate of the subsequent reaction, the absorption is followed at a particular wavelength, chosen so that the absorption for one of the reacting species is a maximum. This may be done by passing white light from a tungsten-filament lamp or xenon arc through the solution to a monochromator and thence to a photo-multiplier; alternatively (as shown in the figure) one may use a

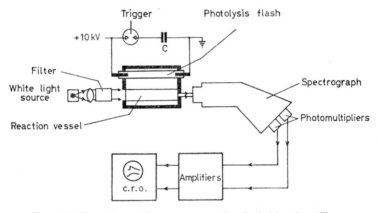

FIG. 6.1. Experimental arrangement for flash kinetics. (From Bridge and Porter.[3])

spectrograph whose plate-holder has been replaced by a photo-multiplier set in the appropriate position. [4] The response of the photomultiplier is displayed on the screen of an oscillograph, whose time-base is triggered by the initiating discharge. The trace is photographed, and an absorption–time plot extending over perhaps a millisecond is obtained; for an example, see Fig. 6.3, p. 117.

The absorption spectrum of the solution can be recorded a short time after the initiating flash, if the white-light source is replaced by a subsidiary flash-lamp, which is fired automatically through an electronic delay circuit by a photocell which detects the first flash.

[4] Instead of a white-light source, a mercury lamp may be used and the appropriate line isolated by means of a monochromator: Hatchard and Parker, *Trans. Faraday Soc.* 1961, **57**, 1093.

The photomultiplier is replaced by a photographic plate and the spectrum is recorded in the usual way. A series of spectra taken after various intervals gives very useful information about the course of reaction. Time-intervals down to a few microseconds can be arranged. The main experimental difficulties are that oxygen must be thoroughly removed from the solution, and that small quantities of impurity may be important.

Range of rates accessible[1a]

The factor which determines the fastest reaction that can be studied is the finite duration of the primary flash. The greater the energy output, the longer the duration. The energy required to produce a sufficient concentration of the primary product in a reaction tube 10 cm long and 2 cm in diameter is in the region of 100 to 1000 joules. To achieve this, the minimum duration of the flash must be 2 to 10 μsec. A duration of 10 μsec (10^{-5} sec) is at present typical.

The least half-time that can be studied is thus about 10^{-5} sec. The highest first-order rate constant that can be determined is then about 10^5 sec^{-1}; this allows the study of reactions of triplet states, but not that of the singlet excited states which are the first products of absorption. (These can often be studied by fluorescence techniques, and the results of the two methods are then complementary; see chapter 8). The highest second-order constant accessible[5] is about $10^7 \epsilon$ l mole^{-1}sec^{-1}, where ϵ is the extinction coefficient in l mole^{-1}cm^{-1}. An extinction coefficient of the order of 10^4 l mole^{-1}cm^{-1} in the visible or ultraviolet region is quite common for dyestuffs and free radicals. Thus rate constants can be determined up to about 10^{11} l mole^{-1}sec^{-1}. At the other end of the scale, reactions lasting several milliseconds have been followed.

General comments on the flash method

In summary, the flash method permits the measurement of rates up to the limit set by diffusion control, and flash spectroscopy gives very useful (though not always conclusive) evidence about the

[5] If we have equal concentrations c of the two reactants, $-dc/dt = kc^2$, and $t_{1/2} = 1/kc$. The optical density D is related to c by the equation $D = \epsilon cl$, where l is the length of the tube. Hence $k = \epsilon l/Dt_{1/2}$. Typically, $l = 10$ cm, and $D = 0 \cdot 1$; so if $t_{1/2} = 10^{-5}$ sec, $k = 10^7 \epsilon$.

species present in solution. The temperature can be varied down to $-196°$.[18b] Low concentrations can be used, because of the high sensitivity of photoelectric photometry, especially with pathlengths as long as 10–20 cm. Only photochemically-initiated processes can be studied; and the change in the system on absorption of light is usually considerable. This excludes some reactions, but makes accessible others of great interest.

Applications of flash methods

(i) *Relaxation studies*

Iodine dissociation and recombination. When iodine vapour is subjected to a flash, it is partly dissociated, and the atoms subsequently recombine:

$$I_2 \xrightarrow{h\nu} I + I \longrightarrow I_2$$

The rate of recombination of the atoms can be determined by the photometric method, since the iodine molecule absorbs in the visible and the iodine atom does not. In presence of various added gases M, the rate is proportional to $(M)(I)^2$. The interpretation of this third-order expression is that for an iodine molecule to be formed from two atoms a third body is necessary, to carry away surplus kinetic energy so that the molecule does not fly apart again. The effectiveness of M, measured by the third-order rate constant, varies considerably from one substance to another; it is correlated with the activation energy, which is negative, the reaction rate decreasing with rise of temperature.[6a] These facts are explained if the mechanism involves a first stage in which a complex IM is formed in a rapid equilibrium:

$$I + M \rightleftharpoons IM; \quad IM + I \longrightarrow I_2 + M$$

In solution, however, the iodine atoms are always adjacent to solvent molecules which can remove excess kinetic energy, and there is no need for a third body. The energy of activation may be assumed to be negligible for recombination of atoms. Iodine atoms

[6] (a) Porter and Smith, *Proc. Roy. Soc.*, A, 1961, **261**, 28. For other references on the gas-phase reaction see (b) Trotman-Dickenson, *Gas Kinetics* (Butterworths, 1955), pp. 85 *seq.*, and (c) Cottrell and McCoubrey, *Molecular Energy Transfer in Gases* (Butterworths, 1961) p. 189.

would therefore be expected to recombine at every encounter. By exposing solutions of iodine in carbon tetrachloride to a flash, and observing the change with time of the absorption due to iodine molecules, Willard[7] has found the rate constant for recombination at room temperature to be $(6 \cdot 9 \pm 0 \cdot 6) \times 10^9$ l mole^{-1}sec^{-1}. This corresponds with the value of about 10^{10} l mole^{-1}sec^{-1} expected for a diffusion-controlled reaction between uncharged molecules (p. 12). Moreover, the apparent energy of activation, obtained by combining the above rate constant with the value $1 \cdot 03 \times 10^{10}$ at $50°$, is $3 \cdot 2$ kcal mole^{-1}, which is of the right order for diffusion control, and indeed agrees almost exactly with the value $3 \cdot 3$ kcal mole^{-1} found for the diffusion of iodine in carbon tetrachloride.[7b] It has also been shown that the quantum yield—that is, the ratio of the number of iodine molecules converted into free atoms, to the number of quanta absorbed—is much less than unity; in carbon tetrachloride it is $0 \cdot 14$. This implies that most of the iodine atoms produced by the photolysing flash recombine without separating, and constitutes evidence that solute molecules are confined within a solvent 'cage'. Similar results are obtained by other methods (p. 137) and are of importance in refining the theory of diffusion control (p. 282).

Solutions of iodine in benzene give rather different results.[8] The flash produces a transient species which absorbs in the visible, and disappears according to a second-order law, with a rate constant at least 1×10^{11} l mole^{-1}sec^{-1}. This species is probably a charge-transfer complex ($C_6H_6 . I$).

Proton-transfer reactions.[9] It is known from fluorescence studies (p. 160) that many organic substances ROH are stronger acids in their first excited states ROH* than in their ground states. The effect of the flash is therefore to increase dissociation, into

[7] (a) Strong and Willard, *J. Amer. Chem. Soc.* 1957, **79**, 2098; (b) Aditya and Willard, *idem*, p. 2680.

[8] (a) Rand and Strong, *J. Amer. Chem. Soc.* 1960, **82**, 5; (b) Strong, Rand and Britt, *ibid.*, 5053; (c) Strong and Perano, *idem*, 1961, **83**, 2843; (d) Gover and Porter, *Proc. Roy. Soc.*, A, 1961, **262**, 476; (e) Strong, *J. Phys. Chem.* 1962, **66**, 2423.

[9] (a) Breitschwerdt and Weller, *Z. phys. Chem.* (*Frankfurt*), 1959, **20**, 353 (spectra); (b) *Z. Elektrochem.* 1960, **64**, 395 (kinetics).

$RO^{*-} + H_3O^+$. The excited anion RO^{*-} then loses energy by fluorescence, giving a solution containing more RO^- than corresponds to the ground-state equilibrium. Recombination therefore occurs; it may be observed spectrophotometrically, because the absorption spectra of RO^- and ROH are different. The relaxation cycle is as follows:

$$ROH.H_2O \xrightarrow{\; h\nu \;} ROH^*.\; H_2O \quad \text{(absorption)}$$

$$RO^- + H_3O^+ + h\nu' \longleftarrow RO^{*-} + H_3O^+$$
$$\text{(fluorescence)} \qquad\qquad \text{(dissociation)}$$

The method has been applied to various sulphonated phenols in aqueous solution at various pH's. The half-times are in the region of 10^{-5} sec. When ROH is 3-hydroxypyrene-5,8,10-sulphonate (I), the rate constant for recombination at about $20°$ is $(2 \cdot 7 \pm 0 \cdot 7) \times 10^{10}$ l mole^{-1} sec^{-1}. This is comparable with the rate constants for other proton-transfer reactions of the type $H_3O^+ + RO^-$, which are invariably so fast as to be diffusion-controlled (p. 262).

I

Haemoglobin reactions.[10] Carboxyhaemoglobin dissociates in light, and the return to equilibrium after a flash may be followed. The rate constants for the addition of the first and fourth molecules of CO (cf. p. 54) have been determined in this way, and also those for the addition of the final molecule of various other ligands. With short flashes, it is possible to detect, as the initial product of photodecomposition, a short-lived quickly-reacting species,[10d]

[10] For a review see (*a*) Gibson, in *Progress in Biophysics*, **9** (Pergamon Press, 1959), pp. 1–53. Some experimental papers are: (*b*) Gibson, *J. Physiol.* 1956, **134**, 112, 123 (apparatus); (*c*) Ainsworth and Gibson, *idem*, 1957, **137**, 26P; (*d*) Gibson, *Biochem. J.* 1959, **71**, 293; (*e*) Gibson, *Discuss. Faraday Soc.* 1959, **27**, 142; (*f*) Gibson, *Biochem. J.* 1960, **76**, 46P; (*g*) Gibson and Greenwood, *idem*, 1963, **86**, 541.

possibly a haemoglobin molecule which has lost its ligand molecules in a time so short that the reorganization of the protein normally associated with the loss of the second ligand molecule has not had time to occur.[10e] Gibson has also combined the flash technique with the regenerative stopped-flow procedure of Chance (p. 41) to study reactions of cytochrome oxidase.[10f,g]

Electron-addition to aromatic anions.[11] In certain ethers such as tetrahydrofuran, alkali metals form blue solutions, analogous to those in liquid ammonia. They also react with aromatic hydrocarbons such as naphthacene (N) producing successively the singly and doubly charged anions of the hydrocarbon (N^-, N^{2-}) which have characteristic absorption bands. Flash excitation of N^{2-} solutions leads to a decrease of intensity of the band due to N^{2-} and an increase of that due to N^-. These changes are attributed to the process $N^{2-} \rightarrow N^- + e$. The reverse reaction follows accurately second-order kinetics, with rate constant 4×10^9 l mole^{-1}sec^{-1}.

(ii) *Studies of the triplet state*[12]

General. The lowest excited state of nearly all stable molecules is a triplet state. This has two unpaired electrons with parallel spins. The interaction of the unpaired electrons in a triplet state is much stronger than in diradicals in which the electronic spins are uncorrelated. Transitions between this triplet state and the singlet ground state or excited states are normally forbidden, by spin-momentum conservation rules. In large molecules, however, this selection rule partly breaks down, and transitions can occur. The triplet state, already well known to spectroscopists, became the object of much attention through studies of phosphorescence in solid solution.[12a, 13] The phosphorescence of aromatic molecules

[11] Linshitz and Eloranta, *Z. Elektrochem.* 1960, **64**, 169; (*b*) Eloranta and Linshitz, *J. Chem. Phys.* 1963, **38**, 2214. For related work by e.s.r. methods see pp. 209 *seq.*

[12] For general reviews on the triplet state see (*a*) Reid, *Quart. Rev. Chem. Soc.* 1958, **12**, 205; (*b*) Simons, *idem*, 1959, **13**, 3; (*c*) Porter, *Proc. Chem. Soc.* 1959, 291; (*d*) Reid, *Excited States in Chemistry and Biology* (Butterworths, 1957), chapter 5.

[13] (*a*) Jablonski, *Z. Physik.*, 1935, **94**, 38; (*b*) Lewis and Kasha, *L. Amer. Chem. Soc.* 1944, **66**, 2100; (*c*) Lewis and Calvin, *idem*, 1945, **67**, 1232; (*d*) Kasha, *Chem. Rev.* 1947, **41**, 407.

dissolved in rigid media such as glassy boric acid was attributed by Jablonski[13a] in 1935 to transitions from a metastable state, reached by radiationless deactivation from the lowest singlet excited state, to the ground singlet state. This metastable state was identified by Lewis and Kasha[13b] in 1944 with the lowest triplet state. The demonstration of paramagnetism in the phosphorescent state[13c] confirmed the presence of unpaired electrons. The energy relations are shown in the Jablonski diagram (Fig. 6.2). They are well illustrated by the behaviour of (for example) umbelliferone in a boric acid glass.[14] When exposed to ultraviolet light, this shows

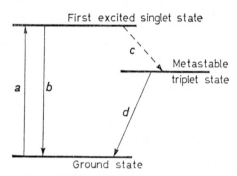

FIG. 6.2. Jablonski diagram. *a*, absorption; *b*, fluorescence; *c*, radiationless deactivation; *d*, phosphorescence.

a blue fluorescence; when removed, a green phosphorescence, decaying in a few seconds. The longer wavelength of the phosphorescence shows that the triplet–singlet transition *d* involves a smaller energy drop than the singlet–singlet transition *b* responsible for fluorescence. The persistence of the phosphorescence also shows that in a rigid medium the transition *d* is much slower than transition *b*.

Rate of decay of the triplet state in solutions. In fluid solutions, phosphorescence is not observed under ordinary conditions; most triplet-state molecules lose their energy without radiating, because their natural lifetime is long enough to allow deactivation by collision before emission occurs. Triplet-state molecules can, however, be detected by the flash method, and their rate of disappearance

[14] I am indebted to Dr. E. J. Bowen for this illustration.

studied.[15] The first experiments were those of Porter and Windsor on anthracene (10^{-5} M) in hexane.[16a] A series of spectra photographed by flashes at intervals of 30 to 300 μsec after the main flash showed two new bands, at wavelengths longer than those of the fluorescence bands; these were ascribed to the first triplet state. The absorption due to these bands decreased steadily, with a half-time of about 200 μsec. Similar results were obtained with naphthalene, phenanthrene, and other aromatic hydrocarbons and their derivatives. (Single-ring compounds do not appear to give triplet spectra.) The kinetics of the decay in solution have been studied with anthracene[16a, 16b, 17] and naphthalene[12c, 16b]; the results with the two substances are similar. The decay is predominantly first-order, though there is some second-order reaction also. The rate constants for the second-order reaction in solvents of low viscosity are high, around 10^{10} l mole^{-1}sec^{-1}; they decrease with increasing viscosity, as would be expected of diffusion-controlled reactions. For the first-order reaction, the rate constant is again found to vary with the viscosity of the solvent, apparently because the decay is due (except at low temperatures) to quenching by traces of impurity in the solutions.[18]

Deactivation of the triplet state by paramagnetic molecules. The disappearance of triplet-state molecules is accelerated by paramagnetic ions.[16b] The second-order rate constants vary from about 10^6 to nearly 10^8 l mole^{-1}sec^{-1}. They cannot be correlated with the magnetic susceptibilities of the ions. It has been suggested that the function of the paramagnetic molecule is to form a complex with the triplet which can dissociate to give a molecule in the ground singlet state without violation of the spin conservation rules. The

[15] For another method see p. 159.
[16] (a) Porter and Windsor, ref. 2; (b) Porter and Wright, *Discuss. Faraday Soc.* 1959, **27**, 18. In the earlier work the reactions were followed by measuring the density of the absorption bands on the spectrograms taken at various times after the main flash.
[17] (a) Livingston and Tanner, *Trans. Faraday Soc.* 1958, **54**, 765; (b) Jackson, Livingston and Pugh, *idem*, 1960, **56**, 1635.
[18] (a) Hoffman and Porter, *Proc. Roy. Soc., A*, 1962, **268**, 46; (b) Hilpern, Porter and Stief, *Proc. Roy. Soc., A*, 1963, forthcoming (low temperatures).

excess energy is removed by the solvent after the transition, as in the intramolecular conversion.

Deactivation of the triplet state by molecules with triplet states of lower energy.[19] The transfer of electronic energy by the following process is allowed by the spin-conservation rules, and is possible provided that the triplet state of B (^{3}B) lies lower than that of A (^{3}A):

$$^3A + {}^1B \longrightarrow {}^1A + {}^3B$$

Transfers of this type have been shown by phosphorescence measurements to occur from benzophenone to naphthalene, for example, in rigid solvents, but the efficiency is low.[19a] In fluid solutions the efficiency can be very high; rate constants greater than 10^8 l mole^{-1}sec^{-1} are observed.[19b]

The role of triplet states in photochemical reactions. From the foregoing it may be expected that the triplet state will play an important part in photochemical reactions of various types. The lifetime of a triplet state is commonly of the order of 10^{-4} sec, and so is several orders of magnitude longer than that of excited singlet states (*ca.* 10^{-8} sec). The chemical behaviour is usually that characteristic of a biradical, so that high reactivity may be expected. The reactions may be quite different from those of the singlet state; the photo-oxidation of anthracene (below) is a case in point. Energy can be transferred to singlet-state molecules with high efficiency, as we have just seen; this suggests that the triplet state may be important in biological systems exposed to radiation, and in particular in photosynthesis (p. 115). Some instances of photochemical reactions in which the triplet state plays a part are given below.

Photo-oxidation of anthracene.[20] When anthracene solutions are irradiated with ultraviolet light, they produce a stable dimer (dianthracene); if oxygen is present, the transannular anthracene peroxide is also formed. Fluorescence studies (pp. 153–156) indicate that the two reactions are independent, and that the singlet excited

[19] (*a*) Terenin and Ermolaev, *Trans. Faraday Soc.* 1956, **52**, 1042; (*b*) Porter and Wilkinson, *Trans. Faraday Soc.* 1961, **57**, 1686.

[20] For a review see R. M. Hochstrasser and G. B. Porter, *Quart. Rev. Chem. Soc.* 1960, **14**, 146.

state is concerned in dimerization, but not (except at high concentrations) in photo-oxidation, which must be ascribed to some other excited state, presumably the lowest triplet state. Flash methods confirm and extend these conclusions.[16a, 16b, 17] The triplet state is not affected by encounters with normal anthracene, and so is not concerned in dimerization. It is deactivated by oxygen, however, at nearly every collision, as would be expected if it is the excited state responsible for photo-oxidation. The rate constants in various solvents are of the order of 10^9 l mole^{-1}sec^{-1}.

Chlorophyll.[21] Solutions of chlorophyll *a* and chlorophyll *b* immediately after flashing show new absorption bands, which rapidly disappear; the mean lifetime is of the order of 10^{-3} sec. These bands are evidently due to a relatively long-lived excited species. Some such species is also required to account for the weak phosphorescence shown by chlorophyll *b* in rigid solvents at low temperatures, and for the results of photochemical and fluorescence work. This species is commonly assumed to be the lowest triplet state. The kinetics of the decay show that several processes contribute: (1) spontaneous first-order decay (2) encounters with other triplet molecules, and (3) encounters with unexcited molecules. The rate constants for process 2 in various solvents are around 10^9 l mole^{-1}sec^{-1}; those for process 3 are of the order of 10^7 l mole^{-1} sec^{-1}. The decay is also accelerated by various substances including oxygen, benzoquinone, and *m*-dinitrobenzene; for these reactions the rate constants are in the region of 10^9 l mole^{-1}sec^{-1}. These values are about ten times smaller than those for the quenching of fluorescence, which agree with the diffusion-controlled limit of about 10^{10} l mole^{-1}sec^{-1} (p. 158). The reason may be that the unpaired electrons of the triplet state are to a large extent localized on nitrogen atoms near the middle of the molecule. The mechanism of quenching is not fully understood. It is of interest in connection with energy-transfer in photosynthesis, to which flash methods have been applied.[22]

[21] Livingston, *Quart. Rev. Chem. Soc.* 1960, **14**, 174.
[22] (*a*) Brody, *Z. Elektrochem.* 1960, **64**, 187; (*b*) Witt, Moraw, Müller, Rumberg and Zieger, *idem*, p. 181. For other references see Bewick and Fleischmann, *Ann. Rep. Chem. Soc.* 1960, 96.

Visual pigments.[23] The visual chromophore retinene when irradiated by a flash produces a long-lived excited state, which is tentatively identified as a triplet. It decays by a first-order process, which in hexane has a rate constant of about 10^5 sec^{-1} and an activation energy of 0·9 kcal mol^{-1}.[23c] Such studies are relevant to the problem of the primary photochemical process in vision.

(iii) *Photochemically-initiated irreversible reactions*

Quinones.[24] Quinones in solution when exposed to a flash give transient intermediates with characteristic absorption spectra. The products from duroquinone were studied by flash spectroscopy,[24a] with various solvents and pH's, and identified as follows: (a) the semiquinone radical QH·, with absorption maximum at about 405 mμ, appearing in all solvents containing abstractable hydrogen at pH 7 and below; (b) the semiquinone radical ion Q$^-$, with absorption maximum at 430 mμ, appearing only at pH 7 and above; and (c) the triplet state of the quinone, with absorption maximum at 490 mμ, appearing only in viscous solvents. Absorption–time curves at various wavelengths (Fig. 6.3) show that the radical is not formed via the triplet state, and give rate constants for various reactions as follows.[24b]

$$2QH\cdot \; \rightarrow \; Q + QH : \quad ca. \; 10^9 \; \text{l mole}^{-1} \text{sec}^{-1} \; \text{in ethanol–water}$$

$$2Q\cdot^- \; \rightarrow \; Q + Q^{2-} : \quad ca. \; 5 \times 10^6 \; \text{l mole}^{-1} \text{sec}^{-1} \; \text{in ethanol–water}$$

$$QH\cdot \; \rightarrow \; Q\cdot^- + H^+ : \quad 7 \times 10^3 \; \text{sec}^{-1} \; \text{in ethanol}$$

$$Q\cdot^- + H^+ \; \rightarrow \; QH\cdot : \quad ca. \; 10^{10} \; \text{l mole}^{-1} \text{sec}^{-1} \; \text{in ethanol–water}$$

Thus the radical QH·disproportionates much faster than the nonprotonated form Q·$^-$. The effects of oxygen and metal ions have

[23] (a) Abrahamson, Marquisee, Gavuzzi and Roubie, *Z. Elektrochem.* 1960, **64**, 177; (b) Reid, *Excited States in Chemistry and Biology* (Butterworths, 1957), chapter 8; (c) Grellman, Memming and Livingston, *J. Amer. Chem. Soc.* 1962, **84**, 546; (d) Rushton, *Visual Pigments in Man and their Relation to Seeing*, in *Progress in Biophysics*, **9** (Butterworths, 1959), pp. 239–83.

[24] (a) Bridge and Porter, *Proc. Roy. Soc.*, A, 1958, **244**, 259; (b) *idem, ibid.*, 276; (c) Land and Porter, *Proc. Chem. Soc.* 1960, 84; (d) Bridge and Reed, *Trans. Faraday Soc.* 1960, **56**, 1796; (e) Bridge, *idem, ibid.*, 1001 (quantum yields).

also been investigated.[24d] These results bear on the mechanism of photosensitization of oxidation by quinones.

Photoreduction of methylene blue and thionine.[25] The dyestuff

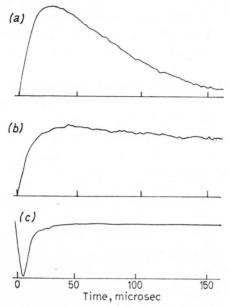

FIG. 6.3. Oscillograph record of absorption by duroquinone after flash: *a*, absorption at 490 mμ, due to triplet state; *b*, absorption at 405 mμ, due to radical; *c*, record showing duration of flash (*ca.* 10 sec). From Bridge and Porter[3].

methylene blue (I) in dilute sulphuric acid is bleached on exposure to light, to the reduced leuco-form. Thionine (II) behaves similarly. The general features of the results of flash work are the same for

$$\left[(CH_3)_2N \cdots S \cdots N(CH_3)_2 \right]^+ \qquad \left[H_2N \cdots S \cdots NH_2 \right]^+$$

I   II

both substances; we will therefore use the symbol D to denote either of them. When orange-red light is used, the spectrum shows

[25] (*a*) Parker, *Nature*, 1958, **182**, 130; (*b*) *ibid.* p. 245; (*c*) Parker, *J. Phys. Chem.* 1959, **63**, 26 (methylene blue); (*d*) Hatchard and Parker, *Trans. Faraday Soc.* 1961, **57**, 1093 (thionine).

9

a new absorption band, with a lifetime of less than 30 μsec; this is assumed to be due to the triplet state ^3D, formed no doubt from the singlet excited molecules initially produced by the flash. In presence of ferrous sulphate, this spectrum is no longer observed, but that of the free radical analogous to semiquinone (DH·) appears; this has a much longer lifetime. It is not formed from the singlet excited state (unlike the corresponding durosemiquinone radical mentioned above), for its concentration is not correlated with the quenching of fluorescence by ferrous ion; presumably it is formed from the triplet state. Its disappearance, which has been studied by following the absorption at various wavelengths in presence of various concentrations of ferrous ion, is attributed to disproportionation into the original dyestuff D and the leuco-form DH_2. The scheme is thus as follows:

$$D \xrightarrow{h\nu} D^* \longrightarrow {}^3D \xrightarrow[k_8]{Fe^{2+}} DH\cdot \xrightarrow{k_d} D+DH_2$$

$$D + h\nu'\text{(fluorescence)}$$

The rate constants have been determined for thionine.[25d] For the quenching of the triplet state by ferrous ion, $k_8 = 3 \times 10^7$ l mole^{-1} sec^{-1}; for the dismutation, $k_d = 2\cdot4 \times 10^9$ l mole^{-1}sec^{-1}. Experiments with added ferric ion have given the rate constant for quenching of the triplet state by Fe^{3+} as 3×10^7 l mole^{-1}sec^{-1}. For the oxidations by Fe^{3+} of semithionine and the leuco-form (which are responsible for reversal of bleaching in the dark), the rate constants are $7\cdot9 \times 10^4$ and $2\cdot6 \times 10^2$ l mole^{-1}sec^{-1}. The rate constants for quenching of the triplet state are several powers of ten less than for the singlet state as shown by fluorescence methods (p. 158).

Ferrous sulphate in water.[26] When an aqueous solution of ferrous sulphate (*ca.* 10^{-4} M) is exposed to a flash, ferric ions are progressively produced; the process may be followed by observing the absorption at 3130 Å. Three stages are observed; the first lasts a few milliseconds, the second a few hundred milliseconds, and the third a few seconds. The rate constant for the slowest reaction

[26] (*a*) Baxendale and Mansell, *Nature*, 1961, **190**, 622; (*b*) Baxendale, *Radiation Research*, 1962, 17,

agrees with the value determined independently for the reaction of ferrous ion with H_2O_2. The oxidizing species in the other two steps may be respectively HO_2 and OH, but these are not definitely established. The effects of adding various organic compounds have also been studied.

Reactions of free radicals. Besides the above examples, many other free radicals can be produced by photolysis and their kinetics studied. Thus benzyl chloride solutions yield benzyl radicals, which disappear in a second-order reaction with a rate constant in the region of 10^9–10^{10} l mole^{-1}sec^{-1}.[27a] Phenol and anisole solutions similarly give phenoxyl radicals.[27b,c] The study of the reactions of free radicals will probably become one of the main fields for work on flash photolysis in solution.

PULSE RADIOLYSIS

General

Pulse radiolysis[28] is the analogue of flash photolysis in radiation chemistry; a pulse of high-energy radiation such as X-rays or electrons takes the place of the light flash. To be of comparable usefulness, the method requires a pulse with an energy not less than 100 J and a duration not more than 50 μsec, if the yield of the radiation chemical reaction is comparable with typical photochemical ones.[28a] In the work so far published, a linear electron accelerator has been used, powered by a klystron and giving pulses of 1–10 MeV for 1–5 μsec. The earliest paper was published in 1960.[28b]

Applications

Aromatic compounds.[28c] Electron pulses were applied to benzene, toluene, chlorobenzene, *p*-xylene and mesitylene. The oscillograph

[27] (a) Porter and Windsor, *Nature*, 1957, **180**, 187; (b) Land, Porter and Strachan, *Trans. Faraday Soc.* 1961, **57**, 1885; Porter *et al.*, *Trans. Faraday Soc.* 1963, **59**, 2016, 2027, 2038, 2051 (phenol derivatives, anilines, benzophenones).

[28] (a) Porter, *Radiation Research*, 1959, Supplement 1, p. 489; (b) MacLachlan and McCarthy, *Trans. Faraday Soc.* 1960, **56**, 1187; (c) *J. Amer. Chem. Soc.* 1962, **84**, 2519; (d) Dorfman, Taub and Bühler, *J. Chem. Phys.* 1962, **36**, 3051; (e) Anderson and Hart, *J. Phys. Chem.* 1962, **66**, 70; (f) Taub and Dorfman, *J. Amer. Chem. Soc.* 1962, **84**, 4053.

records showed in each case an absorption, attributed to free radicals, falling off to zero in less than a millisecond. The decrease followed second-order kinetics and was presumed to be due to combination of radicals. The rate constants range from 3×10^8 to 7×10^9 l mole^{-1}sec^{-1}.

Benzene in water.[28d] Aqueous solutions of benzene when exposed to an electron-pulse give a transient absorption spectrum attributed to a complex formed from hydroxyl radicals:

$$C_6H_6 + OH \cdot \longrightarrow OH \cdot C_6H_6 \cdot$$

The rate constant for the reaction is found to be $(4 \cdot 3 \pm 0 \cdot 9) \times 10^9$ l mole^{-1}sec^{-1}; for the corresponding reaction of C_6D_6, it is $(4 \cdot 7 \pm 0 \cdot 9) \times 10^9$ l mole^{-1}sec^{-1}.

Water.[28e] The results on pure water give relative rate constants for the reactions of H and H_2O_2 with hydrogen atoms.

Ethanol and aqueous ethanol[28f] give an absorption spectrum attributed to the radical CH_3CHOH. The absorption falls off according to a second-order law, and the rate constant for the reaction between two radicals is estimated as about 10^9 l mole^{-1}sec^{-1}.

CHAPTER 7

Photochemical and Related Methods

INTRODUCTION

In the methods now to be considered, reactions are initiated by light at the intensities normally used in photochemical work, rather than at the much higher intensities used in the work described in the last chapter. These methods make use of standard photochemical techniques and apparatus, with various additions. Reactions initiated by high-energy radiation have been studied by similar methods. By measuring the steady rate of polymerization at constant light intensity, and the rate of initiation under the same conditions, one can determine the ratio k_p^2/k_t, where k_p is the rate constant for propagation of the polymer chain, and k_t is that for its termination. Several methods are available for determining in addition the ratio k_p/k_t, and hence the separate rate constants. Rotating-sector methods have been much used; alternatively it is possible to observe the initial acceleration of the polymerization reaction when illumination begins, or its deceleration when light is cut off. The measurement of the concentration of radicals when a steady rate has been set up is theoretically attractive but seldom practicable.

We consider the theory of these methods, the techniques, and finally their applications to polymerization and to the recombination of iodine atoms. In dealing with the theory of polymerization, we shall consider simple linear polymerizations only, such as that of styrene, and refer the reader elsewhere for details of more complex mechanisms.[1]

[1] General accounts of the kinetics and mechanisms of polymerization reactions will be found in (a) Burnett, *Mechanism of Polymer Reactions* (Interscience, 1954); (b) Walling, *Free Radicals in Solution* (Wiley, 1957);

The mechanism of photochemical free-radical polymerization reactions

Let us consider the straight-chain addition polymerization of a pure monomer. Extensive researches[1] have shown that, in the simplest case, polymerization proceeds by the stages: (1) initiation by photochemical production of radicals $P_1^.$ from monomer molecules M; (2) propagation by successive addition of monomer units M to a growing radical chain $P_i^.$; and (3) termination of the reaction by a bimolecular reaction (whether combination or disproportionation) between two such radical chains to give a 'dead' polymer P.

(1) $M \xrightarrow{h\nu} P_1^.$

(2) $P_1^. + M \xrightarrow{k_p} P_2^. \ldots \xrightarrow{k_p} P_i^. \ldots \xrightarrow{k_p} P_j^.$

(3) $P_i^. + P_j^. \xrightarrow{k_t}$ inactive products P.

It will be assumed that the rate constants k_p and k_t are independent of the length of the chain. There is experimental support for this assumption, at least for the initial stages of polymerization.

Another reaction called 'chain transfer' is possible; here a growing radical chain $P_i^.$ attacks a monomer M producing not a radical chain $P_{i+1}^.$ as in step 2 above, but a monomer radical M· and a 'dead' polymer P_i:

(4) $P_i^. + M \longrightarrow P_i + M·$

In presence of a solvent, a similar transfer reaction between a growing radical chain $P_i^.$ and a solvent molecule XS may occur (see also p. 137):

(5) $P_i^. + XS \longrightarrow P_iX + S·$

In simple cases, however, especially in the pure liquid monomer, reactions 4 and 5 do not contribute appreciably to the rate of the overall reaction, and we shall say little about them. We shall also

(c) Bevington, *Radical Polymerization* (Academic Press, 1961); (d) Dainton, *Chain Reactions* (Methuen, 1956); (e) Flory, *Principles of Polymer Chemistry* (Cornell University Press, 1953); (f) Burnett, in *Investigation of Rates and Mechanisms of Reactions*, ed. Friess, Lewis and Weissberger (Interscience, 1963), Part II, chapter 21.

leave aside the complication that thermal initiation may occur alongside the photochemical reaction 1.

Determination of k_p^2/k_t by conventional photochemical methods

The rate of conversion of monomer to polymer may be determined by various methods, such as dilatometry. Our problem is to relate this rate of polymerization to the rates of the individual steps 1, 2 and 3. Under continuous illumination at constant intensity, the observed rate reaches a steady value after a few seconds, or at most minutes. This so-called 'steady state' may be understood as follows. The rate of conversion of monomer is proportional to the concentration of growing radicals of all lengths (P·). This concentration is fixed by the balance between the initiation step 1 and the termination step 3. (The propagation step 2 does not affect the number of radicals present.) The rate of destruction of radicals is $k_t(\text{P·})^2$. The rate of initiation by process 1, expressed as moles of radical produced per litre per second, is proportional to the light intensity absorbed; suppose that at a given light intensity it is R_i. In the 'steady state' there must be a constant concentration (P·)$_s$ of growing radicals, which will be given by[2]:

$$R_i = k_t(\text{P·})_s^2 \tag{7.1}$$

The rate of polymerization R at any time is:

$$R = -d(\text{M})/dt = k_p(\text{M})(\text{P·}) \tag{7.2}$$

The rate R_s in the 'steady state' is therefore, by virtue of equation 7.1,

$$R_s = k_p(\text{M})(\text{P·})_s = k_p k_t^{-1/2}(\text{M}) R_i^{1/2} \tag{7.3}$$

This equation shows that the observed steady rate R_s is proportional to $R_i^{1/2}$ and hence to the square root of the absorbed light intensity. This is characteristic of bimolecular terminations; it is of importance for the sector method (p. 130). Our present purpose, however, is to note that the ratio k_p^2/k_t is given by equation 7.3 as:

$$k_p^2/k_t = R_s^2/R_i (\text{M})^2 \tag{7.4}$$

We can therefore find k_p^2/k_t by determining R_i under the same

[2] Many workers, especially in America, define a rate constant half as large, so that equation 7.1 becomes

$$R_i = 2k_t(\text{P·})_s^2. \tag{7.1a}$$

conditions as R_s. In such experiments, the mode of initiation need not be photochemical; the same value of k_p^2/k_t should be obtained when the initiation is by high-energy radiation, or by decomposition of an initiator, provided that R_i and R_s are determined under the same conditions.

There are two general ways[1c, 1e] of determining the rate of initiation R_i. (a) The first of these is to make use of a 'scavenger' which reacts with all or most of the radicals as they are produced, so that the polymerization is retarded or completely inhibited. Ferric chloride is one substance that behaves in this way ($P\cdot + FeCl_3 \rightarrow PCl + FeCl_2$); another is diphenylpicrylhydrazyl, whose rate of disappearance can be determined photometrically. If the polymerization is completely inhibited until all the scavenger is used up, the rate of initiation can be determined by dividing the initial concentration of inhibitor by the inhibition period. Such methods are exact only if the stoichiometry of the scavenging reaction is known, and if the product is unreactive. The use of diphenylpicrylhydrazyl, for example, is open to objection on the second of these counts, and also because it absorbs light and so acts as an internal filter. For reasons such as these, different inhibitors often give different values for the rate of initiation, and the results are subject to some uncertainty.

(b) The other general method of determining R_i makes use of initiation by a reagent. Dibenzoyl peroxide, for example, decomposes thermally giving phenyl radicals which combine with monomer and start radical chains. After a known time, the polymerization is stopped, and the polymer recovered and analysed for phenyl groups. The rate of initiation R_i is equal to x/vt, where x is the number of moles of initiator fragment found in the polymer recovered after t sec from v litres of solution. It is convenient to label the benzoyl peroxide in the ring with ^{14}C, and to measure the radioactivity of the polymer. This method is independent of the catalyst efficiency, the mechanism of termination, and the extent to which transfer occurs; it has therefore superseded the earlier methods based on recovery of polymer. The only possible complication is transfer to catalyst, and this can be experimentally checked.

By the use of standard techniques, then, it is possible to determine the value of k_p^2/k_t. The determination of k_p and k_t separately, however, requires further experiments, using photochemical initiation, as follows.

DETERMINATION OF THE RATE CONSTANTS OF POLYMERIZATION REACTIONS

General principles

(a) *Determination of k_p/k_t from build-up and decay of reaction rate.* So far we have considered photochemical polymerization only in the 'steady state' in which the concentration of radicals is constant. When illumination of the monomer is started, there is a period of a few seconds or minutes during which this concentration is building up. The acceleration of the reaction during this period evidently depends on the relative rates of propagation and termination, and it is possible to deduce the value of k_p/k_t. Somewhat similarly, k_p/k_t can be determined from the deceleration of reaction when the light is cut off. From this and the value of k_p^2/k_t determined as described above, the separate rate constants can be found. The theory of these methods is given below (p. 126).

(b) *Mean lifetime of radicals.* Methods have been devised for determining the mean lifetime of the growing radical from initiation to termination. This mean lifetime τ is the ratio of the number of radicals to the number destroyed per second; this is equal to the concentration of radicals divided by the rate of destruction, so that

$$\tau = (\text{P·})_s/k_t(\text{P·})_s^2 = 1/k_t(\text{P·})_s \tag{7.5}$$

or

$$k_t = 1/\tau(\text{P·})_s \tag{7.5a}$$

Combining these relations with equation 7.1, we obtain

$$\tau = (k_t R_i)^{-1/2} \tag{7.6}$$

$$k_t = 1/\tau^2 R_i \tag{7.6a}$$

Equations 7.6a and 7.4 give:

$$k_p/k_t = \tau R_s/(\text{M}) \tag{7.7}$$

and

$$k_p = R_s/(\text{M}) R_i \tau^2 \tag{7.7a}$$

It follows that, if the mean lifetime τ has been determined under given conditions of illumination, a determination of the steady rate of polymerization R_s under the same conditions gives the value of k_p/k_t, by equation 7.7. A determination of the rate of initiation R_i under the same conditions gives the value of k_t, by equation 7.6a, and of k_p by equation 7.7a. An equivalent procedure is to combine the value of k_p/k_t from equation 7.7 with that of k_p^2/k_t from equation 7.4. Determinations of the mean lifetime have therefore been of great importance in determining the rate constants of polymerization reactions. A standard method is to make use of intermittent illumination, usually by the sector technique (p. 130); it is also possible to use observations on the initial build-up period (below).

(c) *Photostationary concentration.* If the concentration of radicals in the 'steady state' can be determined, k_t can be found by means of equation 7.1. This method has been applied to the recombination of iodine atoms (p. 137), but in general the estimation of the low concentration of radicals in photochemical polymerization (10^{-8} to 10^{-9} M) is impossible by present methods, though it may become possible by refinement of e.s.r. techniques (p. 198).

Determination of rate constants from observations during the build-up or decay of radical concentration

General.[3] Under continuous steady illumination, the rate of polymerization generally becomes constant after a few seconds, or at most minutes, during which only a small fraction of the monomer is polymerized. The decay of the rate when light is cut off also generally occurs in a few seconds. The experimental technique for following the polymerization during these periods must therefore be fairly rapid, and capable of detecting about 1 in 10^7 of the complete reaction. It has been found possible to use the measurement of viscosity,[4a] of volume change by dilatometry,[4b] and of

[3] For general accounts, see (a) Burnett, ref. 1a, chapter 7; (b) Walling, ref. 1b, chapter 3; (c) Melville and Burnett, in *Investigation of Rates and Mechanisms of Reactions*, ed. Friess, Lewis and Weissberger (2nd edn., Interscience, 1963), part II, chapter 20.

[4] (a) Bamford and Dewar, *Proc. Roy. Soc.*, A, 1948, **193**, 309, 329; (b) Burnett, *Trans. Faraday Soc.* 1950, **46**, 772; (c) Grassie and Melville, *Proc. Roy. Soc.*, A, 1951, **207**, 285; (d) Burrell, Majury and Melville, *idem, ibid.*, p. 309; (e) Bengough and Melville, *idem*, 1954, **225**, 330; (f) Bengough, *Trans. Faraday Soc.* 1958, **54**, 868.

temperature rise by its effect on refractive index[4c] or dielectric constant[4d]; the simplest method of all is to measure the temperature-rise directly with a thermocouple[4e], or by dilatometry under adiabatic conditions.[4f]

Theory of initial stages of polymerization ('*induction period*'). We shall give a simple form of the theory, applicable to the reaction scheme given above (photochemical initiation, linear propagation, mutual termination), and taking no account of chain-transfer, diradical initiation, or thermal reaction. For fuller accounts the reader is referred to the monographs available.[3]

At any time t, the net rate of increase of the concentration of radicals P· is the difference between the rates of initiation and termination, which is

$$d(\text{P·})/dt = R_i - k_t(\text{P·})^2 \tag{7.8}$$

Integration of this equation gives:

$$(k_t/R_i)^{1/2}\tanh^{-1}[(\text{P·})(k_t/R_i)^{1/2}] = k_t t + C \tag{7.9}$$

Since $(\text{P·}) = 0$ when $t = 0$, the integration constant C is zero. With equation 7.1, we obtain:

$$\tanh^{-1}[(\text{P·})/(\text{P·})_s] = (k_t R_i)^{1/2} t \tag{7.10}$$

In terms of the radical lifetime given by equation 7.6, this may be expressed as:

$$\tanh^{-1}[(\text{P·})/(\text{P·})_s] = t/\tau \tag{7.11}$$

A plot of (P·) against t according to this equation is shown in Fig. 7.1, curve a.

The rate of polymerization at time t is, if the rate constant k_p for the propagation step 2 is independent of the chain length,

$$-d(\text{M})/dt = k_p(\text{M})(\text{P·}) \tag{7.12}$$

With equation 7.11, this leads to:

$$-d(\text{M})/dt = k_p(\text{M})(\text{P·})_s \tanh(t/\tau) \tag{7.13}$$

Substituting $(\text{P·})_s = 1/k_t\tau$ from equation 7.5a, we obtain:

$$-d(\text{M})/dt = (\text{M})(k_p/k_t\tau)\tanh(t/\tau) \tag{7.14}$$

On integration this gives, if the initial concentration of monomer is written $(M)_0$,

$$- \ln (M)/(M)_0 = (k_p/k_t) \ln \cosh (t/\tau) \qquad (7.15)$$

If F is the fraction of monomer converted, so that $(M)/(M)_0 = 1 - F$, this equation becomes, when F is small,

$$F = (k_p/k_t) \ln \cosh (t/\tau) \qquad (7.16)$$

When the time t is greater than about 5τ, the rate of polymerization (equation 7.13) is practically constant, and the progress of

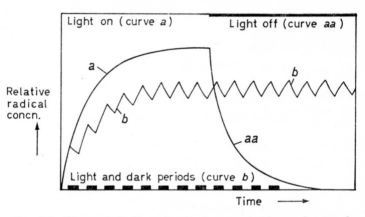

Fig. 7.1. Rise and decline of radical concentration and rate of polymerization when illumination is started and stopped. Curve a, increase when illumination starts; aa, decline in the dark; b, effect of intermittent illumination (p. 130). The concentrations and rates are relative to the values for steady illumination.

the reaction (equation 7.16) is represented (since $\cosh x = \frac{1}{2}[e^x + e^{-x}]$) by:

$$F = (k_p/k_t)(t/\tau - \ln 2) \qquad (7.17)$$

This equation shows that a plot of the fraction of converted monomer F against time (Fig. 7.2) will, when $t > 5\tau$, be a straight line with a slope of $k_p/k_t\tau$, and an intercept on the t-axis ('induction period') of $\tau \ln 2$. The product of slope and intercept thus gives the value of the ratio k_p/k_t. If the value of k_p^2/k_t is already known from observations of the steady rate of polymerization and the rate of initiation (equation 7.4), the separate rate constants may be evaluated. A knowledge of the rate of initiation R_i is actually sufficient, since τ can be determined from the intercept, and k_t can then be evaluated by equation 7.6a as $1/R_i\tau^2$.

Theory of decline of reaction rate in the dark ('after-effect'). The decline of the reaction rate when illumination is cut off can also be

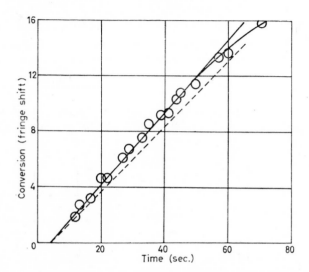

FIG. 7.2. Initial stages of photo-initiated polymerization of methyl methacrylate, using interferometer method.[4c] The ordinate is proportional to the fraction of monomer converted (F). Full curve, experimental; broken curve, corrected for non-adiabaticity of system. From Burnett, *Mechanism of Polymer Reactions* (Interscience, 1954), by permission.

observed by the rapid methods referred to above (p. 126). The rate of decrease of the concentration of radicals is

$$d(P\cdot)/dt = -k_t(P\cdot)^2 \tag{7.18}$$

Hence after a time t in darkness the concentration is given by

$$(P\cdot)^{-1} - (P\cdot)_s^{-1} = k_t t \tag{7.19}$$

A plot of $(P\cdot)$ against time according to this equation is shown in Fig. 7.1, curve aa. The rate of reaction at any time, is, by equation 7.2,

$$R = k_p(M)(P\cdot), \tag{7.20}$$

and at zero time when darkness begins it is R_s, where

$$R_s = k_p(M)(P\cdot)_s \tag{7.21}$$

With equation 7.19, we obtain:

$$R^{-1} - R_s^{-1} = [k_t/k_p(M)]t \tag{7.22}$$

A plot of R^{-1} against time will therefore be a straight line whose slope gives k_t/k_p. This provides an alternative to the use of equation 7.17.

Determination of rate constants by intermittent illumination (sector method)

General.[5] We have seen how the rate constants k_p and k_t may be determined when the mean lifetime τ of the growing radicals is

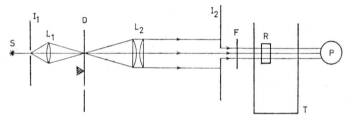

FIG. 7.3. Rotating sector apparatus. S, source; L_1, L_2, lenses; D, rotating disc; I_1, I_2, irises; F, filters; R, reaction cell; P, photomultiplier; T, thermostat.

known (p. 125). In many polymerization reactions, τ is in the region of 10^{-2} to 10 sec, and may be determined by methods in which the reacting solution is illuminated intermittently. This is most simply achieved, with standard photochemical equipment, by interposing a rotating slotted disc, or 'sector', between a steady light source and the solution (Fig. 7.3). The light and dark periods can then be varied together by varying the speed of rotation. If these periods are made short enough, the rate of polymerization as measured by conventional methods such as dilatometry (without fast recording)

[5] For general accounts, see (a) Melville and Burnett, ref. 3c; (b) Burnett, ref. 1a, chapter 7; (c) Walling, ref. 1b, chapter 3; (d) Dainton, ref. 1d, chapters 5 and 7.

is steady but lower than when illumination is continuous, and varies with the speed of rotation. Some experimental results are shown in Fig. 7.4.

This behaviour can be understood as follows. The rate of polymerization is proportional to the radical concentration. This concentration increases during each light period (according to equation 7.11), and decreases during each dark period (according to

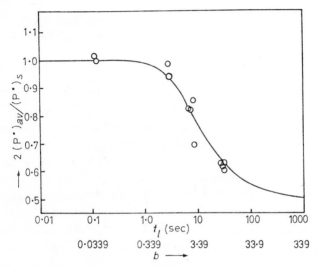

Fig. 7.4. Rate of photo-initiated polymerization of methyl methacrylate in intermittent light for different durations of light periods. Curve, theoretical (assuming no thermal reaction); points, experimental. (From Matheson, Auer, Bevilacqua and Hart, ref. 9).

equation 7.19); this is shown in Fig. 7.1, curve b. These fluctuations in rate are too fast to be observed without special techniques; the observed rate is therefore apparently steady, though actually it is an average. It will evidently depend on the relation of the light and dark periods to the mean lifetime τ, which determines the radical concentration reached in a given time (equation 7.11).

Fast and slow rotation. It is not difficult to derive expressions for the relative rates in the limiting cases of very fast and very slow rotation. Let the durations of light and dark be t_i and t_d respectively.

For very slow rotation (t_l, $t_d \gg \tau$), the radical concentration will be constant for most of the light period, and zero for most of the dark period; the reaction rate will therefore be the same as if the system were illuminated with full intensity for a fraction $t_l/(t_l + t_d)$ of the total duration of the experiment. Thus if the rate with the sector removed is R_0, the rate of reaction for 'slow' rotation is:

$$R_{slow} = R_0 \, t_l/(t_l + t_d) \qquad (7.25)$$

The fraction $t_l/(t_l + t_d)$ is equal to the sector opening, i.e. the angular fraction of the disc occupied by slots, and may be written $1/f$; then equation 7.25 becomes:

$$R_{slow} = R_0/f \qquad (7.25a)$$

For very fast rotation ($t_l, t_d \ll \tau$) the oscillations of the radical concentration shown in curve b of Fig. 7.1 will become negligible, and the rate of reaction will therefore be constant. Radicals are formed, during the light period only, at the same rate as if the sector were removed. The effect on the rate will be the same as if the intensity of illumination were reduced by the factor f to a constant lower value. In the type of reaction under consideration, where termination is by interaction of radicals in pairs, the rate depends on the square root of the intensity (equation 7.3). The rate of reaction for fast rotation if the sector is therefore:

$$R_{fast} = R_0/f^{1/2} \qquad (7.26)$$

Comparing equations 7.26 and 7.25a, we find:

$$R_{fast}/R_{slow} = f^{1/2} \qquad (7.27)$$

This equation shows that as the sector speed is increased from 'slow' to 'fast' (relative to the radical lifetime) the rate of reaction will increase. If, for example, the sector opening is such that $t_l = t_d$ and $f = 2$, the ratio of the limiting rates is $\sqrt{2}$. This has been verified for a number of linear polymerizations; an example is shown in Fig. 7.4. For more complex mechanisms,[3c] the rate will change with sector speed provided that the rate is not directly proportional to the light intensity.

Theory for determination of radical lifetime and rate constants. The complete curve showing the variation of average rate with sector speed (Fig. 7.4) can be calculated in terms of τ, with the help of equations 7.11 and 7.19 which express the growth and decay of radical concentration. In outline the calculation is as follows.

After a number of cycles, the saw-tooth variation of radical concentration with time (Fig. 7.1, curve b) will become uniform. Suppose the concentration at the end of each light period is $(\mathrm{P}\cdot)_l$, and at the end of each dark period $(\mathrm{P}\cdot)_d$. The average radical concentration is given by:

$$(\mathrm{P}\cdot)_{av} = \int_0^{t_l} (\mathrm{P}\cdot)\,dt + \int_0^{t_d} (\mathrm{P}\cdot)\,dt \qquad (7.28)$$

where $(\mathrm{P}\cdot)$ in the first integral is given by equation 7.11, and in the second by equation 7.19. Evaluation of the integrals gives for $(\mathrm{P}\cdot)_{av}/(\mathrm{P}\cdot)_s$, which is equal to the corresponding ratio of rates R_{av}/R_s,

$$(\mathrm{P})/(\mathrm{P}\cdot)_s = R_{av}/R_s$$
$$= f\left[1 + b^{-1}\ln\frac{(\mathrm{P}\cdot)_l/(\mathrm{P}\cdot)_d + (\mathrm{P}\cdot)_l/(\mathrm{P}\cdot)_s}{1 + (\mathrm{P}\cdot)_l/(\mathrm{P}\cdot)_s}\right] \qquad (7.29)$$

where $b = t_l/\tau$. Elimination of $(\mathrm{P}\cdot)_l$ and $(\mathrm{P}\cdot)_s$ from this equation with the help of equations 7.11 and 7.19 gives R_{av}/R_s as a function of b and f alone. The full expression is cumbrous, but for a given sector opening it can be plotted as a function of b alone. Tables and plots for various values of b and f are given in reference 3c. The form of the curves is illustrated by the full line in Fig. 7.4.

From such a curve, the lifetime may be determined as follows. A set of experimental runs at various sector speeds gives R_{av}/R_s at a series of values of t_l; comparison with the theoretical curve gives the corresponding values of b, i.e. t_l/τ, whence τ can be determined. In Fig. 7.4, for instance, the experimental relative rates are plotted against t_l, and the theoretical curve of relative rate against b has been superimposed after choosing the scale of b to give the best fit. The comparison shows that $t_l/b = 1/0\cdot339$ sec, and this is the value of τ. It will be noted that the plot covers a variation of several powers of 10 in t_l; thus if the experimental points are few or scattered, the uncertainty in τ can be considerable. The rate constants for termination and propagation (k_t and k_p) may be obtained from τ

10

by applying equations 7.6a and 7.7a. As these involve both τ and R_i, the values of k_p and k_t reflect the uncertainties in both these quantities. In the best work, the values of k_p and k_t are uncertain by at least 20%.

Experimental methods for intermittent illumination. The arrangement is shown in Fig. 7.3. Lifetimes from about 10 sec down to about 10^{-2} sec can be conveniently measured by the sector technique.[5] The light intensity can be adjusted to bring the rates of many photochemically-initiated reactions into this region. Thermostatting is easy to arrange. Compared with the flash technique, the apparatus is simple, and high-speed recording gear is not needed. Although the lifetimes that can be measured are longer than with flash methods, equally high second-order constants can be determined, because the radical concentrations are lower; the rate of initiation is commonly such that the radical concentration is of the order of 10^{-9} M, whence by equation 7.5a a lifetime of 0·1 sec implies that the rate constant k_t is 10^{10} l mole^{-1}sec^{-1}.

The theory assumes its simplest form if the light and dark periods have a 'square wave' form, and if the generation of radicals occurs uniformly throughout the reaction vessel. With careful design of apparatus and choice of wavelength, these conditions can be approximately realized, and corrections may be applied for unavoidable deviations from them.[6]

The method can also be adapted to reactions initiated by ionizing radiation such as γ-rays. The rotating disc is then replaced by a stainless-steel cylinder several inches thick.[7] Intermittent exposure may also be arranged by moving the reaction cell in and out of the beam,[8a] or by moving the cell to and fro along the beam and so making use of the inverse square law.[8b] A pulsed beam of electrons from a Van der Graaff accelerator has also been used.[8c]

[6] (a) Burns and Dainton, *Trans. Faraday Soc.* 1950, **46**, 411; (b) Burnett and Wright, *Proc., Roy. Soc., A,* 1954, **221**, 37.

[7] (a) Hummel, Freeman, van Cleave and Spinks, *Science,* 1954, **119**, 159; (b) Colebourne, Collinson, Currie and Dainton, *Trans. Faraday Soc.* 1963, **59**, 1357.

[8] (a) Hart and Matheson, *Discuss. Faraday Soc.* 1952, **12**, 169; (b) Dainton and Rowbottom, *Nature,* 1952, **169**, 370; (c) Schwartz, *J. Phys. Chem.* 1962, **66**, 255.

An example of the use of sector methods. The polymerization of methyl methacrylate by light from the mercury line at 3660 Å has been studied by sector methods.[9] The rate of this reaction has been independently shown to depend on the square root of the light intensity. The rate of polymerization was measured dilatometrically at a series of sector speeds. Some of the results are illustrated in Fig. 7.4 (p. 131). There is good agreement between the experimental points and the theoretical curve calculated on the assumption that the thermal reaction is negligible. (For some other reactions there is an appreciable thermal contribution.) The lifetimes at the intensities and temperatures used in this investigation were in the region of 1–10 sec. From these results are derived values of k_p/k_t, by equation 7.7. Separate experiments on rates of initiation, by an inhibitor method, give values of k_p^2/k_t. Combination of the two sets of results gives values of k_p and k_t. At 30°, k_p is 143 l mole^{-1}sec^{-1} and k_t is $6 \cdot 1 \times 10^6$ l mole^{-1}sec^{-1}; the energies of activation are 6·3 and 2·8 kcal mole^{-1} respectively.

THE RATE CONSTANTS OF POLYMERIZATION REACTIONS[10]

Rate constants for termination and propagation in liquid monomers

We have seen that the values of the rate constants for propagation and termination in photochemically-initiated polymerizations can be obtained either by sector methods or by observations made just after illumination is begun or ended. Both types of measurement have been applied to the polymerization of vinyl acetate, styrene, methyl methacrylate, and methyl acrylate. The values found by various investigators for the rate constants agree within a factor of about 10, apart from some anomalous results obtained by dielectric-constant measurements; the values for the ratio k_p/k_t agree somewhat better. The discrepancies may be due partly to difficulties of purification, and partly to the fact that in some early work the

[9] Matheson, Auer, Bevilacqua and Hart, *J. Amer. Chem. Soc.* 1949, **71**, 497.
[10] For reviews see (*a*) Burnett, ref. 1*a*, chapter 7; (*b*) Walling, ref. 1*b*, chapters 3 and 4; (*c*) Bevington, ref. 1*c*.

activating light appears to have been absorbed mainly at the front of the cell instead of uniformly. Selected values are given in Table 7.1.

TABLE 7.1

Selected rate constants for chain propagation and termination in polymerization reactions

k_p, k_t, A_p and A_t in l mole^{-1}sec^{-1}; E_p and E_t in kcal mole^{-1}. k_t is defined by equation 7.1a (p. 123, note). Data from Walling, ref. 1b, p. 95.

Monomer	k_p at 30°	E_p	$10^{-7}A_p$	$10^{-7}k_t$ at 30°	E_t	$10^{-9}A_t$
Vinyl acetate	990	6·3	3·2	2·0	3·2	3·7
Methyl methacrylate	350	4·7	0·09	1·5	1·2	0·11
Styrene	49	7·3	0·45	0·24	1·9	0·058
Methyl acrylate	720	ca. 7·1	ca. 0·10	0·22	ca. 0·5	ca. 0·15
Vinyl chloride	6800	3·7	0·33	1200	4·2	600
Methacrylonitrile	29	11·5	600	ca. 1·1	5·0	45

For the termination reaction, the values of k_t mentioned are in the region of 10^7 to 10^{10} l mole^{-1}sec^{-1}, and the corresponding energies of activation are 1–5 kcal mole^{-1}. In the more viscous media the reaction is diffusion-controlled.[1c] The values of k_p are in the region of 10–10^4 l mole^{-1}sec^{-1}, with energies of activation 3–12 kcal mole^{-1}.

Rate constants for termination and propagation in solution

The polymerization of methacrylamide in aqueous solution has been studied by the rotating-sector technique[11a]. The reaction is first-order with respect to monomer, as in the simple reaction scheme. The rate constants and Arrhenius parameters lie within the ranges given above. In many instances, however, the kinetics of radical-catalysed polymerizations of vinyl monomers in solution are not simple; in particular, the order with respect to monomer is commonly between 1 and 1·5. Various modifications of the

[11] (a) Dainton and Sisley, *Trans. Faraday Soc.* 1963, **59**, 1369; (b) George and Onyon, *ibid.*, p. 1390.

mechanism have been suggested, such as complex formation, cage effects, termination by primary radicals, and recombination of primary radicals with participation of solvent.[11b]

Rate constants in solution for chain transfer reactions in thermal polymerization

When polymerization reactions take place in solution, the transfer reaction between solvent molecules (XS) and growing radical chains may occur (reaction 5, p. 122):

$$P_i^{\cdot} + XS \xrightarrow{k_{tr}} P_i X + S\cdot$$

This reaction stops the growth of the polymer chain and reduces the average degree of polymerization, i.e. the number of monomer units per molecule of polymer. If the average degree of polymerization in presence of solvent is $\bar{P}$, compared with $\bar{P}_0$ in the liquid monomer, it may be shown that, if the chains are not too short,

$$\bar{P}^{-1} = \bar{P}_0^{-1} + (k_{tr}/k_p)(XS)/(M) \tag{7.30}$$

A plot of $\bar{P}^{-1}$ against the ratio of solvent to monomer concentration will therefore be a straight line with a slope of k_{tr}/k_p, so that the rate constant k_{tr} for transfer can be determined.

The thermal polymerization of styrene in various solvents has been studied in this way.[12] The values of k_{tr} vary by a factor of 10^7 from solvent to solvent. The energies of activation vary from 4 to 21 kcal mole^{-1}; these variations are partly compensated by changes of A.

THE RECOMBINATION OF IODINE ATOMS

The photochemical dissociation of iodine in solution has already been mentioned (p. 108). The results of flash experiments indicate that the mechanism is:

$$I_2 \xrightarrow{h\nu} 2I,$$

$$I + I \xrightarrow{k} I_2.$$

[12] (a) Bamford and Dewar, *Discuss. Faraday Soc.* 1947, **2**, 214; (b) Burnett, ref. 1a, chapter 7; (c) Walling, ref. 1b, pp. 150–159; (d) Flory, ref. 1e, chapter 4.

That the recombination is bimolecular has been confirmed by experiments on the rate of exchange of radioactive iodine with trans-diiodoethylene.[13a] This is no doubt a reaction of atomic iodine:

$$RI + I' \underset{\longleftarrow}{\overset{k'}{\longrightarrow}} RI' + I.$$

Under continuous illumination the reaction reaches a constant rate which is proportional to the square root of the light intensity. This is what would be expected if the iodine atoms are destroyed by combining in pairs; the equations for the 'steady state' are then analogous to equations 7.1 and 7.3:

$$R_i = k(I)_s^2 \tag{7.31}$$

$$R_s = k'(I)_s(RI) = k'(RI)(R_i/k)^{1/2} \tag{7.32}$$

so that R_s is proportional to $R_i^{1/2}$ and hence to the square root of the intensity. Because of this fact, the sector method can be used (p. 132) to find the mean lifetime of the iodine atoms under given conditions of light intensity, wavelength, temperature and solvent. The whole of the mathematical treatment given above for simple photochemical polymerizations holds good, if for k_t, k_p, (P·) and (M) respectively we substitute k, k', (I) and (RI). In particular, in place of equation 7.5a we have

$$k = 1/\tau(I)_s \tag{7.33}$$

and in place of 7.6a we have

$$k = 1/\tau^2 R_i \tag{7.34}$$

The lifetimes observed for solutions in hexane at 25°, with light of wavelength 4358 Å, were in the region of 0·1 to 1 sec, depending on the intensity.[13a,b] To determine the rate constant k from these values of τ, two different methods were used. (a) The concentration of iodine atoms in the photostationary state under continuous

[13] (a) Zimmerman and R. M. Noyes, J. Chem. Phys. 1950, 18, 658 (τ and (I) under same conditions); (b) Rosman and Noyes, J. Amer. Chem. Soc. 1958, 80, 2410 (τ under same conditions as in ref. 13c); (c) Lampe and Noyes, J. Amer. Chem. Soc. 1954, 76, 2140 (quantum yield under same conditions as in ref. 13b). Cf. Noyes, in ref. 1f, pp. 846–850.

illumination at the same set of intensities had been measured spectrophotometrically.[14] When the solution of iodine was strongly illuminated by a carbon arc, there was a slight decrease in the optical density, which was attributed to dissociation of iodine molecules into atoms. The concentration of atoms $(I)_s$ so determined was of the order of 10^{-10} M. An approximately square-root dependence of this concentration on the incident intensity was found. By application of equation 7.33, k was found to be $1 \cdot 1 \times 10^{10}$ 1 mole^{-1}sec^{-1}. In view of the difficulty of determining the atomic concentration, this must be regarded as a preliminary value.

(b) The rate of initiation R_i was measured under the same conditions, by a scavenger method.[13c] The principle of this is that iodine atoms react quantitatively with allyl iodide in presence of oxygen, each atom producing one molecule of iodine, so that the number of iodine atoms produced in a given time under the experimental conditions can be determined. The quantum yield is also found, as the ratio of R_i to the measured rate of energy input. From the rate of initiation and the lifetime, the rate constant for recombination of the iodine atoms is found by equation 7.34. The results are shown in Table 7.2.

TABLE 7.2

Recombination of iodine atoms in solution at 25°

Rate constants in 1 mole^{-1}sec^{-1}.

Solvent	Quantum yield	Rate constant
Hexane	0·5	$(13 \cdot 1 \pm 1 \cdot 6) \times 10^9$
Carbon tetrachloride	0·1–0·2	$(8 \cdot 2 \pm 2 \cdot 1) \times 10^9$
Hexachlorobutadiene-1,3	0·075	$(6 \cdot 1 \pm 1 \cdot 2) \times 10^9$

The rate constant in hexane agrees with the value from the photostationary concentration within experimental error. The results for carbon tetrachloride solutions agree within experimental error with those obtained by the flash method (p. 109). The rate constant in

[14] Rabinovitch and Wood, *Trans. Faraday Soc.* 1936, **32**, 547.

each solvent is close to the value for a diffusion-controlled reaction. The marked decrease of quantum yield in the series is further evidence for a solvent 'cage' from which the chance of escape is lower the heavier the solvent molecules.[15]

Diffusion control and proximity effects. Further experiments in various solvents showed that the quantum yield of iodine atoms

TABLE 7.3

Qunatum yields for iodine dissociation at 25° in various solvents [16a]

Solvent	Viscosity poise	Wavelength Å	Quantum yield calc.	obs.
Hexane	0·0029	4047	0·54	0·75
		4358	0·52	0·66
		5461	0·46	0·47
		5790	0·44	0·46
		6430	0·40	0·13
		7350	0·31	0·13
Hydrocarbon	0·017	4358	0·145	0·18
fractions	0·54	4358	0·0052	0·086
	0·8	4358	0·0035	0·048
	1·8	4358	0·0016	0·038
	3·8	4358	0·0007	0·036
Hexachlorobuta-	0·030	4358	0·087	0·075
diene		5461	0·070	0·041
		5790	0·065	0·023
		6430	0·055	0·016
		7350	0·040	0·017

decreased with increase of viscosity, and with increase of wavelength, i.e. decrease in the energy quantum absorbed.[16] These effects are qualitatively in accord with a simple theory of motion in a viscous medium, omitting all consideration of cage effects. It is

[15] The efficiency of thermal initiation of polymerization in various solvents shows a similar variation, which is likewise attributable to a cage effect; cf. Walling, ref. 1b, pp. 73 *seq.*
[16] (a) R. M. Noyes, *Z. Elektrochem.* 1960, **64**, 153. For a review see (b) Noyes in *Progress in Reaction Kinetics*, ed. Porter (Pergamon Press, 1961), chapter 5.

assumed that the energy of the quantum in excess of that required
for dissociation appears as kinetic energy of two iodine atoms
separating in opposite directions, and that the atoms are brought to
rest by the viscous drag of the solvent, at a distance depending on
the size of the energy excess and on the viscosity. Quantitatively
the agreement is imperfect, as might be expected since cage effects
have been ignored. The discrepancies can indeed be interpreted
on the cage model. For instance, the predicted quantum yield is too
high at the longer wavelengths and too low at the shorter. This
suggests that when the separating iodine atoms have low velocity
they are turned back towards each other by the solvent cage, and
when they have high velocity they separate so far that solvent
molecules come between them and hinder recombination. It
appears therefore that our picture of diffusion control should here be
modified to take account of 'proximity effects' due to the solvent
cage. Diffusion control is further discussed in chapter 12 (pp. 279
seq.).

CHAPTER 8

Fluorescence methods

GENERAL PRINCIPLES

Introduction

Fluorescence methods for studying fast reactions are concerned with the rates of reaction of photochemically-excited molecules, usually with an added substance which reduces the intensity of fluorescence. This 'quenching' reaction competes with deactivation by other mechanisms that occur even in the absence of reaction, such as loss of energy to the solvent. A steady state is set up, depending on the relative rates of these processes; the resulting fluorescence intensity can be observed without fast-recording apparatus. From the relation between the intensity and the concentration of reagent, the rate constant for the reaction can be derived. The method is applicable only to excited molecules, and to very fast reactions (p. 153). The fluorescence and flash methods often give complementary information on a given system; fluorescence quenching can be used to investigate the singlet excited states of systems whose triplet states are studied by the flash technique (cf. pp. 155, 158, 159).

Fluorescence quenching

Mechanism of fluorescence quenching

Many substances in solution fluoresce when irradiated continuously with ultraviolet light; examples are anthracene, β-naphthol and quinine sulphate.[1] Fluorescence occurs because some of the

[1] For general accounts of fluorescence see (*a*) Förster, *Fluoreszenz organischen Verbindungen* (Vandenhoeck and Ruprecht, 1951); (*b*) Bowen and Wokes, *Fluorescence of Solutions* (Longmans, 1953); (*c*) Pringsheim, *Fluorescence and Phosphorescence* (Interscience, 1949). For a general account of the application of fluorescence methods to fast reactions see Weller, in *Investigation of Rates and Mechanisms of Reactions*, ed. Friess, Lewis and Weissberger (2nd edn., Interscience, 1963), part II, chapter 16.

molecules are raised to an electronically excited state, by absorbing quanta of the exciting light, and re-emit light of visible or near-ultraviolet wavelength as they drop back to the ground state. These processes may be represented, for a molecule X:

Excitation: $\qquad X + h\nu \longrightarrow X^*$ (8.1)

Emission: $\qquad X^* \xrightarrow{\ k_f\ } X + h\nu'$ (8.2)

The molecules always drop to the zero vibrational level of the lowest singlet excited state before fluorescing. The emission spectrum is therefore characteristic of the substance, and independent of the wavelength of the exciting light. The average interval between excitation and emission is very short, of the order of 10^{-8} sec. However, some of the excited molecules (a small proportion, for strongly fluorescent substances) are deactivated before they can emit, either by interaction with the solvent or by 'internal quenching' processes[2] within the molecule:

Solvent and internal quenching:

$$X^* \xrightarrow{\ k_i\ } X \qquad (8.3)$$

In the absence of any other reactive substance, a steady state is set up, in which process 8.1 is balanced by 8.2 and 8.3. In presence of a suitable reagent Q, the excited molecule X^* may react before it emits. The effect of adding Q is then to reduce the intensity of the fluorescence; this is called 'external quenching'. It will be noticed only when the reaction is fast, since the normal lifetime of the excited molecule is so short. The product may be an unexcited molecule Y or sometimes an excited molecule Y^*. A special case is a reaction of X^* with X to form a dimer. The alternative reactions may be written:

External quenching:

$$X^* + Q \xrightarrow{\ k_Q\ } Y + Q' \qquad (8.4)$$

$$X^* + Q \xrightarrow{\ k_Q\ } Y^* + Q' \qquad (8.5)$$

$$X^* + X \longrightarrow X_2 \text{ or } XX^* \qquad (8.6)$$

[2] Examples of mechanisms for 'internal' quenching are given on pp. 158 and 162.

As the concentration of Q increases, the intensity of fluorescence due to X* decreases, while if an excited molecule Y* is formed, the intensity of its fluorescence increases; the two intensities can be separately measured if the two frequencies are far enough apart.

In this ideally simple scheme, therefore, the excited molecule formed in process 8.1 may take part in one of three subsequent processes: emission (8.2), internal quenching (8.3), or external quenching (8.4, 8.5 or 8.6). The external quenching has been supposed to take place in a simple bimolecular encounter with Q. This scheme was developed to account for the simplest observed relations between the concentration of the quenching solute Q and the intensity of fluorescence (see below, Figs. 8.1 and 8.3). These relations are derived from the scheme in the following section.

The relation between fluorescence intensity and concentration of quenching reagent; the Stern-Volmer equation.

The rate of production of excited molecules X* by process 8.1 is constant, since the intensity of the exciting light is kept constant. When no 'external' quencher is present, the overall rate of disappearance of X* by the two competing processes 8.2 and 8.3 is:

$$-d(X^*)/dt = (X^*)(k_f + k_i) \qquad (8.7)$$

The corresponding relaxation time τ_i, usually called the 'mean lifetime' of the excited species X* in the given solvent in absence of quencher, is the reciprocal of the overall first-order rate constant (p. 62), so that:

$$1/\tau_i = k_f + k_i \qquad (8.8)$$

The rate of loss of X* by emission of fluorescent light (process 8.2) is $k_f(X^*)$. Hence the X* molecules that fluoresce form a fraction F_o of the total number produced, given by:

$$F_o = k_f/(k_f + k_i) \qquad (8.9)$$

This fraction is called the quantum yield of fluorescence.

In presence of a quenching reagent Q, the fluorescence has to compete with process 8.4, 8.5 or 8.6, as well as 8.3. The overall rate of disappearance of X* is then:

$$-d(X^*)/dt = (X^*)[k_f + k_i + k_Q(Q)] \qquad (8.10)$$

The mean lifetime $\tau_{(Q)}$ in presence of quencher is thus related to the concentration (Q) by:

$$1/\tau_{(Q)} = k_f + k_i + k_Q(Q) \tag{8.11}$$

The quantum yield becomes:

$$F = k_f/[k_f + k_i + k_Q(Q)] \tag{8.12}$$

The intensity I of the fluorescent light depends on the number of molecules that fluoresce per second, and so is proportional to the quantum yield. Consequently the ratio of the fluorescence intensity in the absence of added quencher (I_0) to that in presence of a given concentration of quencher (I) is

$$\frac{I_0}{I} = \frac{F_0}{F} = \frac{k_f + k_i + k_Q(Q)}{k_f + k_i} = 1 + \frac{k_Q(Q)}{k_f + k_i} \tag{8.13}$$

In terms of τ_i (equation 8.8), this may be written:

$$I_0/I = 1 + k_Q\tau_i(Q) \tag{8.14}$$

Writing $k_Q\tau_i = k$, this becomes:

$$I_0/I = 1 + k(Q) \tag{8.15}$$

where $$k = k_Q\tau_i = k_Q/(k_f + k_i) \tag{8.16}$$

The important relation 8.15 is known as the *Stern-Volmer equation*. It enables us to determine the rate constant k_Q for the quenching reaction, from the variation of the relative fluorescence intensity I/I_0 with the concentration of quencher. Absolute values of the intensity are not required; this greatly simplifies the measurements. A plot of I_0/I against (Q) will be linear; examples are shown in Fig. 8.1. A plot of I/I_0 against log (Q) has the form seen in Fig. 8.3, curve a. As (Q) increases, the intensity decreases from I_0 towards 0, and has the value $\frac{1}{2}I_0$ at a concentration $(Q)_c$ such that $k_Q\tau_i(Q)_c = 1$. We can therefore find k_Q, as $1/\tau_i(Q)_c$, if we know τ_i. The value of τ_i has to be determined independently, by one of several methods (see below).

Another method of determining k_Q is to measure the fluorescence lifetime $\tau_{(Q)}$ in presence of a series of concentrations of quencher.

The relation between $\tau_{(Q)}$ and (Q), obtained by combining equations 8.8 and 8.11, is

$$1/\tau_{(Q)} = 1/\tau_i + k_Q(Q) \tag{8.17}$$

Thus k_Q can be found as the slope of a linear plot of $1/\tau_{(Q)}$ against (Q). Rate constants have been determined to $\pm 15\%$ by this method.[12b]

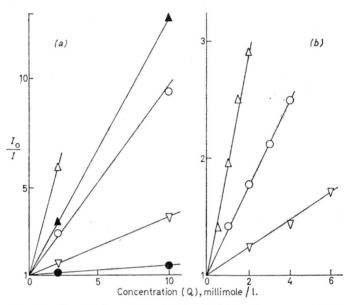

FIG. 8.1. Stern-Volmer plots of I_o/I against quencher concentration (Q) for quenching of fluorescence of various substances by (a) oxygen and (b) biacetyl, in cyclohexane at $25°$: $\triangle$ naphthalene; $\blacktriangle$ phenanthrene; $\bigcirc$ chrysene; $\triangledown$ fluorene; $\bullet$ azulene. (Stevens and Dubois, unpublished work.)

Internal quenching, and temperature-variation of F_0

The rate constant k_i for solvent and internal quenching can be determined if we know both τ_i and F_0, the quantum yield in absence of quencher. Solving equations 8.8 and 8.12, we obtain:

$$k_i = (1 - F_0)/\tau_i \tag{8.18}$$

The variation of k_i with temperature, however, can be determined simply from that of F_0, as follows. By equation 8.9,

$$k_i/k_f = (1/F_0) - 1 \tag{8.19}$$

Since k_f depends only on the properties of the excited molecule, it may be assumed independent of temperature, so that

$$\ln k_i = \text{const.} + \ln\left[(1/F_0) - 1\right] \qquad (8.20$$

In practice, the fluorescence intensity increases gradually with decrease of temperature, and linear plots of $\ln\left[(1/F_0) - 1\right]$ against $1/T$ are found for a number of systems. The slope of such a plot is evidently, by equation 8.20, equal to $d\ln k_i/d(1/T)$, and so gives the activation energy E_i corresponding to k_i. Absolute quantum yields must be measured (p. 151), but τ_i need not be known. Some results are discussed on pp. 162–163.

A more detailed kinetic scheme for external quenching

In deriving the Stern-Volmer equation 8.15, the external quenching reaction 8.4 (or 8.5 or 8.6) was treated as if it occurred in a single collision. However, when the molecules X and Q have come together, by diffusion through the solution, they will find themselves in a solvent cage and undergo several collisions before separating (p. 282). They may then be said to form an 'encounter complex'. An excited complex may therefore be formed in two ways, either by a molecule Q meeting an excited molecule X* by diffusion, or by unexcited X and Q molecules forming an encounter complex which then becomes excited by absorption of light. (This second path was ignored in the simple treatment above.) The excited encounter complex formed by either path then gives the deactivated product. The two paths are distinguished as 'diffusional' and 'static' quenching.[3]

Diffusional quenching:

$$X^* + Q \underset{k_{-D}}{\overset{k_D}{\rightleftharpoons}} X^*.Q \overset{k_2}{\longrightarrow} \text{product} \qquad (8.21)$$

Static quenching:

$$X + Q \overset{K}{\rightleftharpoons} X.Q \overset{h\nu}{\longrightarrow} X^*Q \overset{k_2}{\longrightarrow} \text{product} \qquad (8.22)$$

[3] For a review see (a) Weller, in *Progress in Reaction Kinetics*, vol. I, ed. Porter (Pergamon Press, 1961), pp. 187 *seq.* See also (b) Weller, *Discuss. Faraday Soc.* 1959, **27**, 25; (c) Bowen and Metcalf, *Proc. Roy. Soc., A,* 1951, **206**, 437; (d) Melhuish and Metcalf, *J. Chem. Soc.* 1954, 976.

This scheme leads to the following equation[3a] for the concentration-dependence of the relative fluorescence intensity, in place of equation 8.15:

$$I_0/I = [1 + \gamma k_D \tau_i(Q)]/(1 - \gamma\alpha) \tag{8.23}$$

Here k_D is the rate of encounter by diffusion (p. 11), while α is the fraction of the XQ complexes excited by process 8.22, and is given by the following equation, where ϵ and ϵ' are the extinction coefficients of X and XQ:

$$1/\alpha = 1 + \epsilon/\epsilon' \, K(Q) \tag{8.24}$$

The factor γ in equation 8.23 is the probability of reaction during the lifetime of the excited complex, given at higher quencher concentrations by the following expression, where τ_{XQ} is the fluorescence lifetime of the complex X^*Q:

$$\gamma = k_2/(k_2 + k_D + 1/\tau_{XQ} + k_D \, \tau_i(Q)/\tau_{XQ}) \tag{8.25}$$

The Stern-Volmer quenching constant k (equation 8.15), which is determined by experiment as $(I_0/I - 1)/(Q)$, now includes γ and will vary with the concentration of Q, instead of being independent of it. This behaviour was observed for the fluorescence of anthracene, for instance, and it was possible to determine K and γ.[3c]

There are two limiting cases. When there is a high equilibrium concentration of XQ, as may occur when Q is the solvent, static quenching (process 8.22) may dominate. Then $\alpha = 1$, and the limiting value of I_0/I at high quencher concentrations is, from equations 8.23 and 8.25,

$$I_0/I = 1 + k_2 \tau_{XQ} \tag{8.26}$$

Diffusional quenching (process 8.21), on the other hand, will dominate when the concentration of XQ is small and in general for efficient quenching in solvents of moderate viscosity. Then α is negligible, and equation 8.23 reduces to a form of the Stern-Volmer equation 8.15.

$$I_0/I = 1 + \gamma k_D \, \tau_i(Q) \tag{8.27}$$

Here the k_Q of the simple treatment has been replaced by γk_D. This quantity may be found from the experimental plots of I_0/I against (Q), and one can then evaluate γ by comparison with the values of k_D calculated from diffusion theory. This has been done for various proton-transfer reactions (p. 269).

A further complication is that for diffusion-controlled reactions the time required to reach the steady state may be comparable with the reaction time.[3a] It is then necessary to modify equation 8.23, which was derived by straightforward steady-state kinetics. The new equation is:

$$I_0/I = [1 + \gamma k_D \tau_i(Q)]/W \qquad (8.28)$$

Here $(1 - W)$ represents the fraction of excited molecules which react immediately after excitation and so do not contribute to the quantum yield. The value for W thus depends on γ; it approaches unity very rapidly as γ decreases. It can be calculated from γ when the rate constant is approximately known, and by a few successive approximations the stationary rate constant can be found. The rate constants of some fast proton transfers have been found in this way (p. 160).

The 'inner mechanism' of quenching. The kinetic treatment above is mainly concerned with the encounters that occur between molecules, or what has been called the 'outer mechanism' of quenching. Little is known of the 'inner mechanism' of the quenching within the encounter complex X*Q in processes 8.21 and 8.22, which controls k_2 and γ. It probably involves an electron-transfer.[1a, 3a] Steric requirements are suggested by the values of γ in certain reactions[3a] (p. 269); and there is some evidence that solvent relaxation is also concerned.[3b]

EXPERIMENTAL INVESTIGATION OF FLUORESCENCE

Relative fluorescence intensity (I/I^0) and quantum yield (F/F^0) in presence of quencher[4]

In principle the arrangement is simple (Fig. 8.2). The solution is contained in a quartz cell and irradiated with ultraviolet light from a mercury lamp through filters. The fluorescent light emitted is

[4] For general accounts, see, e.g., refs. 1a and 1b; also Wotherspoon and Oster, in *Physical Methods of Organic Chemistry*, ed. Weissberger (3rd edn., Interscience, 1960), part 3, pp. 2063–2105.

11

measured by means of a photomultiplier or spectrophotometer placed at an angle to the exciting beam. Two solutions may be compared by substituting one for the other, if the lamp is adequately stabilized. To eliminate variations in the intensity of the lamp, it is better to divide the ultraviolet light by means of a quartz plate at 45° to the beam; the two resulting beams may be passed through the two solutions, and the two fluorescent intensities measured by separate photomultipliers. Measurements of the fluorescent intensity at a single wavelength are often adequate. By passing the light

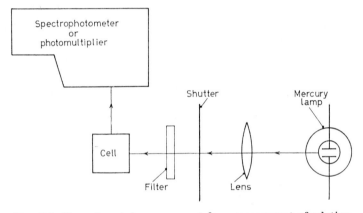

FIG. 8.2. Experimental arrangement for measurement of relative fluorescence intensities (schematic).

through a spectrophotometer, the intensity may be observed as a function of wavelength.[5] Commercial spectrofluorimeters are now available. In the Perkin-Elmer instrument,[5b] a rotating sector is used to pass the light first through one solution and then through the other in rapid succession; the two fluorescent beams are brought through a spectrophotometer system to a single photomultiplier, and any difference of intensity is amplified and recorded as a function of frequency. For temperature control, the cells may be surrounded by a copper block,[6] or a small unsilvered quartz Dewar vessel may be used; temperatures down to 90°K have been

[5] (a) Parker and Rees, Analyst, 1960, 85, 587; (b) Lippert, Nägele, Seibold-Blankenstein, Staiger and Voss, Z. anal. Chem. 1959, 170, 1.
[6] Lippert, Lüder and Moll, Spectrochim. Acta, 1959, 10, 378.

employed. The exciting light must be monochromatic. The materials used must be carefully freed from fluorescent or absorbing impurities, especially as the concentration of the fluorescent substance may be less than 10^{-5} M. Oxygen (which often acts as a quencher) must be expelled, by bubbling nitrogen or carbon dioxide through the solution.

Absolute quantum yields (*F*) are sometimes needed (p. 162). The direct determination of *F* requires measurements of the quanta absorbed and emitted over the entire frequency range, with corrections for scattered light, reabsorption, and refractive-index effects. The relative number of quanta emitted per second by the fluorescent solution may be determined by means of a 'quantum counter', consisting of a combination of a second fluorescent solution (such as rhodamine B in glycerol) and a photomultiplier; since fluorescence yields are independent of the wavelength of the exciting light (above a long-wave limit), the response of this system depends on the number of quanta absorbed, irrespective of wavelength.[7] The number of incident quanta is determined by the same quantum-counter after replacing the solution by a magnesium oxide surface, whose light-scattering properties are known, or better still by a purified protein solution of calculable scattering power.[8] The number of quanta absorbed by the fluorescent solution can then be found from measurements of light absorption. The ratio of emitted to absorbed quanta gives *F*. For quinine bisulphate in water, for example, the value 0·55 is accepted.[7b]

Given such a standard, *F* is more easily determined by comparative measurements.[5] The fluorescent intensities of the two solutions under the same conditions are determined as a function of frequency by means of a spectrofluorimeter, whose response curve is determined with the aid of a tungsten lamp of known colour temperature. Curves representing relative numbers of quanta emitted against frequency can thus be constructed; the areas under these curves are proportional to *F*, and so the unknown value can be derived from that of the standard. Correction is necessary

[7] (a) Bowen and Sawtell, *Trans. Faraday Soc.* 1937, **33**, 1425; (b) Melhuish, *N.Z. J. Sci. Tech.*, B, 1955, **37**, 142.

[8] Weber and Teale, *Trans. Faraday Soc.*, 1957, **53**, 646

for refractive-index effects, which depend on the geometry of the apparatus and affect the spatial distribution of fluorescence. To minimize these effects, the cell may be surrounded by a 5-litre flask coated internally with magnesium oxide, to act as an integrating sphere.[9]

Determination of the mean lifetime of a fluorescent molecule (τ)[10]

Several methods are available, each considerably more elaborate than those used for determining relative intensities. (*a*) A direct method[11] is to excite fluorescence by a light-pulse lasting less than 10^{-9} sec, from a hydrogen lamp, and observe the intensity of the emitted light by means of a photomultiplier connected to an oscillograph. The decay of fluorescence may then be followed as a function of time. (*b*) The phase-shift method is more convenient.[12] Fluorescence is excited by light modulated at a high frequency $(\omega/2\pi$ c/sec). The difference in phase (ϕ) between the exciting light and the emitted fluorescent light is determined, by means of photomultipliers and suitable electronic circuits. The mean lifetime is given by $\omega\tau = \tan\phi$. This method has been applied to acridine, quinine sulphate, and fluorescein, with a precision of ± 1–2%. (*c*) An indirect method[13] makes use of the fact that the area under the fluorescence emission band can be related theoretically to the mean lifetime. This area could be found directly by means of a spectrofluorimeter; it has commonly been found by determining the integrated extinction coefficient, i.e. the area under the absorption band, which is approximately the mirror-image of the emission band. This method gives the true radiative life τ_0 in the absence of quenching, which corresponds to $k_i = 0$, so that by equation 8.8 $\tau_0 = 1/k_f$. Thus the actual mean life in a given solvent is given, according to equation 8.9, by $\tau_i = \tau_0 F_0$; its determination therefore requires a knowledge of the absolute quantum efficiency F_0.

[9] Bowen and Sahu, *J. Phys. Chem.* 1959, **63**, 4.

[10] For a survey with references see Förster, ref. 1*a*, chapters 2 and 8.

[11] Brody and Rabinowitch, *Science*, 1957, **125**, 555.

[12] (*a*) Rollefson and Bailey, *J. Chem. Phys.* 1953, **21**, 1315; (*b*) Ware, *J. Phys. Chem.* 1962, **66**, 455.

[13] (*a*) Forster, ref. 1*a*, chapters 6 and 8; cf. (*b*) Bowen, *Trans. Faraday Soc.* 1954, **50**, 97.

General comments on fluorescence methods

The fastest reactions may be measured with comparative ease by fluorescence methods. Since τ_i is of the order of 10^{-8} sec, a concentration of 10^{-2} M for half-quenching corresponds to a rate constant of 10^{10} $M^{-1}sec^{-1}$. Diffusion-controlled processes can therefore be studied in detail, as the examples below will show. Some depend on energy-transfer alone, some on reversible interactions, and some on irreversible photochemical reactions. They nearly all involve singlet excited states; comparisons may be made with the behaviour of triplet states studied by flash methods (p. 111). The temperature can be varied over wide ranges.

The main restriction is on the reactions that can be studied, since one of the reagents must belong to the restricted class of fluorescent substances; moreover, its mean lifetime τ_i must be known. Once τ_i has been determined, however, the measurements of relative intensity are not especially difficult. The uncertainty in the rate constant in the most favourable cases is ± 5–10%.

KINETIC APPLICATIONS OF FLUORESCENCE MEASUREMENTS

Dimerization and self-quenching

Anthracene.[14] Solutions of anthracene in benzene are fluorescent:

$$A + h\nu \rightarrow A^* \rightarrow A + h\nu'$$

However, they show a marked decrease of fluorescence intensity as the concentration is increased. A stable dimer (dianthracene) is formed photochemically in high yield in solutions stronger than 10^{-2} M. The intensity-concentration relation is consistent with a reaction scheme in which the excited molecule A^* reacts on collision with a ground-state molecule A:

$$A + A^* \rightarrow AA^* \rightarrow AA$$

[14] (a) Bowen and Norton, *Trans. Faraday Soc.* 1939, **35**, 44; (b) Bowen and Tanner, *idem*, 1955, **51**, 475; (c) Dammers-de Klerk, *Mol. Phys.* 1958, **1**, 141.

The rate constant for dimerization is of the order of 10^{10} l mole^{-1} sec^{-1}.[14b]

Pyrene.[15] Solutions of pyrene in benzene show an additional feature: at low concentrations the fluorescence is violet, at high concentrations blue. The concentration-dependence is shown in Fig. 8.3. It agrees with the interpretation that the violet fluor-

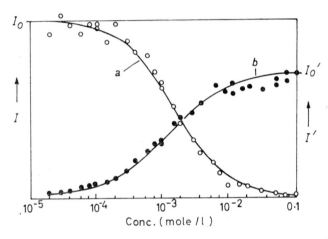

FIG. 8.3. Concentration-dependence of fluorescence of pyrene in benzene.[15] Curve a, intensity I of violet fluorescence (monomer); curve b, intensity I' of blue fluorescence (dimer). The concentration scale is logarithmic. (From Förster and Kasper, ref. 15a.)

escence is due to excited monomer and the blue to a metastable excited dimer; the violet band is quenched by dimerization:

$$A + A^* \rightarrow AA^* \rightarrow AA \rightarrow A + A$$
$$\quad\;\; \downarrow \qquad \downarrow$$
$$\quad\;\; h\nu' \qquad h\nu''$$

Application of the Stern-Volmer equation 8.14 to the results gives $k_Q \tau_i = 650$ l mole^{-1}; as τ_i is independently known to be $1 \cdot 2 \times 10^{-7}$ sec, the rate constant for dimerization is 5×10^9 l mole^{-1}sec^{-1}.

[15] (a) Förster and Kasper, *Z. Elektrochem.* 1955, **59**, 976; (b) Kasper, *Z. phys. Chem. (Frankfurt)*, 1957, **12**, 52.

Oxygen quenching of naphthalene and anthracene fluorescence:
energy exchange and irreversible oxidation[16]

Dissolved oxygen often quenches fluorescence.[14a, 17] Sometimes
this is accompanied by oxidation of the fluorescent molecule
to a peroxide, but not always. With naphthalene, for example,
no peroxide can be detected; the quenching appears to be due
to deactivation by collision, probably by a charge-transfer
mechanism[18]:

$$A^* + O_2 \rightarrow (A^+, O_2^-)^* \rightarrow A + O_2 + k.e.$$

With anthracene, fluorescence quenching is accompanied by
irreversible oxidation to a transannular peroxide, but the two
processes are not directly related. The results can be fitted to a
kinetic scheme in which quenching involves the removal of energy
from a singlet excited molecule, while photo-oxidation involves a
triplet state, of lower energy than the singlet. Flash methods
confirm this (p. 114), The rate constants for fluorescence quenching
are considered below.

Quenching of anthracene fluorescence: diffusion control. Measurements of fluorescence quenching in solution are of interest in connection with the theory of diffusion control, since with their aid
high rate constants can be determined, in solvents of differing
viscosities, over a wide range of temperature. For bimolecular
reactions occurring at every encounter between uncharged molecules, an approximate value (p. 12) for the calculated rate con-
stant is $(8RT/3000\eta)$ l mole^{-1}sec^{-1}, where η is the viscosity. This
equation predicts (*a*) an inverse dependence of rate on viscosity;
(*b*) a rate constant of the order of 10^{10} l mole^{-1}sec^{-1} at 25° in water
($\eta = 0.01$ poise) and in organic solvents of comparable viscosity;
and (*c*) a temperature-variation determined by that of T/η, giving
an apparent activation energy of a few kilocalories per mole.

The quenching by oxygen of the fluorescence of anthracene and
substituted anthracenes has been investigated in various organic

[16] For reviews see (*a*) Simons, *Quart. Rev. Chem. Soc.* 1959, **13**, 3; (*b*)
    Hochstrasser and Porter, *idem*, 1960, **14**, 146.
[17] Bowen, and Williams, *Trans. Faraday Soc.* 1939, **35**, 765.
[18] Evans, *J. Chem. Soc.* 1961, 1987.

solvents over a range of temperature from $-50°$ to $+20°$, at concentrations where the dimerization is negligible.[19] The rate constants in benzene, acetone, chloroform, etc., are in the range 2×10^{10} to 8×10^{10} l mole^{-1}sec^{-1}. These values agree within 50% with the values calculated from simple diffusion theory, provided that the directly-observed value for the diffusion coefficient of oxygen is used,[12b] rather than the Stokes-Einstein value ($kT/6\pi\eta r$) used in the approximate theory. (The values for quenching by sulphur dioxide are comparable; those for carbon tetrachloride and bromobenzene are about 100 times smaller.) A close dependence on viscosity is shown by solutions in various paraffin fractions whose viscosities range from $0\cdot003$ to $1\cdot9$ poise.[19a] The temperature coefficients are small compared to those of most chemical reactions; the rate constant increases by a factor of only two or three between $-50°$ and $+20°$.[19c] Thus the general features expected of a diffusion-controlled process are all at least qualitatively verified.

It is of interest that rate constants for quenching by oxygen and sulphur dioxide can also be determined in the gas phase.[19a] They are found to be of the same order as the collision numbers calculated from kinetic theory; the fraction of effective collisions in the gas is $\frac{1}{2}$ to $\frac{1}{6}$. The rate constants in solution are 10 to 20 times smaller than those in the gas phase. Numerical values of the parameters of the Arrhenius equation are available for the quenching of the fluorescence of β-naphthylamine by carbon tetrachloride[20a]; in iso-octane the rate constant is $(2\cdot0 \times 10^{11})\exp(-1100/RT)$, and in cyclohexane it is $(4\cdot5 \times 10^{11})\exp(-2470/RT)$ l mole^{-1}sec^{-1}. Here A is slightly larger than the rate constant found for the gas phase, which is temperature-independent: $5\cdot9 \times 10^{10}$ l mole^{-1}sec^{-1}. The encounter diameter in solution thus appears to be slightly larger than the collision diameter in the gas. A possible interpretation[20b] is that when the two molecules have approached within a distance comparable with molecular dimensions, they are forced together by the surrounding solvent molecules, as in the cage effect (p. 282).

[19] (a) Bowen and Metcalf, *Proc. Roy. Soc.*, A, 1951, **206**, 437; (b) Bowen, *Trans. Faraday Soc.* 1954, **50**, 97; (c) Bowen and Sahu, ref. 9.

[20] (a) Curme and Rollefson, *J. Amer. Chem. Soc.* 1952, **74**, 3766; (b) Noyes, *J. Chem. Phys.* 1954, **22**, 1357.

Fluorescence quenching by ions[21]

Fluorescent ions are present in aqueous solutions of (for example) fluorescein and quinine sulphate. The fluorescence is quenched by addition of salts such as potassium iodide. The rate constants k_Q derived from the Stern-Volmer equation, when compared with those calculated for diffusion control (p. 12), indicate that quenching occurs in all or most encounters, presumably by energy-transfer.[21a] When the viscosity of the solution is increased by adding glycerol, the rate constant decreases, as would be expected.[21c] When the ionic strength is varied, the rate constant varies in the same way as that of an ordinary second-order ionic reaction; that is, at fairly low concentrations (0·01 M) the plot of $\log k$ against the square root of the ionic strength approaches the straight line predicted by the Debye-Hückel theory[21b] (see also p. 160 below).

Energy transfer at long range[22]

Transfer of energy from fluorescent molecules to quenching molecules may occur over distances considerably longer than the encounter distance, when the quenching molecule absorbs at a longer wavelength than the fluorescent molecule. The critical distance for energy transfer from acriflavine to rhodamine B in methanol, for instance, is of the order of 70 Å.[22c] The rate is not determined by diffusion; it is nearly independent of the viscosity of the solvent[22a] This remarkable phenomenon is attributed to long-range dipole–dipole interaction, which can be sufficient for transfer when the energy change for deactivation in one molecule corresponds closely to that for absorption in the other; it is often called 'resonance transfer'. It appears to be involved in photosynthesis.[23]

[21] (a) Umberger and La Mer, *J. Amer. Chem. Soc.* 1945, **67**, 1099; (b) Stoughton and Rollefson, *idem*, 1939, **61**, 2634; (c) *idem*, 1940, **62**, 2264.

[22] For reviews see Förster; (a) *Discuss. Faraday Soc.* 1959, **27**, 7; (b) *Z. Elecktrochem.* 1960, **64**, 157. For experimental work and discussion see (c) Förster, *Z. Naturforsch.* 1949, **4A**, 321; (d) Bowen and Livingston, *J. Amer. Chem. Soc.* 1954, **76**, 6300.

[23] Brody, *Z. Elektrochem.* 1960, **64**, 187.

Chlorophyll[24]

The fluorescence of chlorophyll is strongly quenched by oxygen, quinones and various other substances. The mechanism is not certain. The rate constants for quenching are in the region of 10^{10} l mole^{-1}sec^{-1}, and agree with those calculated for diffusion control. They are about ten times larger than the rate constants for quenching of the triplet state, determined by the flash-photolysis method (p. 115). A similar difference is observed for anthracene (p. 155), and a larger one for thionine (below). These results are of interest for the study of photo-synthesis.

Thionine: singlet and triplet states

The fluorescence of thionine in aqueous acid solution has been investigated in close relation with a study of its photo-reduction.[25] The connection arises because the singlet excited state T*, which is responsible for fluorescence, can drop to a lower triplet excited state ^{3}T, whose behaviour can be studied by flash methods (p. 117). This is a form of internal quenching. The constant k_i (p. 143) is thus the sum of two terms, one (k_2) for solvent quenching and the other (k_3) for the reaction T* $\rightarrow$ ^{3}T.

In absence of quenchers, the fluorescence yield F_0 has been determined by comparison with rhodamine B as 0·024, so that (by equation 8.19) $k_i'/k_f = 41$. The mean lifetime (from the integrated extinction coefficient) gives $k_f = 1·5 \times 10^8$ sec^{-1}, so that $k_i = k_2 + k_3$ $= 6·1 \times 10^9$ sec^{-1}. The values of k_2 and k_3 cannot be found separately from fluorescence measurements, but from flash experiments on the quantum efficiency of bleaching in presence of ferrous ions it appears that they are of the same order of magnitude.

The fluorescence is quenched by ferrous and ferric ions. The constant k in the Stern-Volmer equation (8.15) is found to be 0·6 l mole^{-1} for Fe^{++} and 2·6 l mole^{-1} for Fe^{+++}. Hence the rate constant k_Q for the bimolecular quenching by ferrous ion is (by equation 8.16) 4×10^9 l mole^{-1}sec^{-1}, and for ferric ion $1·6 \times 10^{10}$

[24] For a review see Livingston, *Quart. Rev. Chem. Soc.* 1960, **14**, 174.
[25] Hatchard and Parker, *Trans. Faraday Soc.* 1961, **57**, 1093.

l mole^{-1}sec^{-1}. These are considerably larger than the rate constants for quenching of the triplet state, and fairly close to the values calculated for diffusion-controlled reactions in water $(7 \times 10^9$ l mole^{-1}sec$^{-1})$.

Eosin: triplet–singlet transitions

It was remarked earlier (p. 112) that phosphorescence, which is due to triplet–singlet transitions, is not normally observed in fluid solutions, because the triplet state has a comparatively long natural radiative lifetime and deactivation by collision is frequent compared with emission. With eosin, however, in glycerol or ethanol, it has been found possible to observe phosphorescence, and to measure the ratio of its intensity to that of fluorescence.[26a] This was done by means of a spectrofluorimeter and two rotating sectors, one of which was made to chop the beam of exciting light and the other the emitted beam. When the two choppers were in phase, the measured intensity was due to phosphorescence plus fluorescence; when out of phase, it was due to phosphorescence alone. This is a promising technique for determining the rates of transitions between triplet and singlet states. Compared with the flash method, it has the advantages that monochromatic light of various frequencies can be used for irradiation, that quantum yields can be precisely determined, and that the standing concentration of triplet-state molecules is small, so that triplet–triplet quenching can be neglected. On the other hand, when the natural lifetime is long, or when quenching is strong, the emission will be very weak in systems where the triplet state could still be readily observed by flash spectroscopy.

Besides the phosphorescence band, the spectrum of the long-lived emission from eosin shows a band similar to the normal fluorescence band.[26b]. This is attributed to the formation of an excited singlet molecule by interaction of two triplet-state molecules. Similar results have been obtained with proflavine hydrochloride, anthracene, phenanthrene, and pyrene solutions.[26b,c,d]

[26] Parker and Hatchard, (a) Trans. Faraday Soc. 1961, 57, 1894; (b) J. Phys. Chem. 1962, 66, 2506; (c) Proc. Roy. Soc., A, 1962, 269, 574; (d) Trans. Faraday Soc. 1963, 59, 284.

Proton-transfer reactions[27]

The rates of proton-transfer to or from certain aromatic amines and hydroxy-compounds can be determined by fluorescence studies. Acridine, for instance, in water is a base of pK 5·45. Its fluorescence in acid or neutral solution is green, and remains unchanged up to a pH of about 10, above which it becomes blue. The interpretation is that excited acridine is a much stronger base, of pK 10·65; the green fluorescence is due to the cation, the blue to the unchanged molecules.[22e] Since the frequencies are different, the intensities of the light emitted by the two excited species may be determined separately. The curves of intensity against pH for one such reaction are shown in Fig. 8.4. They have been analysed by Weller, taking account of the effect of transient reaction rates, with the aid of equation 8.28. Rate constants can be determined for various proton-transfers, such as the following, which have been studied in ammonium-ammonia buffers:

$$Acr^* H_2O \rightleftharpoons Acr^* H^+ + OH^-$$

$$Acr^* + NH_4^+ \xrightarrow{k_a} Acr^* H^+ + NH_3$$

For this last reaction, k_a is $(5·7 \pm 0·25) \times 10^8$ l mole^{-1}sec^{-1} at 25°; the energy of activation is $4·1 \pm 0·6$ kcal mole^{-1}.

Similar behaviour is shown by β-naphthol and other naphthols. Rate constants can be determined for reactions such as:

$$ROH^* . H_2O \rightleftharpoons RO^{*-} + H_3O^+$$

$$ROH^* + Ac^- \rightleftharpoons RO^{*-} + HAc$$

The rate constants for the ionic reactions depend on the ionic strength (0·001 to 0·02) in the way predicted by the Debye-Hückel equation, and can be extrapolated to zero ionic strength. A collection of rate constants determined in this way is given in the table on p. 270, and the results are there discussed. From a comparison of the rate constants with those calculated from diffusion theory, it is concluded that the transfer of a proton during the encounter

[27] For discussions see Weller, (a) ref. 3a; (b) Z. Elektrochem. 1960, **64**, 55; (c) ref. 3b. Experimental papers include (d) Weller, idem, 1957, **61**, 956; (e) Weller, Z. phys. Chem. (Frankfurt), 1958, **18**, 163.

is effected in a time much less than the mean lifetime of the excited molecules, with the exception of some transfers from nitrogen to nitrogen involving an ion of high charge.[27b]

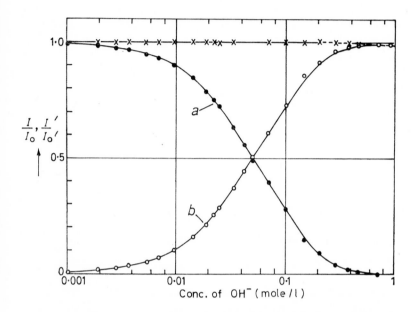

FIG. 8.4. Fluorescence intensity of DH^{3-}-* as a function of OH^- concentration   (DH^{3-} = 3-monoacetylamino-pyrene-5-8-10-sulphonate). Curve a, relative intensity I/I_0 of blue fluorescence due to undissociated form. Curve b, relative intensity I'/I_0' of green fluorescence due to dissociated form. The concentration scale is logarithmic. (From Weller, ref. 27e.)

Formation of hydrogen-bonded complexes[28]

Pyridine (Py) and 3-hydroxypyrene (ROH) form a hydrogen-bonded complex; the equilibrium constant may be determined from the absorption spectrum:

$$ROH + Py \rightleftharpoons (ROH.Py)$$

The hydroxypyrene is fluorescent, and measurements show that

[28] (a) Grellmann and Weller, Z. *Elektrochem.* 1960, **64**, 145; (b) Weller, ref. 3a, pp. 196 seq.

I/I_0 decreases with increasing concentration of pyridine. The rate constant k_1 may therefore be determined for the reaction:

$$\text{ROH}^*_+ + \text{Py} \xrightarrow{\ k_1\ } (\text{ROH}^* . \text{Py})$$

Correction is made for the simultaneous formation of the excited complex by excitation of the ground-state complex (p. 147). The results (accurate to about $\pm 8\%$) are given in Table 8.1.

TABLE 8.1

Rate constants for formation of hydrogen-bonded complex

Solvent	$10^{-10}k_1$ (l mole^{-1}sec^{-1})	
	Pyridine	α-Chloropyridine
Methylcyclohexane	1·6$_5$	1·2$_5$
Benzene	0·86	0·55
o-Chlorotoluene	0·67	0·39

The reactions are evidently fast enough to be diffusion-controlled. The difference between pyridine and α-chloropyridine, which appears in all three solvents, may be attributed to steric hindrance. The lower rate constants in the aromatic solvents are tentatively ascribed to an activation energy of around 0·5 kcal mole^{-1}, which may be necessary to effect partial desolvation of the reactants before hydrogen bonding can occur.

Internal and solvent quenching

The preceding examples have been mostly concerned with bimolecular interactions between a fluorescent substance and an added quencher. It remains to mention some instances of internal and solvent quenching in absence of quenchers. As we noticed earlier, it is possible to determine the energy of activation E_i for internal and solvent quenching, from the temperature-variation of the absolute quantum yield (p. 147). In general E_i will include contributions both from solvent quenching and from internal quenching, as in example (a) below; in example (b) the contribution from internal quenching appears to be dominant.

(a) *Anthracene derivatives.*[29] The absolute quantum yields of various 9-substituted anthracenes have been measured in various solvents over the temperature range $-70°$ to $+70°$, and show approximate agreement with equation 8.20. The energies of activation E_i depend both on the fluorescent substance and on the viscosity of the solvent if this is high. The interpretation may be that deactivation of the excited molecule involves not only an internal process requiring activation energy, but also a sufficient amplitude of vibrational movement against the solvent viscosity.

(b) *Acridine fluorescence and hydrogen bonding.* The absolute quantum yield of acridine has been measured[30] over a range of temperature in a series of mixtures of water with ethanol, formamide, dioxane and dimethylformamide at a pH such that fluorescence is due entirely to the uncharged molecule and not to the protonated cation (p. 160). The quantum yield varies with the water content; it decreases to zero in pure dioxane or dimethyl-formamide, but not in pure ethanol or formamide. The energy of activation E_i is found to have values in the region of 4·7 to 6·6 kcal mole^{-1}; this is approximately the energy required to break a hydrogen bond. It is suggested that fluorescence occurs only from excited acridine molecules that are hydrogen-bonded to solvent molecules, and that the decrease in fluorescence intensity with rise of temperature is due to breaking of the hydrogen bonds to give a non-fluorescent molecule. However, other interpretations are possible, such as changes in the relative energies of π, π^* and n, π^* transitions with change of solvent.

[29] Bowen, *Discuss. Faraday Soc.* 1959, **27**, 40, and ref. 19c.
[30] Bowen, Holder and Woodger, *J. Phys. Chem.* 1962, **66**, 2491.

CHAPTER 9

Electrochemical methods

GENERAL PRINCIPLES

The general principle that governs the applications of electro-chemical techniques to the measurement of rates of reaction in solution may be illustrated[1] by considering polarography. A voltage is applied to a cell at whose cathode some species O is electrochemically reduced: $O + ze \rightleftarrows R$. Assuming this electrode reaction to be fast, the current in the cell is controlled by the rate at which the reducible species O diffuses to the cathode. Suppose that O can take part in a chemical equilibrium such as $A + B \rightleftarrows O$, where A and B are not reduced at the cathode. Then O will be produced by the forward reaction, while it is being removed from the solution by electrochemical reduction. The two processes are opposed; the rate of the forward reaction influences and may control the flux of O near the electrode, and therefore the observed current. The equations for diffusion accompanied by reaction can be solved for idealized conditions, such as linear or spherical diffusion in an infinite depth of solution; the actual experimental conditions are less simple, but the theoretical expressions for the current are quite good approximations. (The same is true of course if the electrode reaction is an oxidation.) This diffusion control of a current which depends on the motion of a species towards an electrode must evidently be distinguished from the diffusion control of a rate of reaction (chapter 1) in which reactant molecules meet by diffusion and react at every encounter.

[1] For general accounts see (a) Strehlow, in *Investigation of Rates and Mechanisms of Reactions*, ed. Friess, Lewis and Weissberger (2nd ed., Interscience, 1963), part II, chapter 15; (b) Delahay, *New Instruments Methods in Electrochemistry* (Interscience, 1954), especially chapters 3, 5, 8, 16. For references see also (c) Fleischmann and Bewick, *Ann. Rep. Chem. Soc.* 1960, pp. 99–102.

There are four electrochemical techniques by which rate constants can be determined:

(i) The *polarographic* method, in which the cell contains a dropping-mercury electrode; the other may be a calomel electrode. A steady voltage is applied and an average current measured.

(ii) The *rotating-disc* method, in which the cathode consists of a spinning platinum disc; a steady voltage is applied and the current in the steady state is measured at a series of rotation speeds.

(iii) The *potentiostatic* method, in which the cathode is commonly a pool of mercury; the potential difference between the cathode and

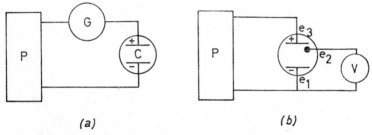

(a)   (b)

FIG. 9.1. (*a*) Arrangement for coulometry at constant voltage as in polarography. C, cell; P. power supply giving constant p.d. across cell; G, galvanometer and recorder. (*b*) Arrangement for voltammetry at controlled current (galvanostatic method). P, power supply giving constant current; C, cell; e_1, cathode; e_2, reference electrode; e_3, auxiliary electrode; V, voltmeter and recorder. (After Delahay, ref. 1*b*.)

the reference electrode is kept constant, while the fall of current with time is recorded.

(iv) The *galvanostatic* method, in which the cell is similar to that for the potentiostatic method, but conversely the current is kept constant and the rise of voltage with time is recorded.

The generic term 'coulometry' may be used for (i), (ii) and (iii), and the term 'voltammetry' for (iv). (Some authors, including Delahay, have used the terms 'voltammetry at constant voltage' and 'voltammetry at constant current' instead.) The arrangements for coulometry at constant voltage and voltammetry at constant current are illustrated schematically in Figs. 9.1*a* and 9.1*b*. The polarographic and rotating-disc methods are differentiated from

12

the other two by the fact that a steady current is observed instead of a transient or time-dependent current. In this chapter we first deal with the theory of each method, then outline the experimental arrangements, and finally consider the applications of the methods to various problems.

THEORY OF ELECTROCHEMICAL METHODS

Coulometry at constant voltage

The factors determining the current

Our problem is to calculate the current in a cell in which some species O is reduced at the cathode, and is formed in the solution by a preliminary reaction whose rate constants are to be measured, such as:

$$A + B \underset{k_b}{\overset{k_f}{\rightleftharpoons}} O \overset{+ze}{\rightleftharpoons} R \qquad (9.1)$$

It is assumed that there is always a large excess of potassium chloride or some other 'supporting electrolyte' which does not take part in the reaction but carries most of the current and reduces the potential gradient in the bulk of the solution nearly to zero.

The current i in the cell is proportional to the rate at which O is reduced at the cathode, and may be expressed as follows:

$$i = zFA \times \text{(flux of O at electrode surface)} \qquad (9.2)$$

where F is the Faraday, A is the area of the electrode in cm², and the flux of O at the electrode surface is the rate at which O is reduced per unit area of the electrode surface, in moles $cm^{-2} sec^{-1}$. This flux depends on several factors.

(*a*) The first is the rate constant of the electrode reaction $O \rightarrow R$. We shall assume that this reaction is fast and is not the rate-determining step. (If the contrary is true, it is easily detected, by an unusually flat polarographic wave, for example).

(*b*) A second factor is the equilibrium ratio of the concentrations of O and R, which may be written c_O/c_R. This ratio depends on the electrode potential E, according to the familiar relation (from which activity coefficients have been omitted):

$$E = E^0 - (RT/zF) \ln (c_R/c_O) \qquad (9.3)$$

When the electrode reactions are fast, as we are assuming, the potential difference is practically equal to the applied voltage, and the concentrations of O and R adjust themselves to the imposed e.m.f. according to equation 9.3. This explains why in polarography variation of the voltage leads to the characteristic 'wave' or S-shaped curve of current against voltage. We shall not, however, be concerned here with variation of the voltage; we shall assume that it is always so high that the equilibrium lies far to the right, so that the reaction $O \rightarrow R$ at the electrode is complete, as well as fast. In polarography this corresponds to the top of the wave and to the limiting current.

(c) Given that the electrode reaction is fast and complete, the flux of O depends on the rate at which it arrives at the electrode. This depends both on the rate at which O is produced by the preliminary reaction $A + B \rightarrow O$ in the bulk solution, and on the rate at which O diffuses to the electrode. These are the two opposed rate processes for which we now seek quantitative relations. We consider first the case where there is no preliminary reaction and the current is controlled by diffusion alone; then the case where diffusion is modified by reaction.

Current determined by diffusion alone[2]

We consider a cell in which O is reduced to R at the cathode, and there is no preliminary reaction. The problem is to calculate the rate of arrival of O at the electrode by diffusion, supposing it to be completely removed by reduction immediately on arrival.

Fick's laws. The fundamental assumption, known as Fick's first law, is that at any point the flux, or rate of diffusion per unit area perpendicular to the electrode, of the solute is proportional to its concentration gradient in the solution. The proportionality constant is the diffusion coefficient D_O. Thus if the concentration of O is c_O at a distance x from the electrode at time t, the flux q is given by Fick's first law as:

$$q = D_O(\partial c_O/\partial x)_t \qquad (9.4)$$

Consider two parallel planes at distances x and $x + dx$ from the electrode. The flux through the first plane is given by equation 9.4,

[2] Cf. Delahay, ref. 1b, chapter 3.

while that through the second plane, if D_0 is independent of x, is similarly given by

$$D_0\left[\left(\frac{\partial c_0}{\partial x}\right) + \left\{\frac{\partial}{\partial x}\left(\frac{\partial c_0}{\partial x}\right)_t dx\right\}\right]$$

The difference is

$$D_0\left(\frac{\partial^2 c_0}{\partial x^2}\right) dx \tag{9.5}$$

and this is the rate of increase in the number of moles of O between the two planes, per unit area. As the volume between the planes per unit area is dx, the rate of increase of concentration between the planes, which may be expressed as $(\partial c_0/\partial t)_x$, is obtained by dividing the expression 9.5 by dx. We thus obtain the equation known as Fick's second law for diffusion towards a plane:

$$(\partial c_0/\partial t)_x = D_0(\partial^2 c_0/\partial x^2)_t \tag{9.6}$$

This is the general equation, which has to be solved for appropriate initial and boundary conditions. If it can be solved, the flux at the electrode surface can be deduced, and the current then found from equation 9.2.

Solutions for plane and spherical electrodes. Equation 9.6 can be solved rigorously for a plane electrode in an unstirred solution that extends to infinity; this case is known as 'semi-infinite linear diffusion'. The result for the current at time t from the start of electrolysis is:

$$i_d = zFAD_0^{1/2} c_0 \pi^{-1/2} t^{-1/2} \tag{9.7}$$

We write i_d for the current to indicate that the calculation refers to control by diffusion alone. The equation shows that the current decreases with time, proportionally to $t^{-1/2}$. This has been experimentally verified for certain processes with plane electrodes.[3]

For a spherical electrode, the equation corresponding to 9.6 can again be solved rigorously; the result reduces practically to equation 9.7 provided that the time of electrolysis is not longer than a few seconds. This condition is fulfilled by the dropping-mercury

---

[3] (a) Kolthoff and Laitinen, *J. Amer. Chem. Soc.* 1939, **61**, 3344 (oxidation of ferrocyanide on platinum); (b) Laitinen, *Trans. Electrochem. Soc.* 1942, **82**, 289 (deposition of silver).

electrode as used in polarography (p. 181), although the differential equation now contains an extra term because the mercury drop expands continuously.[1b] An equation of type 9.7 may therefore be applied to calculate the limiting current in a polarographic experiment, but modifications have to be made for two reasons. The first is that the area A increases with time; it is easily shown that $A = 0.85m^{2/3} t^{2/3}$, where t is the time in seconds and m is the rate of flow of mercury in g sec^{-1}. The second is that the concentration gradient is larger than for a static electrode, because the surface moves outwards towards regions of solution where there is less depletion; a factor $(7/3)^{1/2}$ is introduced to take account of this. The current after t seconds of the drop-life is then given by equation 9.7 as:

$$i_d = 0.73zFD_O^{1/2} c_O(m^{2/3} t^{1/6}) \qquad (9.8)$$

where c_O is in mole ml^{-1}; the other units have already been defined. The average current $\bar{i}_d$ over the complete drop-life t_1, which is $(1/t_1) \int_0^{t_1} i \, dt$, is 6/7 of the maximum current, so that:

$$\bar{i}_d = 0.63zFD_O^{1/2} c_O(m^{2/3} t_1^{1/6}) \qquad (9.9)$$

This is the Ilkovič equation,[4] which predicts the average current as measured in a polarographic experiment, in the limit at the top of the wave. (The diffusion coefficient D_O can be estimated for a non-electrolyte by the Stokes-Einstein equation, and for an ion from its mobility.) The experimental conditions do not correspond exactly with those assumed in the theory; the dropping-mercury electrode is not a perfect sphere, and the solution is stirred to some extent. Neverthless the equation fits the experimental data well, so long as the concentration of O is not dependent on the rate of an antecedent reaction. The observed current agrees with the

[4] The original papers are those of (a) Ilkovič, Coll. Czech. Chem. Comm. 1934, **6**, 498; (b) MacGillavray and Rideal, Rec. trav. chim. 1937, **56**, 1013. For reviews see, e.g., (c) Kolthoff and Lingane, Polarography (2nd edn., Interscience, 1952), chapter 2 and 4; (d) Milner, Principles and Practice of Polarography (Longmans, 1957), chapter 3; (e) Müller, in Physical Methods of Organic Chemistry, ed. Weissberger (3rd edn., Interscience, 1960), part IV, chapter 48.

calculated value within a few per cent. (This is true even when the electrode reaction is irreversible; the polarographic wave is then flatter, but the limiting current still obeys the Ilkovič equation.) Further, according to equation 9.9 the current should be proportional to $m^{2/3}t_1^{1/6}$ and so to the square root of the head of mercury; this also is observed, with only minor deviations.

Current dependent on antecedent reaction: rate constants from coulometry at constant voltage[5]

When the species O is produced by a reaction in solution, as in equation 9.1, Fick's equation 9.6 must be modified by adding terms involving the rate constants, to take account of the changes in concentrations due to the reaction.

First-order antecedent reaction. Let us suppose first that the reaction precedes the electrochemical reduction and is a reversible first-order reaction:

$$A \underset{k_b}{\overset{k_f}{\rightleftarrows}} O \overset{ze}{\underset{\longleftarrow}{\longrightarrow}} R \qquad (9.10)$$

The modified equation for c_O, the concentration of O, is then:

$$(\partial c_O / \partial t)_x = D_O (\partial^2 c_O / \partial x^2)_t + k_f c_A - k_b c_O \qquad (9.11)$$

There is a similar equation for c_A. We make the simplifying assumptions that the diffusion coefficients of A and O are effectively equal (D); and that the equilibrium constant K, defined as the equilibrium value of c_A/c_O, is large, so that c_A is equal to the formal concentration c_A°. The equation can then be solved for the case of semi-infinite linear diffusion. The solution, due to Koutecký and

[5] The solutions of the diffusion equations are given by (a) Delahay, ref. 1b, chapter 5. (It may be noted that Delahay defines K as the equilibrium value of c_O/c_A, which is the inverse of our definition.) For the simplified treatment based on the concept of a reaction layer (p. 175) see e.g. (b) Brdička, *Z. Elektrochem.* 1960, **64**, 16. The mathematical theory of constant-voltage methods has been summarized by (c) Reinert, *Z. Elektrochem.* 1962, **66**, 379, and that of polarography by (d) Brdička, Hanuš and Koutecký, in *Advances in Polarography*, ed. Zuman and Kolthoff (Interscience, 1962).

Brdička, [6] gives the following expressions for the initial current i_0 and the current i at time t[5a]:

$$i_0 = zFAD^{1/2} c_A^{\circ}(k_f^{1/2} K^{-1/2}) \tag{9.12}$$

$$i/i_0 = \exp(\lambda^2)\,\mathrm{erfc}\,(\lambda) \tag{9.13}$$

where $\qquad \lambda = (tk_f/K)^{1/2} \tag{9.14}$

and $\mathrm{erfc}\,(\lambda)$ is the complement of the error function,

$$\mathrm{erfc}\,(\lambda) = 1 - \frac{2}{\pi^{1/2}} \int_0^{\lambda} e^{-z^2}\,dz \tag{9.14a}$$

The time-dependence of the current is given by the expression on the right-hand side of equation 9.13. It is evidently different from the time-dependence in the absence of reaction, expressed by equation 9.7. A specimen plot of i/i_0 against λ is shown in Fig. 9.3. Since λ varies as $t^{1/2}$, the plot shows that i/i_0 falls off with time; it declines from unity to about 0·4 when $\lambda = 1$, which corresponds to a time K/k_f sec from the start. The time-scale for the decline of current in a given experiment is therefore fixed by a characteristic time-interval K/k_f. This may be written τ'; then $\lambda = (t/\tau')^{1/2}$.

Measurements of current-time transients by the potentiostatic method fit the theoretical equation 9.13 reasonably well. Some observed current-time plots are shown in Fig. 9.2. From such a plot the rate constant is found as follows. A value of τ' is chosen so that the plot of i/i_0 against λ agrees with the theoretical plot according to equation 9.13. From this value of τ', k_f can be found if K is known, since $k_f = K/\tau'$. An example is shown in Fig. 9.3.[7] It is of interest that the slope of the curve does not depend on the diffusion coefficient, but on K and k_f which are characteristic of the reaction $A \rightleftarrows O$ alone. The fastest reaction that can be followed by the potentiostatic method corresponds to a value of τ' of about 10^{-4} sec, or k_f/K about 10^4 sec^{-1}.

Alternatively, we can compare the observed current i with the maximum current i_d^0 which would be observed if there were no

[6] Koutecký and Brdička, Coll. Czech. Chem. Comm. 1947, 12, 337.
[7] Gerischer, Z. Elektrochem. 1960, 64, 29.

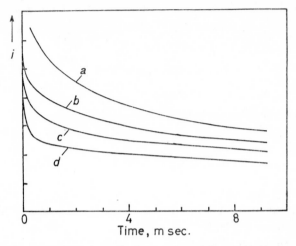

FIG. 9.2. Potentiostatic method: experimental current–time curves for aqueous cadmium chloride solutions (0·001 M) containing CN^-, with $NaClO_4$ (3 M) as supporting electrolyte. Applied voltage 1·439 V. Concentrations of CN^-: a, 0·02; b, 0·04; c, 0·06; d, 0·09 M. (From Gerischer, ref. 7.) The reactions in the solution and at the electrode are:

$$Cd(CN)_4{}^{--} \; \rightleftarrows \; CN^- + Cd(CN)_3{}^- \; \overset{2e}{\rightleftarrows} \; Cd + 4CN^-.$$

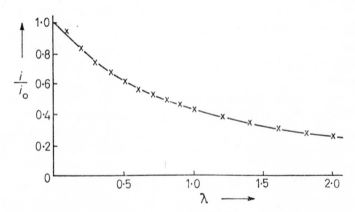

FIG. 9.3. Potentiostatic method: plot of i/i_0 against λ (see text). Theoretical curve, with experimental points corresponding to curve c of Fig. 9.2 assuming $K/k_f = 9$ msec. (From Gerischer, ref.7.)

antecedent reaction and the species O were present at concentration c_A°. Using equation 9.7 to find i_d^0, and combining it with equations 9.12 and 9.13, we find:

$$i/i_d^0 = \pi^{1/2}\lambda \ \exp(\lambda^2)\,\text{erfc}\,(\lambda) \qquad (9.15)$$

The values of i_d^0 at various times for a given reaction may be calculated from equation 9.8, using an independent value of D, and thence a plot of i/i_d^0 against time constructed. This may be compared with the theoretical plot, to find k_f.

In *polarographic measurements* the average current at a growing nearly-spherical electrode is determined. By starting with equations 9.12 and 9.13, one obtains[8] for the average limiting current the approximate equation:

$$\bar{i} = 0\!\cdot\!51zFD^{1/2}c_A^\circ(m^{2/3}t_1^{2/3})(k_f^{1/2}\,K^{-1/2}) \qquad (9.16)$$

This current $\bar{i}$ is less than that predicted by the Ilkovič equation, since it is limited by the rate at which O is produced, as well as by the rate of diffusion. Comparing with $\bar{i}_d^0$ from equation 9.9, we find:

$$\bar{i}/\bar{i}_d^0 = 0\!\cdot\!81t_1^{1/2}(k_f^{1/2}\,K^{-1/2}) \qquad (9.17)$$

This equation shows that the effect of the antecedent reaction on $\bar{i}$ depends on the value of $(t_1 k_f/K)^{1/2}$. The slower the forward reaction the smaller is $\bar{i}$ compared with $\bar{i}_d^0$. The fastest reaction that can be investigated has a value of k_f/K around 10 sec^{-1}.

If the equilibrium does not lie far to the left, as we have assumed, the concentration c_O can be expressed in terms of $\bar{i}_d^0$ by means of equation 9.9, and we obtain in place of equation 9.17:

$$\bar{i}/(\bar{i}_d^0-\bar{i}) = 0\!\cdot\!81t_1^{1/2}(k_f^{1/2}\,K^{-1/2}) \qquad (9.17a)$$

The shape of the polarographic wave for such systems as we are discussing is much as usual; it is the height of the wave $(\bar{i})$ that differs

[8] See Delahay, ref. 1b. Historically, polarography was the first electrochemical method by which reaction rates were determined. Early investigations on formaldehyde (cf. p. 191) showed anomalies which were explained kinetically by Vesely and Brdička (*Coll. Czech. Chem. Comm.* 1947, **12**, 313) following the suggestion of Wiesner (*Z. Elektrochem.* 1943, **49**, 164) and the work of Brdička and Wiesner (*Naturwiss.* 1943, **31**, 247; *Coll. Czech. Chem. Comm.* 1947, **12**, 39, 138).

from the usual Ilkovič value. This contrasts with the situation when the electrode reaction is irreversible. (p. 170); it is a criterion for a current-controlling reaction in solution. Another criterion may be deduced from equation 9.16. If the head of mercury is varied, the current is proportional to $t_1^{2/3}$ instead of $t_1^{1/6}$ as for pure diffusion (equation 9.9); and since the current is proportional also to $m^{2/3}$ it is independent of the head of mercury, in contrast with the square-root dependence for diffusion alone. A third criterion is that the temperature-dependence of the current is of the order of 10% per degree for reaction control, compared with less than 2% for pure diffusion control.

For the *rotating-disc* method,[9] the conditions are different because the solution is stirred by the rapid rotation of the disc. The hydrodynamic equations governing mass transfer can be solved for an infinite disc in an infinite depth of solution, and experiments have shown that the results are valid for a disc a few cm in diameter in an ordinary vessel. The conditions are very simple: near the electrode there is a diffusion layer, to which the reactant is brought by the stirring motion; movement within this layer occurs by diffusion only; and the concentration gradient in the steady state is constant across the layer. The diffusion equation can then be solved. For diffusion alone, the limiting current when the electrode reaction is fast and complete may be expressed in terms of the angular velocity of rotation ω and the kinematic viscosity ν (i.e. the product of viscosity and density) by the equation:

$$i_d = zFAD_0^{2/3} c_0^\circ \, \omega^{1/2}/a\nu^{1/6} \tag{9.18}$$

where a is a numerical constant. If a first-order reaction precedes the electrode process, the limiting current i is given by:

$$i/\omega^{1/2} = i_d/\omega^{1/2} - i(k_f/k_b)/aD^{5/6}\nu^{1/6} \, (k_f + k_b)^{1/2} \tag{9.19}$$

[9] For theory see (a) Delahay, ref. 1b, chapter 9; (b) Lewitsch, *Acta physicochem. U.R.S.S.* 1942, **17**, 257; 1944, **79**, 117, 133; (c) Dogonadzhe, *Zhur. fiz. Khim.* 1958, **32**, 2437. For experiments verifying eqn. 18 and elucidating the constant a, see (d) Gregory and Riddiford, *J. Chem. Soc.* 1956, 3756. Experimental work on reaction rates has been done by (e) Vielstich and Jahn, *Z. Elektrochem.* 1960, **64**, 43; (f) Albery and Bell, *Proc. Chem. Soc.* 1963, 169.

A plot of $i/\omega^{1/2}$ against i should therefore be linear, on the above assumptions, with a slope determined by k_f and k_b. So far there have been few studies of rates of reaction by this method (see pp. 182, 185).

Other types of reaction. So far we have dealt only with antecedent reactions. Rate constants can also be determined[5a] for reactions subsequent to the electrode process:

$$O \underset{}{\overset{ze}{\rightleftharpoons}} R \underset{k_b}{\overset{k_f}{\rightleftharpoons}} Z \qquad (9.20)$$

including regenerative reactions (sometimes called 'parallel' or 'catalytic' reactions) in which the reducible species is reproduced:

$$O \overset{ze}{\rightleftharpoons} R; \quad R+Z \rightleftharpoons O \qquad (9.21)$$

Second-order reactions. The earlier rigorous treatments applied to first-order reactions only. The equations were later solved for second-order reactions also[10].

Theory in terms of reaction-layer thickness

So far we have made use of the rigorous theory based on solving the Fick equation as modified by terms involving rate constants. A less rigorous treatment in terms of the thickness of a 'reaction layer' next to the electrode is also of interest.[11] We consider again the processes denoted by equation 9.10, namely, $A \rightleftharpoons O \rightleftharpoons R$.

The calculation turns on a deduction from the simple theory of diffusion in liquids that in a time t the mean distance traversed by a diffusing molecule is about $D^{1/2} t^{1/2}$. Suppose now that the molecules of O formed in the bulk of the solution by the reaction $A \rightarrow O$ have a mean lifetime τ, before disappearing by the reverse reaction $O \rightarrow A$. Then the distance corresponding to diffusion

[10] (a) Koryta, *Coll. Czech. Chem. Comm.* 1955, **20**, 667; (b) Koutecký, *idem*, 1957, **22**, 160; (c) Čižek, Koryta and Koutecký, *idem*, 1959, **24**, 3844. Cf. also refs. 5c, 5d.

[11] For reviews see (a) Brdička, *Z. Elektrochem.* 1960, **64**, 16; (b) Koryta, *ibid*, p. 23. For a comparison of the reaction-layer treatment with the exact treatment of Koutecký, see (c) Pospíšil, *Coll. Czech. Chem. Comm.* 1953, **18**, 337. The original treatment is due to (d) Brdička and Wiesner, *Coll. Czech. Chem. Comm.* 1947, **12**, 138.

during this lifetime ($D^{1/2}\tau^{1/2}$) may be identified with the thickness μ of a 'reaction layer' within which all the O molecules produced by reaction reach the electrode and are reduced there. The volume of this reaction layer is, if A is the area of the electrode,

$$V = \mu A = AD^{1/2}\tau^{1/2} \qquad (9.22)$$

The initial current, on the same assumption, is proportional to the number of moles of O produced per second by reaction within this reaction layer, which is $Vc_A k_f$. With the proportionality factor zF, we have for the current:

$$i_0 = zFVc_A k_f \qquad (9.23)$$

Substituting for V from equation 9.22 we obtain:

$$i_0 = zFAD^{1/2}c_A\tau^{1/2}k_f \qquad (9.24)$$

The mean lifetime τ may be identified with $1/k_b$ (p. 62), which is equal to $1/Kk_f$. Hence

$$i_0 = zFAD^{1/2}c_A k_f^{1/2}K^{-1/2} \qquad (9.25)$$

This is the general equation for a first-order preliminary reaction. If the equilibrium lies well to the left, for example, c_A is nearly equal to c_A°, and the equation becomes identical with equation 9.12. Thus in simple cases the reaction-layer treatment gives the same result as the rigorous solution of the diffusion equations, with much less mathematical difficulty. Though only approximate, the treatment can be used in favourable instances without leading to large errors.[11c] The main error arises from taking the thickness of the reaction layer as constant over the whole drop-life. This error is less the faster the reaction.

With very fast reactions, however, other uncertainties appear, because the thickness of the reaction layer becomes very small. In the above calculation it is $(D\tau)^{1/2}$ or $(D/k_b)^{1/2}$. As the diffusion coefficient D is of the order of 10^{-5} cm^{2}sec^{-1}, this implies that the reaction layer is of the order of 1000 Å thick when k_b is 10^5 sec^{-1}, 100 Å when k_b is 10^7 sec^{-1}, and so on. The normal diffusion equations cannot be expected to hold when the thickness is comparable with molecular dimensions; moreover the abnormal potential gradient in the diffuse double layer near the electrode may be of importance. These complications may be the origin of some anomalies in the rate constants found experimentally (pp. 187–189).

Voltammetry at controlled current (galvanostatic method)[12]

We turn now to the method in which the current, instead of the voltage, is held constant, and the experiments lead to a curve of potential against time, such as that in Fig. 9.4 below. The experimental arrangement is described on p. 183.

Since the current is fixed, the flux of O at the electrode surface is constant. The current i_0 is expressed by equation 9.2 (p. 166), and the flux by Fick's equation 9.4. We thus obtain:

$$i_0 = zFAD_O(\partial c_O/\partial x)_{x=0} \tag{9.27}$$

This is the boundary condition which has to be used in the solution of the appropriate differential equation. It applies both when diffusion alone has to be considered and when reaction in solution occurs as well.

Diffusion alone at constant current

As before, we consider first the reduction of the solute O at the cathode ($O \to R$) when no other reaction intervenes. The diffusion equation 9.6 can be solved with 9.27 for a plane electrode in an unstirred solution of infinite depth—the case of semi-infinite linear diffusion (p. 168). The concentrations c_O and c_R are found as functions of time. The voltage E is related to c_R/c_O by equation 9.3. The final result is:

$$E = E_{1/2} + \frac{RT}{zF}\left(\frac{\Delta t_d^{1/2} - t^{1/2}}{t^{1/2}}\right) \tag{9.28}$$

Here Δt_d is the 'transition time' after which the calculated value of E becomes infinite, the subscript denoting that it is determined by diffusion only; $E_{1/2}$ is the value of E when $(t/\Delta t_d)^{1/2} = \frac{1}{2}$, and can be shown to be the same as the 'half-wave potential' of polarographic theory; and the transition-time is given in terms of the

[12] General accounts are given by Delahay, (a) ref. 1b, chapter 8; (b) *Discuss. Faraday Soc.* 1954, **17**, 205.

constant current i_0, the diffusion coefficient D_O, and the bulk concentration c_O° by the expression:

$$\Delta t_d^{1/2} = \pi^{1/2} zFAD_O^{1/2} c_O^\circ / 2i_0 \qquad (9.29)$$

A plot of potential against time is shown in Fig. 9.4. The general shape of the curve reflects the fact that the voltage which must be applied to keep the current constant increases as the species O is removed

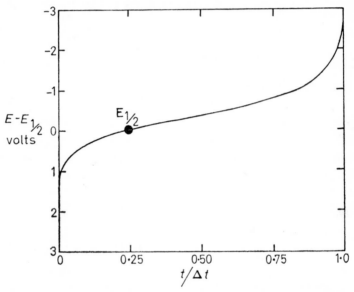

FIG. 9.4. Galvanostatic method. Plot of $(E - E_{1/2})$ against $(t/\Delta t)$ for diffusion process alone (equation 9.28). Similar curves are obtained when there is an antecedent reaction. From Delahay, ref. 1b, *New Instrumental Methods in Electrochemistry* (Interscience, 1954), by permission.

from the solution near the electrode. It is evident that a well-defined transition time is to be expected.[13]

The curves obtained by experiment for simple electrochemical

[13] Delahay (ref. 12a) notes that equation 9.29 was derived by Karaoglanoff (*Z. Elektrochem*. 1906, **12**, 5) long before the corresponding equation in polarography, the Ilkovič equation; and that a solution of the equation for c_O was first given by Weber, *Wied. Ann*. 1879, **7**, 536. The form of a plot of E against $t^{1/2}$ from equation 9.28 is the same as that of the polarographic 'wave' of E against current.

reductions are in good agreement with equation 9.28, apart from minor deviations, provided that the transition time lies between a few milliseconds and a few minutes.[12a] The predictions of equation 9.29 have also been verified. The proportionality of the transition time to the square of the concentration c_O° has been made the basis of quantitative analysis by the galvanostatic method. When the current i_0 is varied, the transition time is proportional to $1/i_0^2$; more specifically, it is inversely proportional to the square of the current density (i_0/A). This fact permits adjustment of the transition time within wide limits.

Rate constants by the galvanostatic method

As in the treatment of coulometry at constant voltage (p. 170), we consider a first-order reaction A $\rightleftarrows$ O with $K = c_A/c_O$, preceding the electro-chemical reduction as in equation 9.10. The general shape of the observed voltage–time plots is similar to that for diffusion alone (cf. Fig. 9.4). In the theoretical calculation, the modified Fick equation 9.11 must again be used, and the same simplifying assumptions are made. The solution of the equation, giving the rate constants in terms of the transition time, is[14]:

$$\Delta t^{1/2} = \frac{\pi^{1/2} zFAD_O^{1/2} c_O^\circ}{2i_0} - \frac{\pi^{1/2} K \operatorname{erf}[(k_f+k_b)^{1/2} \Delta t^{1/2}]}{2(k_f+k_b)^{1/2}} \quad (9.30)$$

The equation may be simplified if $(k_f+k_b)\Delta t \geqslant 4$, since the error function is then practically unity, and we obtain:

$$\Delta t^{1/2} = \pi^{1/2} zFAD_O^{1/2} c_O^\circ/2i_0 - \pi^{1/2} K/2(k_f+k_b)^{1/2} \quad (9.31)$$

Substituting from equation 9.29 for the first term on the right,

$$\Delta t^{1/2} = \Delta t_d^{1/2} - \pi^{1/2} K/2(k_f+k_b)^{1/2} \quad (9.32)$$

The first term on the right is evidently the contribution of diffusion. The second term depends on the rate constants and is due to the antecedent reaction. If we multiply equation 9.31 by i_0, we obtain:

$$i_0 \Delta t^{1/2} = \pi^{1/2} zFAD_O c_O^\circ/2 - i_0[\pi^{1/2} K/2(k_f+k_b)^{1/2}] \quad (9.33)$$

[14] Delahay and Berzins, *J. Amer. Chem. Soc.* 1953, **75**, 2486. Equation 9.30 differs slightly from the equation given by these authors because (a) the symbol i_0 denotes current rather than current density; and (b) K has been defined above as c_A/c_O rather than c_O/c_A.

This equation predicts that if we measure the transition-time for a given system at a series of currents i_0 (more specifically, at a series of current densities i_0/A), the product $i_0 \Delta t^{1/2}$ will no longer be constant, as it is for diffusion alone (equation 9.29), but will decrease linearly with increase of the current. This is a criterion for a preliminary reaction of measurable rate. From the slope of the plot

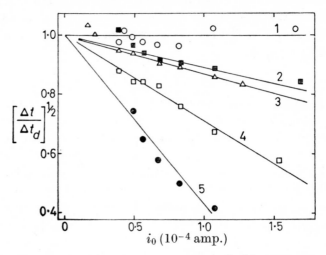

FIG. 9.5. Galvanostatic method. Plots of $(\Delta t/\Delta t_d)^{1/2}$ against current i_0 for the reduction of various complexes at a dropping-mercury electrode, area about 0.02 cm^2. (1) 0.001 M Zn^{++}, 2 M ammonium hydroxide, 2 M ammonium chloride; (2) 0.001 M Cd^{++}, 1 M potassium iodide, 1 M potassium nitrate; (3) 0.001 M Ni^{++}, 1 M potassium cyanide, 1 M potassium nitrate; (4) 0.002 M Cd^{++}, 0.5 M sodium tartrate, 1 M sodium nitrate; (5) 0.001 M Cd^{++}, 0.1 M dipyridyl, 1 M potassium nitrate. From Delahay, ref. 1b, *New Instrumental Methods in Electrochemistry* (Interscience, 1954), by permission.

(the quantity in square brackets), k_f and k_b can be determined if $K(= k_b/k_f)$ is known.

Another way of expressing the theoretical result is as follows. Dividing equation 9.31 by equation 9.29, we obtain;

$$\Delta t^{1/2}/\Delta t_d^{1/2} = 1 - i_0[K/zFAD_O\, c_O^0(k_f + k_b)^{1/2}] \qquad (9.34)$$

A plot of $(\Delta t/\Delta t_d)^{1/2}$ against i_0 will therefore be linear, with a slope depending on the rate constants. The slope will be less the larger is $(k_f + k_b)$.

Some experimental results are shown in Fig. 9.5, for the reduction of various metal ions preceded by the dissociation of complexes.[12b] For each system, values of Δt were determined at a series of currents, and Δt_d was found by extrapolating a plot of $i_0 \Delta t^{1/2}$ to zero current. The results confirm the predicted linear variation of $(\Delta t / \Delta t_d)^{1/2}$ with current, and rate constants can be deduced for the dissociation of the complexes. Transition times down to a few milliseconds can be determined. The fastest reaction that can be studied corresponds to a value of $(k_f + k_b)/K^2$ of the order of 10^5 sec^{-1}. By reversing the current after the transition time, the reverse reaction may be studied.

Besides reactions preceding the electrode process, one can handle reactions subsequent to it, as with coulometry at constant voltage (p. 175)[12a].

Reaction-layer treatment. An approximate treatment of antecedent reactions in terms of the thickness of a reaction layer can be devised, as before (p. 175)[12a], and gives the same result as the rigorous treatment when $k_f \ll k_b$.

TECHNIQUES FOR ELECTROCHEMICAL METHODS

Polarography

The apparatus is well known and need not be described in detail (Fig. 9.6).[15] The dropping electrode gives more reliable results than a stationary electrode when electrolysis is prolonged. The rate of flow of mercury is controlled, by adjusting the head of mercury; the time per drop is a few seconds. The current varies as the drop grows, but with a well-damped galvanometer the observed current for a given applied voltage is steady and gives directly the average value. The advantages of the method are that the electrode surface is continually renewed, that one obtains directly the average current over a period short enough to be unaffected by convection, and that the apparatus is comparatively simple.

[15] See, e.g., (a) Kolthoff and Lingane, ref. 4c, chapter 14; (b) Milner, ref. 4d, chapters 2 and 6; (c) Müller, ref. 4e.

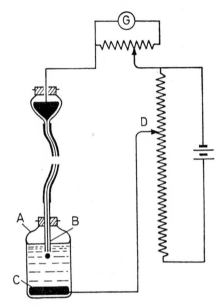

Fig. 9.6. Apparatus for polarography (schematic): A, cell containing solution; B, dropping-mercury cathode; C, mercury-pool anode acting as calomel electrode; D, rheostat; G, galvanometer with shunt.

Rotating-disc method[9f,g]

The working electrode is the plane end of a cylindrical platinum rod about 1 mm in diameter, which can be rotated about its axis at speeds up to around 100 revolutions per second. The platinum rod is embedded in a glass or plastic cylinder whose plane end is flush with the surface of the electrode. By this means the correct hydrodynamic conditions are set up (p. 174). Current-voltage curves are recorded as in polarography.

Potentiostatic method[16]

The power supply is controlled so that the potential of a working electrode is kept constant within about a millivolt. The working

[16] For apparatus see (a) Meites, in *Physical Methods of Organic Chemistry*, ed. Weissberger (3rd ed., Interscience, 1960), part IV, chapter 49; (b) Bewick, Fleischmann and Liler, *Electrochim. Acta*, 1959, **1**, 83; Bewick and Fleischmann, *idem*, 1963, **8**, 89.

electrode is commonly a pool of mercury (e_1 in Fig. 9.7), with a reference electrode e_2 and an auxilary platinum electrode e_3. An e.m.f. applied across e_1 and e_3 is controlled by a feedback regulator, called a potentiostat, so that the potential difference between e_1 and e_2 is kept constant. The current-time curves (Fig. 9.2) are

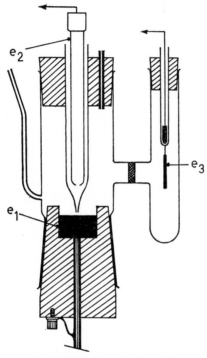

FIG. 9.7. Mercury-pool cell for potentiostatic or galvanostatic method: e_1, mercury electrode; e_2, reference calomel electrode; e_3, platinum auxiliary electrode. (From Delahay, ref. 12b).

recorded by means of an oscillograph or a fast pen-and-ink recorder.

Galvanostatic method[12b]

The cell is similar to that used in the potentiostatic method.[12b] A sufficiently constant current is produced by connecting a resistance in series with the cell and applying a voltage of 200–300 volts;

or an electronically-regulated source of current can be used. The potential difference between the mercury and calomel electrodes is applied to a fast recording system. A dropping-mercury electrode can be used, provided that the transition time is short compared with the drop-life.

Some general comments on electrochemical methods

Of these methods, the polarographic is experimentally the simplest, especially since it needs no fast-recording apparatus, and the results are reproducible. Low concentrations of reagent can be used—a typical concentration is 10^{-4} M—but a supporting inert electrolyte is required. The method is restricted to the use of a mercury cathode, and the maximum value of k_f/K is lower than for the potentiostatic or galvanostatic methods. Rate constants up to the highest values (corresponding to diffusion control of the bulk reaction) have been determined by all these methods. None of them is of high accuracy; rate constants can commonly be estimated within about $\pm 20\%$.

The rate constants found by electrochemical methods often differ considerably from those determined by other methods. The most important discrepancies are shown by the fastest reactions, such as the recombination of the ions of a weak acid. Such differences must be expected when the thickness of the reaction layer is comparable with that of the double layer near the electrode, since the potential gradient is then very high and will affect the distribution of the ions (p. 188). A correction for this effect can be calculated for some reactions, but not as yet for the fastest. It must therefore be borne in mind that the rate constant as determined electrochemically refers to a reaction occurring in a thin layer, and is not necessarily equal to that in the bulk of the solution.

APPLICATIONS OF ELECTROCHEMICAL METHODS

Dissociation of weak acids and recombination of ions

A considerable amount of work has been done on the reversible dissociation of weak acids:

$$\mathrm{HA + H_2O} \underset{k_2}{\overset{k_1}{\rightleftarrows}} \mathrm{A^- + H_3O^+}$$

Either the forward or the reverse reaction may be made to precede an electrode reaction, in suitable instances, as a rate-controlling step. Since the equilibrium constant can be independently determined, both rate constants can be found. It is not convenient to use the reduction of hydrogen ion itself as the cathode reaction, except when a rotating platinum disc is used as electrode, because of the considerable overvoltage of hydrogen on mercury. There are several means of overcoming this difficulty, as follows.

(a) *Reduction of a base.* The dissociation of acids can be studied by making use of an electrode reaction specifically involving hydrogen ions,[17] namely the reduction of a base such as azobenzene:

$$\phi N{=}N\phi + 2H^+ + 2e \rightarrow \phi NH{\cdot}NH\phi$$

The hydrogen ions are provided by the dissociation of a weak acid HA in a buffer solution; the rate of this preliminary dissociation is made to control the overall rate. In principle this method is applicable to any system in which neither component of the buffer (HA, A$^-$) is reducible. Because of the low solubility of azobenzene in water, solutions in 50–50 aqueous ethanol have been used. Solutions in water can be studied by using p-nitraniline as base in place of azobenzene;[17d] or a base such as pyridine or dipyridyl adsorbed on a mercury surface may be employed.[17e]

The polarographic, potentiostatic and galvanostatic techniques have all been used.[17a,b,c] Some results are shown in Table 9.1. The results for acetic acid in water agree moderately well with Eigen's value from the electric-impulse method ($k_2 = 5 \cdot 1 \times 10^{10}$ l mole^{-1} sec^{-1}; Table 4,2, p. 75).

(b) *Reduction of hydrogen ions at a rotating-disc cathode.* With a rotating platinum disc as cathode, it is possible to make use of the sequence of reactions:

$$HA + H_2O \rightleftharpoons A^- + H_3O^+; \quad H_3O^+ + e \rightarrow H_2O + \tfrac{1}{2}H_2$$

[17] (a) Ruetschi, Z. phys. Chem. (Frankfurt), 1956, 5, 323; (b) Delahay and Oka, J. Amer. Chem. Soc. 1960, 82, 329; (c) Delahay and Vielstich, J. Amer. Chem. Soc. 1953, 77, 4955; (d) Giner and Vielstich, Z. Elektrochem. 1960, 64, 128; (e) Nürnberg, Riesenbach and von Stackleberg, Z. Elektrochem. 1960, 64, 130.

TABLE 9.1

Dissociation of weak acids in water studied by electrochemical reduction of base, etc.

$$HA + H_2O \underset{k_2}{\overset{k_1}{\rightleftharpoons}} H_3O^+ + A^-$$

k_1 in sec^{-1}; k_2 in l mole^{-1} sec^{-1}.

Acid	Solvent	Technique	Temp. (°C)	pK	k_1	k_2	Ref.
Formic	Aq. ethanol, 1 M KCl	Azobenzene, Hg, galvanostatic	25	4·3	6×10^4	1×10^9	17c
Acetic	Aq. ethanol, 1 M KCl	Azobenzene, Hg, galvanostatic	25	5·5	3×10^5	9×10^{10}	17c
,,	Aq. ethanol	Azobenzene, Hg, polarographic	20	5·3	2×10^5	$4 \cdot_4 \times 10^{10}$	17a
,,	Water, 2 M KCl	p-Nitraniline, Hg, galvanostatic	25	4·7	5×10^5	$2 \cdot_5 \times 10^{10}$	17d
,,	Water, 1 M KCl	Rotating disc, Pt, constant voltage	25	4·5	3×10^5	1×10^{10}	9e
,,	Water	,,	25	4·8	$9 \cdot 1 \times 10^5$	$5 \cdot 2 \times 10^{10}$	9f
Trimethyl-acetic	Water	,,	25	5.0	$1 \cdot 4 \times 10^5$	$1 \cdot 5 \times 10^{10}$	9f
Monochloro-acetic	Aq. ethanol $I = 1$	Azobenzene, Hg, potentiostatic	25	3·9	2×10^6	1×10^{10}	17b
$H_2PO_4^-$	Water (buffer + KCl, $I = 2 \cdot 0$)	Dipyridyl, polarographic	25	6·4	6×10^4	$1 \cdot 5 \times 10^{11}$	17e

Acetic acid has been investigated in this way[9e]; the value reported for k_2 is 1×10^{10} l mole^{-1} sec^{-1}. The difficulty arises, however, that in the acetate buffer solutions the current does not reach a limiting value as the voltage is increased; the current-voltage plot does not show a flat portion, but a point of inflection. This behaviour appears to be due to electrochemical decomposition of water at the cathode. This complication may be eliminated by using two electrodes differentially, one in the buffer and the other in strong acid[9f]; the result then agrees with Eigen's ($k_2 = 5 \cdot 2 \times 10^{10}$ l mole^{-1} sec^{-1}). For trimethylacetic acid, a lower value of k_2 is found, attributed to the steric blocking effect of the t-butyl group.[9f]

(c) *Reduction of the acid.* The recombination of anions with hydrogen ion can be made to control the rate if the potential can be so adjusted that the acid HA is reduced while the anion A^- is not. Pyruvic acid is an example.[18] The sequence of reactions is then:

$$H_3O^+ + A^- \underset{k_1}{\overset{k_2}{\rightleftharpoons}} H_2O + HA \overset{e}{\longrightarrow} \text{products}$$

Polarography has been applied to such reactions, especially by the Czech school. The procedure is limited to reducible acids, but a considerable number of these have been investigated. A collection of results[19] is given in Table 9.2.

Comments on the observed rate constants. It will be noticed from Table 9.2 that the rate constants k_2 for recombination obtained by the polarographic method range from below 10^7 to over 10^{13} l mole^{-1}sec^{-1}, although values determined by other methods for acids with a wide range of pK nearly always lie between about 10^{10} and 10^{11} l mole^{-1}sec^{-1} (p. 267), and agree with the values calculated from simple diffusion theory (p. 12). These peculiarities require attention.[20]

The reason for the low rate constants obtained polarographically for some α-keto-carboxylic acids may be that there is a preliminary hydration equilibrium and only the unhydrated form is reduced. For pyruvic acid (above) the correction brings the rate constant to $1\cdot3 \times 10^{10}$ l mole^{-1}sec^{-1}, which is within the normal range.[20d]

The high rate constants of 10^{12} and 10^{13} l mole^{-1}sec^{-1} are more anomalous, since no reaction can proceed faster than encounter by diffusion. There are several possible explanations. One is that, as in general acid catalysis, the anions may gain protons from the undissociated acid HA present in the buffer solution, as well as

[18] (a) Rüetschi and Trümpler, *Helv. chim. Acta*, 1952, **35**, 1957; (b) Delahay and Adams, *J. Amer. Chem. Soc.* 1952, **74**, 1437.
[19] From Brdička, *Z. Elektrochem.* 1960, **64**, 16, where full references are given.
[20] For discussions, see (a) Strehlow. ref. 1a and (b) *Z. Elektrochem.* 1960, **64**, 45 (general); (c) Bewick and Fleischmann, *Ann. Rep. Chem. Soc.* 1960, 101 (general); (d) Becker and Strehlow, *Z. Elektrochem.* 1960, **64**, 129 (hydration); (e) *idem, ibid.*, p. 43 (influence of other acids in buffer); (f) Koryta, *ibid.*, p. 23 (reaction layer); (g) Gierst and Hurwitz, *ibid.*, 36 (double layer); (h) Delahay and Oka, ref. 17b.

TABLE 9.2

Dissociation of weak acids in water studied by polarographic reduction of acid

$$HA + H_2O \underset{k_2}{\overset{k_1}{\rightleftarrows}} H_3O^+ + A^-$$

k_1 in sec^{-1}; k_2 in l mole^{-1}sec^{-1}. Data from ref. 19.

Acid	pK	k_1	k_2
Trimethylpyruvic	2·30	$2·9 \times 10^4$	$5·7 \times 10^6$
Pyruvic	2·40	$1·8 \times 10^7$	$4·6 \times 10^9$
Phenylpyruvic	2·68	$5·4 \times 10^7$	$2·6 \times 10^{10}$
Diphenylpyruvic	2·78	$1·1 \times 10^8$	$6·6 \times 10^{10}$
3,4-dimethoxypyruvic	3·10	$4·6 \times 10^8$	$5·8 \times 10^9$
Phenylglyoxylic	1·20	$7·2 \times 10^{10}$	$1·2 \times 10^{12}$
β-Acetylacrylic (*cis*)	4·56	$1·1 \times 10^5$	$3·9 \times 10^9$
β-Acetylacrylic (*trans*)	3·57	$7·9 \times 10^7$	$2·9 \times 10^{11}$
Picolinic	5·45	$1·1 \times 10^6$	$6·8 \times 10^{11}$
Isonicotinic	4·90	$1·7 \times 10^7$	$1·3 \times 10^{12}$
Maleic	1·85	$2·8 \times 10^8$	$2·0 \times 10^{10}$
Citraconic	2·29	$6·1 \times 10^6$	$1·2 \times 10^9$
Fumaric	3·02	$1·6 \times 10^6$	$1·7 \times 10^9$
Oxalic	1·42	$2·1 \times 10^6$	$5·5 \times 10^7$
Hydroxylamine	6·05	$1·7 \times 10^7$	$1·9 \times 10^{13}$
Nitrosohydroxylamine	4·28	$4·4 \times 10^5$	$8·3 \times 10^9$
Hydroxylamine o-methyl ether	4·64	$1·7 \times 10^7$	$7·8 \times 10^{11}$
p-Azobenzene monocarboxylic	4·7	$1·1 \times 10^9$	$5·4 \times 10^{13}$
HCrO$_4$	6·5	$1·3 \times 10^6$	$7·4 \times 10^{12}$
H$_3$BO$_3$	9·2	$1·3 \times 10^3$	$2·0 \times 10^{12}$

from H_3O^+.[20e] Another is that adsorbed molecules may take part in the reaction. Perhaps the most important point is that the reaction controls the current in a thin layer near the electrode (p. 176). The thickness of this layer will be less than 100 Å if k_1 is larger than about 10^7 sec^{-1}. This is so close to molecular dimensions that the normal laws of diffusion may not be accurate. Moreover, the diffuse double layer, which extends a few Å from the electrode, will have important effects if it is comparable in thickness with the reaction layer. The steep potential gradient in the double layer will affect the distribution of ions in the solution, and also increase the dissociation constants of weak acids, by the dissociation field effect (p. 71).[21] A correction for the first of these effects has been worked out for a relatively slow reaction (p. 190), but not as yet for the reactions under discussion.

These considerations apply to all the electrochemical methods of determining the rates of fast reactions. The apparent rate constant refers to reaction in a thin film near the electrode, not in the bulk solution, and so is not necessarily comparable with values derived by other methods, unless corrected. The faster the reaction, the more difficult is the calculation of the correction.

Formation and dissociation of metal complexes

Cyanocadmiate ion.[22] The dissociation of the cyanocadmiate ion in presence of excess cyanide has been the object of several investigations. It appears that reduction at the cathode normally involves mainly the species $Cd(CN)_3^-$, so that the dissociation is a first-order process preceding the electrode reaction:

$$Cd(CN)_4^- \underset{k_2}{\overset{k_1}{\rightleftharpoons}} CN^- + Cd(CN)_3^- \overset{2e}{\longrightarrow} Cd + 4CN^-$$

Measurements have been made by the polarographic,[22a] galvanostatic,[22b,c,d] and potentiostatic[22e,f] methods. The rate constant k_1 is about 10^4 sec^{-1} and k_2 is about 10^8 l mole^{-1}sec^{-1}. The results by the potentiostatic method show that the rate constants vary somewhat with the applied voltage, as shown in Table 9.3.

[21] For a general account of the diffuse double layer, see for example Parsons, in *Advances in Electrochemistry*, vol. 1, ed. Bockris (Butterworths 1954). The potential gradient in the double layer is perhaps 10^6 volts per cm; this would increase the dissociation constant by one or two orders of magnitude. Cf. (*b*) Delahay and Vielstich, *J. Amer. Chem. Soc.* 1955, **77**, 4955; (*c*) Delahay in *Progress in Polarography*, vol. 1 (Interscience, 1962) pp. 65–80.

[22] (*a*) Koryta, *Z. Elektrochem.* 1957, **61**, 423; (*b*) Gierst and Juliard, *J. Phys. Chem.* 1953, **57**, 701; (*c*) Gerischer, *Z. Elektrochem.* 1953, **57**, 604; (*d*) Gerischer, *Z. phys. Chem. (Frankfurt)*, 1954, **2**, 79; (*e*) Gerischer, *Z. Elektrochem.* 1960, **64**, 29; (*f*) Gierst and Hurwitz, *Z. Elektrochem.* 1960, **64**, 36 (ref. 20*g*).

TABLE 9.3

Rate constants for dissociation of $Cd(CN)_4^{--}$ by potentiostatic method

$$Cd(CN)_4^{--} \underset{k_2}{\overset{k_1}{\rightleftharpoons}} Cd(CN)_3^- + CN^-$$

Rate constants at $25°$ in water; $(CN^-) = 0.06$ molel^{-1}.

Applied voltage	k_1 (sec^{-1})	k_2 (l mole^{-1}sec^{-1})
-1.339	$(2.3 \pm 0.5)10^4$	$(8.9 \pm 1.8)10^7$
-1.439	$(1.8 \pm 0.5)10^4$	$(7.0 \pm 1.8)10^7$
-1.539	$(1.5 \pm 0.5)10^4$	$(5.8 \pm 1.7)10^7$

The decrease of k_2 with increase of applied voltage has been attributed to the variation of potential within the diffuse double layer, when its thickness is comparable with that of the reaction layer.[22a] Theoretical analysis shows that under limiting conditions

TABLE 9.4

Rate constants for dissociation of complexes with nitriloacetic acid by polarography

Metal ion	Ionic strength	k_1 (l mole^{-1}sec^{-1})
Cd^{++}	0.1	3×10^5
Pb^{++}	0.2	1×10^6
Mn^{++}	0.1	9×10^6

the observed rate constant should vary exponentially with the diffuse double-layer potential ψ_0. This can be varied by changing the applied potential or the solution composition. Extrapolation of the rate constants to $\psi_0 = 0$ gives $k_1 = 1.2 \times 10^5$ sec^{-1} and $k_2 = 5 \times 10^8$ l mole^{-1}sec^{-1}.

Complexes with nitriloacetic acid. These complexes have been studied polarographically.[23] The species reduced at the cathode is the metal ion. The equilibrium which precedes the electrode reaction in acid solution is, if we write H_3X for nitriloacetic acid:

$$MX^- + H^+ \overset{k_1}{\underset{}{\rightleftharpoons}} M^{++} + HX^{--}$$

Some results for complexes with various metals are shown in Table 9.4.

Complex-formation between cadmium ion and EDTA ion.[24] Cadmium ions form a complex with the anion of EDTA (H_4Y) according to the equation:

$$Cd^{++} + HY^{3-} \rightarrow CdY^{2-} + H^+$$

The cadmium ions can be produced at the electrode, by reducing Cd^{++} cathodically and then reversing the current. The reaction can therefore be studied polarographically, using the equations for rate-control by a reaction subsequent to the electrode process (p. 175). The rate constant obtained is $10^9 \ 1 \ mole^{-1} sec^{-1}$.

Other reactions studied electrochemically

The polarographic method has been applied to a wide variety of reactions in solution; among these are the following.

Dehydration of formaldehyde.[25] In aqueous solutions of formaldehyde there is an equilibrium in which the hydrated form preponderates:

$$CH_2(OH)_2 \overset{k_1}{\underset{k_2}{\rightleftharpoons}} CH_2O + H_2O$$

The species CH_2O is reducible at the mercury electrode while $CH_2(OH)_2$ is not. The forward reaction producing CH_2O can therefore be studied polarographically as a reaction preceding the electrode process. The dependence of the observed rate constants on the

[23] Koryta et al., *Coll. Czech. Chem. Comm.* 1959, **24**, 3057, 3796; 1960, **25**, 38.

[24] Koryta and Zabransky, *Coll. Czech. Chem. Comm.* 1960, **25**, 3153.

[25] The rigorous equations were first applied to this reaction by (a) Brdička, *Coll. Czech. Chem. Comm.* 1955, **20**, 387. The earliest treatments, using approximate equations (cf. note 8, p. 173), were by (b) Veselý and Brdička, *idem*, 1947, **12**, 313, and (c) Bieber and Trümpler, *Helv. chim. Acta*, 1947, **30**, 706.

concentrations of the components of buffer solutions shows that the reaction is catalysed by acids and bases.

Interconversion of forms of sugars.[26] The overall rate of interconversion of α-glucose and β-glucose in water can be determined by following the mutarotation. The solution contains also an aldehydic form in equilibrium:

$$\alpha\text{-glucose} \rightleftarrows \text{aldehydic form} \rightleftarrows \beta\text{-glucose}$$

This aldehydic form is reducible at a mercury cathode, whereas the glucoses are not. The interconversions have been studied polarographically, as reactions preceding the electrode process. As the rate of mutarotation is known, all four rate constants can be determined. The equilibrium concentration of the aldehydic form is found to be 0·003 %. Other sugars have been studied in a similar way, but less completely.

Oxidation of transition-metal ions.[27] Ferric iron can be reduced to ferrous at a mercury cathode; in presence of hydrogen peroxide, it is re-oxidized to ferric. The oxidation has been studied polarographically, by applying the relations for a regenerative reaction (p. 175). There are two stages; the first is rate-determining, the second is a radical reaction and very fast:

$$Fe^{++} + H_2O_2 \longrightarrow Fe^{+++} + OH\cdot + OH^-$$

$$Fe^{++} + OH\cdot \longrightarrow Fe^{+++} + OH^-$$

The rate constant for the first step is found to be 78 l mole^{-1}sec^{-1}, in 0·5 M H_2SO_4; this is in good agreement with the results of other measurements.[27a] If the iron is complexed with ethylenediaminetetracetic acid (EDTA) the reaction is considerably faster.[27b] The oxidation of titanous ion by chlorate ion[27c] and of U^{III} by nitrate ion[27d] have been similarly investigated; the rate constants are 2×10^4 and $1\cdot6 \times 10^6$ l mole^{-1}sec^{-1}.

[26] (a) Los and Wiesner, *J. Amer. Chem. Soc.* 1953, **75**, 6346; (b) Los, Simpson and Wiesner, *J. Amer. Chem. Soc.* 1956, **78**, 1564.

[27] (a) Pospíšil, *Coll. Czech. Chem. Comm.* 1953, **18**, 337; (b) Matyska, idem, 1957, **22**, 1758; (c) Koryta and Tenygl, idem, 1954, 839; (d) Koryta, idem, 1955, **20**, 667. For other examples of regenerative reactions, see Brdička, ref. 19.

CHAPTER 10

Electron-spin resonance
(paramagnetic resonance)

GENERAL PRINCIPLES

Introduction

Electron-spin resonance, which is also known as paramagnetic resonance (abbreviated to e.s.r. or e.p.r.), is a phenomenon observed with free radicals possessing an unpaired electron.[1] Such an unpaired electron has a spin S of $\frac{1}{2}$, that is to say, it can be regarded as a spinning charged body with an internal angular momentum of $(h/2\pi)\sqrt{S(S+1)}$ where $S = \frac{1}{2}$. Associated with such a spinning charge is a magnetic moment along the axis of rotation. In a strong magnetic field the electron may be pictured as aligned, somewhat like a bar magnet, with a component of its moment either parallel or anti-parallel to the field. These two orientations differ in energy, so there will be two different energy-levels. Electrons can be made to pass from one orientation to the other by applying a second (much weaker) field which is made to alternate with a particular resonance frequency depending on the strength of the main field. When the frequency or field strength is varied, the resonance gives rise to a peak in the power absorbed. With a field strength of the order of 10^4 gauss, the resonance frequency is in the micro-wave region.

The sensitivity of the method is such that the width and structure as well as the position of the absorption line can be determined. The line usually has a fine structure, characteristic of the molecule,

[1] For general reviews on e.s.r. see (a) Whiffen, *Quart. Rev. Chem. Soc.* 1958, **12**, 250; (b) Ingram, *Free Radicals as Studied by Electron-spin Resonance* (Butterworths, 1958); (c) Fraenkel, in *Physical Methods of Organic Chemistry*, ed. Weissberger (3rd edn. Interscience 1960), part IV, chapter 42; (d) Carrington, *Quart. Rev. Chem.~Soc.* 1963, **17**, 67; (e) Slichter, *Principles of Magnetic Resonance* (Harper and Roe, 1963); (f) *Ann. Rev. Phys. Chem.* 1955, **6**, and subsequent volumes.

because nuclei of various kinds, including protons, also have spins and magnetic moments (p. 220), and can interact with the electron, giving rise to further splitting of the energy levels. The line-width and fine-structure depend on the mean lifetime of the radical, as will be shown below; if a reaction which destroys free radicals occurs at an appropriate rate, so that the mean lifetime is shortened, the e.s.r. spectrum is altered. From the observed changes, the rates of such reactions can be inferred. Rate constants up to about 10^{10} l mole^{-1}sec^{-1} have been determined.[2]

Resonance frequency

Let us consider a free radical containing an unpaired electron, not coupled to any of the nuclei. Such an electron, like a free electron, has a spin of $\frac{1}{2}$, and therefore has a spin quantum number m_S of $+\frac{1}{2}$ or $-\frac{1}{2}$. In an assembly of such free radicals, in the absence of an external field, the magnetic moments of the spinning electrons are oriented at random, and all the electrons occupy states of equal energy. When a magnetic field is applied, the magnetic moments tend to become oriented relative to the field. According to quantum theory, they take up one of two orientations, and intermediate directions are not possible, because the resolved spin angular momentum along the magnetic field[3] is restricted by the quantum rules to the two discrete values $+\frac{1}{2}(h/2\pi)$ and $-\frac{1}{2}(h/2\pi)$. Corre-

---

[2] For reviews on the applications of e.s.r. to chemical kinetics see (a) Weismann, *Z. Elektrochem.* 1960, **64**, 47; (b) Strehlow, in *Investigation of Rates and Mechanisms of Reactions*, ed. Friess, Lewis and Weissberger (2nd edn., Interscience, 1963), part II, chapter 17.

[3] According to the old quantum theory, the total spin angular momentum of a particle, in units of $h/2\pi$, was an integral or half-integral number, which for an electron was $S = \frac{1}{2}$. The component of the spin angular momentum along the field for an electron had to be $\pm\frac{1}{2}$, in the same units. Hence the direction of the magnetic moment had to be parallel or anti-parallel to the field, i.e. at an angle of zero or 180° to it, and no other angles were possible. According to quantum mechanics, however, the total spin angular momentum of a free electron is not S but $\sqrt{S(S+1)}$ or $\sqrt{3}/2$. There are still only two possible orientations, but they are now those in which the *component* of the spin angular momentum along the direction of the field is $\pm\frac{1}{2}$. The magnetic moments may thus be pictured as being at an angle θ to the field, where $\cos\theta = \frac{1}{2}/(\sqrt{3}/2) = 1/\sqrt{3}$, and so $\theta = 54\cdot7°$.

spondingly the component of the magnetic moment in the direction of the field must be restricted to two values, which we may designate as $+\mu$ and $-\mu$. It turns out (see below) that μ is nearly equal to the Bohr magneton. The orientational energies in a field of strength H, for the two permitted orientations, will by ordinary electromagnetic theory be $-\mu H$ and $+\mu H$. The electrons therefore divide into two groups, whose energies differ by $2\mu H$ (Fig. 10.1). There are slightly more in the lower energy state than in the higher, because the electrons exchange energy by various mechanisms with their surroundings, and so maintain a normal energy equilibrium. According to

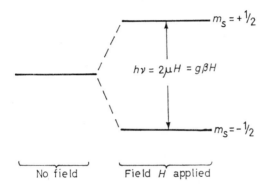

FIG. 10.1. Energy-levels of electrons in magnetic field.

the Maxwell-Boltzmann theorem, the ratio of the numbers in the higher and lower states is $\exp(-\Delta\epsilon/kT)$, where $\Delta\epsilon$ is the energy-separation $2\mu H$, which is much less than kT; in a typical situation the ratio is in the region of 0·998.

If now the sample is exposed to electromagnetic radiation of frequency ν, such that the energy-quantum $h\nu$ is equal to the energy-difference $2\mu H$, some of the electrons in the lower state gain energy and pass into the upper state. At the same time energy is lost from some of the electrons in the higher state, but since there are fewer of these there is on the whole a net absorption of energy. This occurs only at the frequency ν, such that:

$$h\nu = 2\mu H \qquad (10.1)$$

If we vary the field-strength H, keeping the frequency ν constant (since it is more difficult to vary ν than H), we find that there is one value of H at which the power absorbed shows a sharp maximum, corresponding to the condition 10.1 (Fig. 10.2). This is a characteristic resonance phenomenon.

The height of the resonance maximum depends on the number of electrons in the higher state; this, as we noted above, depends on

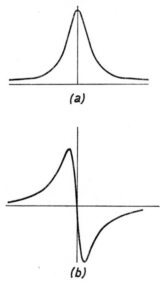

(a)

(b)

FIG. 10.2. E.s.r. absorption line, of approximately Lorentzian shape (p. 200), as shown by e.g. tetrachloro-p-benzosemiquinone ion in solution. (*a*) Absorption plotted against field. (*b*) Gradient of curve *a* plotted against field (derivative curve).

the field strength H. To increase the sensitivity, H is made as large as possible. The upper limit is set by the need for a stable and uniform field over a volume of about 1 ml; it is of the order of 10^4 gauss. A field of about 3000 gauss is convenient. This fixes the frequency required, since

$$\nu = 2\mu H/h \approx 2\beta H/h = He/2\pi m_e c = 2 \cdot 8 \times 10^6 H$$

The resonance frequency is thus about 10^{10} c/sec, corresponding to a wavelength of about 3 cm. The electromagnetic radiation must therefore take the form of microwaves.

We must now consider the value of the resolved magnetic moment μ of the electron, which was stated above to be approximately equal to the Bohr magneton β. The general relation between μ and the resolved angular momentum p is given by electromagnetic theory as:

$$\mu/p = \tfrac{1}{2}ge/m_e c \qquad (10.2)$$

With the quantized value of $|p|$ as $h/4\pi$, this gives:

$$\mu = \tfrac{1}{2}g(he/4\pi m_e c) = \tfrac{1}{2}g\beta \qquad (10.3)$$

Here e and m_e are the electronic charge and mass, c is the velocity of light, h is Planck's constant, and β is the Bohr magneton $(he/4\pi m_e c)$. The constant g depends on the relative contributions of the spin and orbital motions of an electron to its total angular momentum; both motions produce magnetic moments, and the resultant moment is determined by their vector sum. The 'g-value' for free spin is 2·0023 (the difference from 2·0000 is due to the relativity correction).

The condition for resonance (equation 10.1; Fig. 10.1) may now be rewritten, taking account of the value of μ given by equation 10.3, in the form:

$$h\nu = g\beta H \qquad (10.4)$$

For a free radical, the value of g derived by means of equation 10.4 from the observed resonance frequency is usually within $\tfrac{1}{2}\%$ of the free-spin value. This is because the unpaired electron is almost completely delocalized and there is very little coupling between its spin motion and any orbital motion. Diphenylpicrylhydrazyl, for example, has a g-value of 2·0036.

Quantitative estimation of free radicals: reactive intermediates

The rise in the power absorbed at resonance is proportional, other things being equal, to the number of free radicals present. The proportionality constant depends on the experimental arrangement; its determination would be difficult, and is better avoided. Instead, the e.s.r. signal of the sample is compared with that of diphenylpicrylhydrazyl or other substance known to consist entirely of free radicals. The power absorbed is given by the integrated area of the

14

absorption band. The concentration of free radicals in the sample
can thus be determined.

The e.s.r. signal can therefore be used to follow the progress of a
reaction involving a free radical, like any other physical property.
This technique has the advantages that it is sensitive and is specific
to free radicals. Moreover, the radical can be identified, from the
hyperfine structure of the absorption line (p. 202). The recombination of the radicals ($RO\cdot$) formed by photo-dissociation of hydro-
peroxides has been studied in this way.[4]

With a sufficiently sensitive detector, it should be possible to
determine the concentrations of reactive radical intermediates, and
hence their rates of reaction. The first radical to be studied in this
way in a fluid system was the ethyl radical produced in the radiolysis of liquid ethane by high-speed electrons.[5] It was found that
the steady-state concentration of $C_2H\cdot$ was 7×10^{-8} M. With the
known rate of production of radicals, this gave the rate constant
for combination of two ethyl radicals as 4×10^9 l mole^{-1}sec^{-1}. In
general the steady-state concentrations of intermediates in photochemical reactions in solution (10^{-8}–10^{-10}M; cf. p. 126) are somewhat
too small for detection by the present standard techniques (though
in glassy solvents at low temperatures detection is relatively easy).

In such investigations as these, the e.s.r. signal is used simply as a
measure of concentration, and no new principle is involved. We
now turn to the special kinetic methods which depend on magnetic
resonance.

Determination of the lifetimes and rates of reaction of free radicals by e.s.r. spectroscopy

The lifetimes of free radicals: reaction rate from line-broadening

The width of an e.s.r. absorption line can be determined with some
accuracy (cf. Fig. 10.2) because of the high resolution which is
characteristic of the technique (about 0·03 gauss, or 1 in 10^5).
The line for liquid sulphur, for example, which is exceptionally
broad, has a width at half-height of the order of 100 gauss, or
in terms of frequency around 3×10^8 c/sec. The e.s.r. signal is

[4] Piette and Landgraf, *J. Chem. Phys.* 1960, **32**, 1107.
[5] Fessenden and Schuler, *J. Chem. Phys.* 1960, **33**, 935.

attributed to diradicals formed by the following process, for which there is independent evidence:

$$S_8 \rightleftharpoons \; -S(S)_n S-$$

In this instance the line-width can be related to the rate of disappearance of the free radicals. The principles will be outlined here; the details of this particular reaction are given later (p. 207).

The theory of line-width may first be approached in a semi-quantitative way by applying the uncertainty principle. An absorption band of finite width implies that the energy-difference between the upper and lower states ($\epsilon'' - \epsilon'$) is not perfectly definite. This will be so if the lifetime of an electron in either state is uncertain, for energy and time are conjugate quantities in the Heisenberg uncertainty relation $\delta\epsilon\,\delta t \approx h/2\pi$. If the mean lifetime of the electrons in a given state has a mean value τ, we may identify τ with the uncertainty δt in the time. The corresponding uncertainty in the energy-level is then given, as regards order of magnitude, by $\delta\epsilon \approx h/2\pi\tau$. The more stable the state, the less the uncertainty in the level.

Before considering e.s.r. spectra in the light of these ideas, it is interesting to apply them to absorption spectra. In optical spectroscopy, the 'natural' width of an absorption line given by a gas at low pressure may be 0·001 to 0·01 Å.[6a] This width is attributed to an uncertainty in the upper energy-level ϵ'', arising from the short mean lifetime τ'' of the excited state. The ground state is stable and so has a sharp energy-level ϵ'. The Heisenberg relation ($\delta\epsilon \approx h/2\pi\tau$) combined with the general quantum relation for the frequency ($h\nu = \epsilon'' - \epsilon'$) then gives for the line-width $\delta\nu$ in cycles/sec:

$$\delta\nu = \delta(\epsilon'' - \epsilon')/h = \delta\epsilon''/h \approx 1/2\pi\tau'' \qquad (10.5)$$

The lifetime τ'' calculated in this way for an excited state giving a visible absorption line of width 0·001 Å is in the region of 10^{-8} sec. The line-width is increased, however, by addition of an inert gas. This 'pressure-broadening' is attributed to deactivation of the

[6] (a) Herzberg, *Molecular Spectra and Molecular Structure: Spectra of Diatomic Molecules* (2nd edn., Van Nostrand, 1950), pp. 431, 437; (b) Kuhn, *Atomic Spectra* (Longmans, 1962), chapter 7; (c) Townes and Schawlow, *Microwave Spectroscopy* (McGraw Hill, 1955), pp. 338 *seq.*; (d) Van Vleck and Weisskopf, *Rev. Mod. Physics* 1945, **17**, 227.

excited state by collision within a time-interval shorter than the natural lifetime. Because of this decrease of τ'', the energy level becomes more diffuse (equation 10.5); hence $\delta\nu$ increases, and the line broadens. The mathematical theory[6d] of pressure-broadening of absorption lines in gases, due originally to Lorentz, supplements this approximate account. Its predictions are in reasonable agreement with experimental results an optical spectra.[6b] It has been successfully applied to explain the line-shapes of the microwave absorption spectra of gases [6c]; these are easier to investigate than those in the optical region. It is found experimentally, in agreement with the theory, that the shape of the line is 'Lorentzian' (p. 230). i.e. resembles the curve shown in Fig. 10.2; and that the line-width $\delta\nu$ is approximately in accordance with the relation 10.5, when τ'' is calculated from kinetic theory.[7]

The e.s.r. spectrum of liquid sulphur may be treated somewhat similarly. In the absence of reaction the line would be expected to be much narrower than it is; that is, the lifetime of the electron in a given spin state would be relatively long. Most of the line-width is attributed to the removal of free radicals by a rapid chemical reaction, represented by the reverse reaction above. This reduces the mean lifetime of the radical, just as in absorption spectroscopy the mean lifetime of an excited molecule is reduced by the possibility of collisional deactivation. The spin energy-level ϵ of the electron in a radical therefore becomes uncertain, by the Heisenberg relation, and the line is consequently broadened. The line-width, or more accurately the line-broadening $\delta'\nu$, associated with a mean lifetime τ for the radical is then given (as regards order of magnitude) by the Heisenberg relation as:

$$\delta'\nu = \delta\epsilon/h \approx 1/2\pi\tau \tag{10.6}$$

A full mathematical theory of the shape and width of e.s.r. lines has been developed, taking into account various factors that have not yet been mentioned.[8] An analogous theory applies to proton

[7] On the broadening of Raman lines by a proton-transfer reaction, see Kreevoy and Mead, *J. Amer. Chem. Soc.* 1962, **84**, 4596.

[8] In particular, spin–spin interaction and spin–lattice interaction (Ingram, *Free Radicals*, ref. 1*b*, pp. 120 *seq*; Carrington, ref. 1*d*).

magnetic resonance, and its principles will be dealt with more fully in the next chapter (pp. 228–231, 235–237). Here we shall simply note two of its conclusions: (i) that on the simplest assumptions the line-shape is Lorentzian, and (ii) that a more correct expression for the line-broadening in cycles per sec (in place of equation 10.6) is[14c]:

$$\delta'\nu = 1/\pi\tau \tag{10.7}$$

The value of τ can therefore be determined from the line-width, if other line-broadening influences can be shown to be small. For liquid sulphur, the value found in this way is of the order of 10^{-9} sec.

Reaction rate from line-broadening by added reagent

Reactions between free radicals and added substances, such as that between the naphthalenide radical ion $C_{10}H_8^-$ and added naphthalene (p. 209), have been studied by a related method. The line-width increases with the concentration of added reagent; this implies that the mean lifetime τ becomes shorter. If the decrease can be attributed entirely to the reaction removing the radicals, the rate constant for this reaction can be deduced. (Other reasons for line-broadening[8] must first be shown not to apply.)

A quantitative relation can be derived as follows. The electron-exchange reaction is represented by:

$$N^- + N \rightleftharpoons N + N^-$$

Let the second-order rate constant for this reaction be k', so that the rate in either direction is:

$$d(N^-)/dt = -k'(N^-)(N) \tag{10.8}$$

The mean lifetime of the radical N^- is equal to the concentration of radicals divided by their rate of reaction, so that making use of equation 10.8 we obtain:

$$\tau = -(N^-)/[d(N^-)/dt] = 1/k'(N) = 1/k \tag{10.9}$$

where k is a first-order rate constant. Thus by equation 10.7,

$$k = k'(N) = \tau^{-1} = \pi\delta'\nu \tag{10.10}$$

This equation gives us the first-order rate constant in terms of the line-broadening, in the simplest case.

The initial line-width for the radicals concerned in solution is typically in the region of 10^6 c/sec,[9] and values of τ in the region of 10^{-6} sec can be determined. The uncertainty in the line-width is generally of the order of $\pm 10\%$, but the uncertainty in the rate constant is usually greater. This is because the theory assumes a Lorentzian line-shape, which is implicit in the use of equation 10.7; the actual line-shape may not be accurately Lorentzian, and may change with concentration.

Hyperfine structure: identification of free radicals

The e.s.r. absorption spectrum for an organic free radical in solution generally consists not of a single peak but of a system of peaks, covering a range of perhaps 30 gauss or about 10^8 c/sec. The absorption curve for a naphthalene radical ion in solution, for example, is shown in Fig. 10.6 (p. 210). The spectrum is said to show 'hyperfine structure'.[10]

The interpretation of hyperfine structure is briefly as follows. Suppose the unpaired electron is close to a proton, which also has a spin $(I = \frac{1}{2})$ and a magnetic moment. This moment will interact with that of the electron, and each of the electron-spin levels will be split into two (Fig. 10.3). Because the selection rules are $\Delta m_S = \pm 1$ and $\Delta m_I = 0$, the single resonance line will be replaced by a pair of lines, as illustrated in the figure. In the general case of interaction with a nucleus of spin I, the splitting produces $2I + 1$ lines. The separation between the lines is a measure of the interaction between the nucleus and the unpaired electron.

In most free radicals, the unpaired electron is delocalized and may interact with protons in several different environments. Each interaction will give rise to a hyperfine splitting. Other nuclei which may give rise to hyperfine structure are ^2H, ^{13}C, ^{14}N, ^{17}O, ^{19}F, ^{35}Cl and ^{37}Cl, but not ^{12}C nor ^{16}O which have zero spin (p. 220). The resulting

[9] This refers to a single component of the hyperfine structure, which may extend over 10^8 c/sec (see below).

[10] (a) Ingram, *Free Radicals* (ref. 1b), pp. 22 *seq.*, 103 *seq.*; (b) Carrington, ref. 1d.

spectrum may be quite complicated. It is characteristic of the particular substance, and is a very useful means of identification of free radicals.

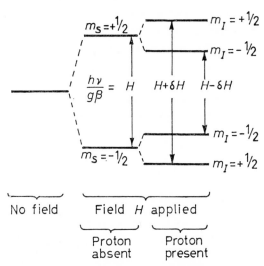

FIG. 10.3. Hyperfine structure: splitting of electronic energy levels by interaction with one proton, and resonance conditions.

Reaction rate from collapse of hyperfine structure

Hyperfine structure can be of kinetic interest.[2] The structure will disappear, and the absorption band will give place to a single line, if the time spent by an electron in each environment is too short for the different resonance lines to be detectable. We may visualize the situation in a preliminary way as follows. A doublet will be detectable if, on the average, the species giving rise to it persists for a period of the order of $1/\Delta\nu$ seconds, where $\Delta\nu$ is the splitting of the doublet—that is, the separation between the peaks in c/sec. If the mean lifetime of the species is much less than this, it will not last long enough to manifest the absorption of radiation throughout its range of frequencies, and the lines will coalesce. For example, the hyperfine structure of the benzophenone radical ion in solution (p. 212) collapses when sufficient benzophenone is added. This implies that the electron-exchange reaction has then become so fast that on the average an electron does not stay long enough near any one proton for the line characteristic of that proton to be observable, and the line that appears represents an average of the several environments. The mathematical theory of the phenomenon is similar to that of the collapse of the multiplet structure of n.m.r. spectra, and will be dealt with further in the next chapter (pp. 235 *seq.*). If the frequency-separation of the components (which determines the minimum time required for their detection), is $\Delta \nu_0$, and the width of the single line after coalescence is $\delta' \nu$, the mean lifetime for the exchange is approximately $\delta' \nu / 4\pi \Delta \nu_0^2$ (p. 237, equation 11.22). Hence it is possible in suitable instances to determine a rate constant for the migration of electrons from one environment to another. The shortest detectable lifetime is less than 10^{-10} sec.

Experimental study of electron-spin resonance

The general principles of experimental work on e.s.r.[11] are exemplified by the simplest type of spectrometer, shown in Fig. 10.4. The specimen to be examined (0·1 to 0·2 ml) is placed between the poles of a strong electromagnet, in a cavity resonator, which concentrates the power from a radar klystron valve emitting 3-cm radiation. The transmitted radiation is led to a crystal detector, whose output voltage is proportional to the power falling upon it. The frequency of the radiation from the klystron is kept as constant as possible, and measured to about 1 in 10^6 by a monitor wavemeter. The magnetic field (about 3000 gauss) is varied, and the absorption at resonance (equation 10.4) is shown by a drop in the crystal output. The absorption line may be examined in detail as follows. A small alternating field, at say 100 c/sec, generated by subsidiary coils, is superimposed on the main field, so that the resultant field varies slightly, by an amount up to say 10 gauss. This 'field-sweep' produces an a.c. output from the crystal, which is amplified and fed to the Y plates of an oscilloscope. The X plates are fed in synchronism with the modulating a.c. field. The trace on the oscilloscope screen thus shows directly the variation of absorption with field-strength during the sweep. As the process is repeated

[11] (*a*) Ingram, ref. 1*b*, chapter 1, pp. 28 *seq.*, and chapter 2; (*b*) Fraenkel, ref. 1*c*, pp. 2824 *seq.*

100 times a second, the trace is stable and can be photographed.
The type of trace obtained is shown in Fig. 10.5a, which also shows
the microwave components needed. This transmission type of
apparatus is very simple and direct; it is sometimes used in work on
paramagnetic ions, but very rarely for studies on free radicals,

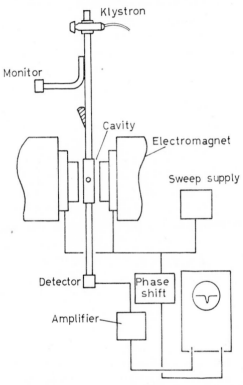

FIG. 10.4. Simple transmission apparatus for electron-spin resonance. (From Ingram, *Free Radicals*, ref. 1b, by permission.)

because it is not easy to adapt for high sensitivity. This is partly
because the amplifier must cover a considerable bandwidth, so that
the ratio of signal to noise is low; and partly because the method of
measuring the absorption leads to a small dip at resonance in a
large measured power.

   Much greater sensitivity can be obtained from a null method,
which makes use of a device known as a 'magic T'. This consists of

four arms, as shown in Fig. 10.5*b*. Microwave power fed into arm 1 is equally divided between arms 2 and 3, and so long as these absorb equally no power appears in arm 4. The cavity resonator is placed at the end of arm 2, and matched with arm 3 so that no power is

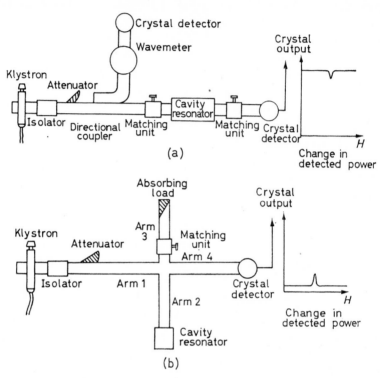

FIG. 10.5. Microwave components for (*a*) transmission and (*b*) reflection types of e.s.r. apparatus. The changes in detected power at resonance are also shown. (From Ingram, *Free Radicals*, ref. 1*b*, by permission.)

detected by the crystal at the end of arm 4, with the field strength at some non-resonant value. When the field strength is changed so that resonance occurs, the absorption by the two arms becomes un-balanced; power appears in arm 4, and is detected by means of the crystal. The optimum sensitivity is actually obtained when the bridge is somewhat unbalanced and a small current flows through the crystal. The detected power is therefore not reduced to zero;

none the less, the absorption at resonance now appears as a considerable change in the signal (Fig. 10.5*b*).

For such high sensitivity, the methods of amplifying and displaying the signal described above are not suitable. The frequency of modulation of the field must be high (10^5 c/sec) and the amplitude is made small (much less than the line-width) so that the amplifier has to cover only a small bandwidth, to eliminate as much noise as possible. The modulated field is moved across the resonance region by a gradual change in the d.c. current producing the main field. The response time of the amplifying system is deliberately made long, to reduce noise; to traverse an absorption line may take perhaps ten minutes. The small-amplitude changes scan the absorption line, and produce a signal proportional to its slope (first derivative). The signal is amplified and rectified by a phase-sensitive detector, and the d.c. output traced by a pen recorder. From the derivative curve, the shape of the absorption line may be computed, For details of this and more elaborate techniques, the reader is referred to monographs.[11] The resolving power of a good e.s.r. spectrometer is about $0 \cdot 03$ gauss (10^5 c/sec). Commercial instruments are available.

APPLICATIONS OF E.S.R. SPECTROSCOPY TO KINETICS OF REACTIONS IN SOLUTION

The polymerization of sulphur[12]: reaction rate from line-width

When liquid sulphur is heated, a sudden change begins to occur about $160° C$; the viscosity starts to rise, reaching a maximum at about $187°$,[12a] and the specific heat also alters.[12b] These and other observations have been interpreted in terms of an equilibrium between S_8 rings and linear polymers, which on ordinary valency rules would be diradicals with an unpaired electron at each end. The increase in viscosity is attributed to a simultaneous increase

[12] (a) Bacon and Fanelli, *J. Amer. Chem. Soc.* 1943, **65**, 639; (b) Powell and Eyring, *idem, ibid.*, p. 645; (c) Gee, *Trans. Faraday Soc.* 1952, **48**, 515; (d) Fairbrother, Gee and Merrall, *J. Polymer Sci.* 1955, **16**, 459; (e) Gardner and Fraenkel, *J. Amer. Chem. Soc.* 1956, **78**, 3279. Cf. the magnetic susceptibility measurements of (f) Poulis, Massen and Leeden, *Trans. Faraday Soc.* 1962, **58**, 474; (g) Poulis and Derbyshire, *Trans. Faraday Soc.* 1963, **59**, 559.

in the concentration and chain-length of the radicals; the maximum and subsequent fall is ascribed to a decrease in chain-length with rise of temperature.

The electron-spin resonance spectrum at a wavelength of 3·2 cm was measured at various temperatures by Gardner and Fraenkel,[12e] who confirmed and extended this interpretation. The general principles have already been outlined (pp. 198 seq.). The spectrum consisted of a single line of nearly Lorentzian shape; the value of g was 2·024. The intensity of absorption gave the concentration of diradicals (p. 197); this increased with temperature, and at 300° C was found to be about 10^{-3} mole l^{-1} in agreement with the specific-heat data. The line-width increased with temperature, from about 40 gauss at 200° C to about 100 gauss at 414°, with a standard deviation of a few per cent at a given temperature. The corresponding values of $\delta\nu$ are of the order of 3×10^8 c/sec. If we ascribe effectively the whole width of the line to the effects of the depolymerization process, the average lifetime τ of the radicals is $1/\pi\delta\nu$ (p. 201). Thus τ is of the order of 10^{-9} sec. The increase in line-width with temperature was attributed to a decrease in the mean lifetime τ of the diradicals. When $\log \delta\nu$ was plotted against $1/T$, a linear plot was obtained, equivalent to an Arrhenius line for the depolymerization reaction. The slope of the line gave $E = 3·08 \pm 0·75$ kcal mole^{-1} for the energy of activation of this reaction. The corresponding A-factor is $(2·8 \pm 1·9) \times 10^8$ sec^{-1}.

Solutions of paramagnetic ions: rate from line-broadening

A paramagnetic ion, like a free radical, has a characteristic e.s.r. spectrum. During collision of such an ion A with another paramagnetic ion B, there will be magnetic interaction, allowing a change of the spin state of the unpaired electron of A. The lifetime of each spin state will be reduced, and the resonance line therefore broadened. In suitable cases the rate of encounter will be rate-determining. It would then be expected that the line-broadening would be proportional to concentration, and would depend mainly on the charge of the other ion B; and that the rate constant k would agree with the value calculated for diffusion control, k_D. Some experiments have been reported on the e.s.r. spectrum of the paramagnetic nitrosyl disulphonate anion $ON(SO_3)_2^{2-}$ in presence of various cations in aqueous solution.[13] It was found that the cations of the first transition series had a much greater effect than others, and that the broadening for these cations in dilute solution (< 0·01 M) was indeed proportional to concentration, and constant for cations of a given charge. The values of $10^{-10} k$ (observed) and $10^{-10} k_D$ (calculated), in l mole^{-1}sec^{-1}, were as follows: for trivalent cations, 3·3 and 1·55; for divalent cations, 3·0 and 1·4; and for monovalent cations, 2·2 and 0·87. The experimental values are of the expected order of magnitude; the significance of the discrepancies is not yet clear.

Naphthalene–naphthalenide exchange[14]: rate from broadening of hyperfine lines by added reagent

When naphthalene, dissolved in a donor solvent such as ether or tetrahydrofuran, is treated with sodium, it produces a free-radical negative ion[14a,b]:

$$C_{10}H_8 + e \longrightarrow C_{10}H_8^-$$

The e.s.r. spectrum of this ion is more complex than that of sulphur[14c]; it has a hyperfine structure, because the electron-spin magnetic moment interacts with the nuclear-spin moments of the protons. From the number of different proton environments, deducible from the symmetry of the molecule, we should expect twenty-five lines, and these have all been resolved[14d]; they cover altogether about 27 gauss (Fig. 10.6).

When naphthalene is added to such a solution the lines broaden, indicating that the mean lifetime of the radicals is being shortened by some new process (p. 201). This is presumed to be the electron-exchange reaction:

$$C_{10}H_8^- + C_{10}H_8 \rightleftharpoons C_{10}H_8 + C_{10}H_8^- \qquad (10.11)$$

[13] Pearson and Buch, *J. Chem. Phys.* 1962, **36**, 1277.
[14] (a) Ward and Weissman, *J. Amer. Chem. Soc.* 1954, **76**, 3612; (b) Paul, Lipkin and Weissman, *J. Amer. Chem. Soc.* 1956, **78**, 116; (c) Weissman and Ward, *idem*, 1957, **79**, 2086; (d) Zandstra and Weissman, *J. Chem. Phys.* 1961, **35**, 757; (e) Weissman, *Z. Elektrochem.* 1960, **64**, 47 (review); (f) Aten, Dieleman and Hoijtink, *Discuss. Faraday Soc.* 1960, **29**, 182. (g) Atherton and Weissman, *J. Amer. Chem. Soc.* 1961, **83**, 1330; (h) Zandstra and Weissman, *idem* 1962, **84**, 4408.

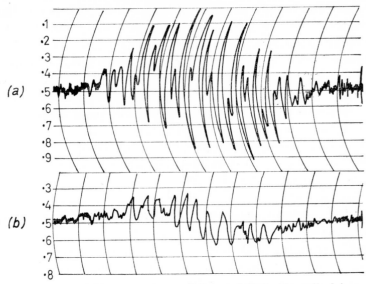

Fig. 10.6. (a) E.s.r. spectrum of the naphthalenide radical ion (derivative tracing) showing hyperfine structure. (b) The same after addition of naphthalene (0·35 M), showing broadening. (From Ward and Weissman, ref. 14a.)

The rate constant was determined from the broadening of one of the component lines,[14c] and later from that of three other lines.[14d] With a concentration of sodium naphthalenide of about 10^{-3} M, broadening began at a naphthalene concentration in the region of

TABLE 10.1

Rate constants at 30–35° for reaction $C_{10}H_8 + C_{10}H_8^-$
DME = dimethoxyethane; THF = tetrahydrofuran.
(From Weissman and Ward, ref. 14c.)

Cation	Solvent	k (1 $mole^{-1}sec^{-1}$)
K^+	DME	$(7\cdot6 \pm 3) \times 10^7$
K^+	THF	$(5\cdot7 \pm 1) \times 10^7$
Na^+	DME	$(0\cdot3 - 4) \times 10^9$
Na^+	THF	$(0\cdot4 - 4) \times 10^7$
Li^+	THF	$(4\cdot6 \pm 3) \times 10^8$

0·1 M. The rate constant at 30–35° was found to depend on the cation (K^+, Na^+, Li^+) and on the solvent (tetrahydrofuran, dimethoxyethane). The values are shown in Table 10.1; they are between 10^7 and 10^9 l mole^{-1}sec^{-1}. It is evident that very large rate constants can be measured in this way, but the accuracy is not of the highest, for reasons mentioned on p. 202. Other systems have been studied in the same way,[15] and rate constants determined for some of them.

It has been pointed out [14f] that the highest rate constant in Table 10.1 is that for solutions of sodium naphthalene in dimethoxyethane, where there is evidence that the sodium and naphthalene ions are completely dissociated; whereas the lowest rate constant is observed in tetrahydrofuran, where they form ion-pairs.[14g] The smaller rate in tetrahydrofuran might be ascribed to a more negative entropy of activation. This could be understood, because when an ion-pair is involved the transition complex will have a sandwich-like structure in which the solvated sodium ion lies between the two naphthalene molecules, so that a considerable degree of order is required. In a later study,[14h] the lines due to the naphthalenide ion and to the ion-pair were distinguished, and the rate constants for the two species determined, in several solvents; the reaction involving the ion-pair was generally the slower.

Since the ions are associated to ion-pairs in tetrahydrofuran, it may be expected that after the electron-exchange the sodium ion will migrate to the new naphthalene ion. There will thus be an exchange of sodium ions as well as of electrons:

$$(ArH^-Na^+) + ArH \rightarrow ArH + (Na^+ArH^-) \qquad (10.12)$$

That this mechanism does occur, in the analogous reaction of sodium benzophenone, may be shown from the collapse of hyperfine splitting, as follows.

[15] These systems include: (a) tetracyanoethylene ($k = 2\cdot1 \times 10^8$ l mole^{-1} sec^{-1}; Phillips, Rowell and Weissman, *J. Chem. Phys.* 1960, **33**, 626); (b) benzophenone, which is considered below (Adam and Weissman, *J. Amer. Chem. Soc.* 1958, **80**, 1518; cf. also ref. 14e); (c) cyclo-octatetraene (preliminary study by Katz and Strauss, *J. Chem. Phys.* 1960, **32**, 1873); (d) tris-*p*-nitrophenylmethide ion (Jones and Weissman, *J. Amer. Chem. Soc.* 1962, **84**, 4269). For a similar system studied by the n.m.r. method, see p. 261.

Benzophenone radical ion exchange: collapse of hyperfine struc-ture[15b, 14e, 14f]

It has been mentioned (p. 203) that the hyperfine structure of the spectrum of a radical ion will collapse if electron-transfer becomes too fast for the lines characteristic of the electron in different proton-environments to be observable. This collapse of hyperfine structure is observed when benzophenone is added to sodium benzophenone in dimethoxyethane. The spectrum of the radical ion contains some eighty lines; the splitting is partly due to protons and partly to sodium nuclei.[16] Benzophenone exchanges electrons with the radical ion in the same way as naphthalene (equation 10.11). At a concentration of 2 M benzophenone, the spectrum collapses to four lines; the structure due to proton interaction dis-appears, while that due to sodium remains. The line-widths indicate mean time-intervals of the order of 10^{-9} and 10^{-6} sec for the two processes. The interpretation suggested is that the unpaired electron wanders rapidly over all the proton environments, but moves relatively rarely from one sodium nucleus to another. This implies that as the electron migrates it usually takes the sodium with it, as in equation 10.12. Conductivity measurements[14f] indicate that the sodium and benzophenone ions are strongly associated, as the mechanism represented by equation 10.12 requires.

Hindered rotation and cis-trans isomerism

E.s.r. methods have been applied to rotational isomerism. In a radical such as $H_3C.CHR\cdot$, the three ^1H nuclei of the methyl group are equivalent if the group rotates freely; but if its rotation is restricted, they become non-equivalent, and the hyperfine struc-ture of the e.s.r. spectrum therefore becomes more complex. Hin-dered rotation has been studied in this way in solid alanine, [17a,b] and in solutions of nitroalkane anions and phenoxyl radicals.[17c,d]. Cis-trans isomerism in the durosemiquinone cation in solution has

[16] Ayscough and Wilson, *Proc. Chem. Soc.* 1962, 229.

[17] (a) Horsfield, Morton and Whiffen, *Mol. Phys.* 1962, **5**, 161; (b) Miyagawa and Itoh, *J. Chem. Phys.* 1962, **36**, 2157; (c) Stone and Maki, *J. Chem. Phys.* 1962, **37**, 1326; (d) Atherton and Harding, *Nature*, 1963, **198**, 987.

been investigated[18]; an alternation of line-widths is observed, and attributed to restricted rotation of the hydroxyl groups about the carbon–oxygen bonds.

General comments on electron-spin resonance methods

The applications of electron-spin resonance to the chemical kinetics of free-radical reactions may be summarized as follows.

(a) The phenomenon reveals the presence of unpaired electrons, and so of free radicals.

(b) The free radical may often be identified by the hyperfine structure of the absorption band; reactive intermediates may thus be detected.

(c) The concentration of free radicals may be determined from the total absorption, and hence the rates of reaction of intermediates. Concentrations as low as 10^{-8} M can be detected, and very high rate constants can therefore be determined (p. 198).

(d) The mean lifetime of a free radical may be estimated from the line-width, and hence the rates of reactions of the radical, if these occur in a comparable time. Lifetimes of around 10^{-9} sec have been determined in this way.

(e) Rates of electron-exchange with an added reagent may also be determined from the concentration of reagent at which the line broadens or the hyperfine structure collapses. Lifetimes from 10^{-9} to 10^{-5} sec have been reported, and second-order rate constants up to about 10^{10} l mole^{-1}sec^{-1}. The precision is not often better than $\pm 10\%$.

The methods are restricted to reactions involving free radicals; but this is sometimes an advantage, in that a single step of a complex reaction can be isolated for investigation. The experimental techniques involve fairly elaborate electronics, as well as a powerful magnet; but with the commercial apparatus now available it is relatively simple to determine e.s.r. spectra.

[18] (a) Bolton and Carrington, *Mol. Phys.* 1962, **5**, 161; (b) Carrington *ibid.*, p. 425.

CHAPTER 11

Nuclear magnetic resonance

GENERAL PRINCIPLES

Introduction

Nuclear magnetic resonance (n.m.r.) may be exhibited by any compound whose molecule contains a nucleus with a spin.[1] Such nuclei include the proton, the common isotopes of nitrogen and fluorine, and less common isotopes of carbon and oxygen, but not ^{12}C nor ^{16}O. A spinning nucleus (like a spinning electron) has a magnetic moment associated with the axis of the spin, and in a magnetic field it will be aligned somewhat like a bar magnet, with its moment at one of certain definite orientations to the field. These orientations differ in energy. Nuclei can be made to pass from one orientation to another by applying a second magnetic field, usually at right angles to the first, alternating with a particular resonance frequency. When the main field is of the order of 10^4 gauss, the resonance frequency is in the radio region. This nuclear magnetic resonance is analogous to electron-spin resonance

For a short account of n.m.r. see (a) Wheatley, *The Determination of Molecular Structure* (Oxford, 1959), chapter 13. Useful reviews include: (b) J. A. S. Smith, *Quart. Rev. Chem. Soc.* 1953, **7**, 279; (c) Wertz, *Chem. Rev.* 1955, **55**, 829. For fuller accounts see (d) Roberts, *Nuclear Magnetic Resonance: Applications to Organic Chemistry* (McGraw Hill, 1959); (e) Jackman, *Applications of N.m.r. Spectroscopy in Organic Chemistry* (Pergamon Press, 1959); (f) Pople, Schneider and Bernstein, *High-resolution Nuclear Magnetic Resonance* (McGraw Hill, 1959); (g) Gutowsky, in *Physical Methods of Organic Chemistry*, ed. Weissberger (3rd edn., Interscience, 1960), part IV, chapter 41; (h) Abragam, *The Principles of Nuclear Magnetism* (Oxford, 1961); (i) Wiberg and Nist, *The Interpretation of N.m.r. Spectra* (Benjamin, 1963); (j) Slichter, *Principles of Magnetic Resonance* (Harper and Roe, 1963). For periodical reviews see (k) *Ann. Rev. Phys. Chem.* 1955, **6** and subsequent volumes.

(chapter 10). As with e.s.r., the structure of the absorption spectrum and the width of the lines can be determined. These depend on the lifetime of the proton (or other nucleus) in a particular environment, and are altered if the compound undergoes a reaction which alters this lifetime. Reaction times from about 1 sec down to 10^{-3} sec are typical of those that have been determined.[2] Rate constants may thence be calculated; values up to about 10^{11} l mole^{-1}sec^{-1} have been reported.

The elementary theory of nuclear magnetic resonance given below is to some extent parallel to that for electron spin resonance, and gives similar equations. However, the structure of the absorption line arises for a slightly different reason, and plays a somewhat larger part in the applications of the method. On the practical side, n.m.r. resembles e.s.r. in requiring a powerful magnet, but differs in that the detection of resonance requires radio techniques rather than microwave.

Resonance frequency

We consider a compound whose molecule contains a nucleus with a spin and an associated magnetic moment. When there is no external field, the magnetic moments of the nuclei are oriented at random and the nuclei all occupy states of equal energy. When a magnetic field is applied, the nuclei may occupy various energy levels, depending on the allowed values of the nuclear spin quantum number m_I, and corresponding to definite orientations of the nuclei to the magnetic field. The simplest case is that of a nucleus such as the proton, for which the spin I is $\frac{1}{2}$; then m_I must be either $+\frac{1}{2}$ or $-\frac{1}{2}$. There are then only two allowed orientations, relative to the direction of the field, namely those in which the component of the nuclear angular momentum in the direction of the field[3] is

[2] These reaction times are longer by several powers of ten than those accessible by e.s.r. methods, because the widths of n.m.r. spectra and their individual lines (in c/sec) are typically smaller by a factor around 10^6 than those of e.s.r. spectra.

[3] The allowed angular directions of the magnetic moments are not parallel or anti-parallel to the field, but at an angle to it. The remarks in footnote 3 of chapter 9 (p. 194) on electrons, with spin $S = \frac{1}{2}$, apply equally to nuclei with spin $I = \frac{1}{2}$.

$+\frac{1}{2}(h/2\pi)$ and $-\frac{1}{2}(h/2\pi)$. Correspondingly, the component along the field of the nuclear magnetic moment (which is related to the angular momentum) can take up only two values, which we may designate as $+\mu$ and $-\mu$. The exact value of μ is considered later. The energies of nuclei in these two orientations are affected by the field; in a field of strength H, they differ from the zero-field value by $-\mu H$ or $+\mu H$. There are thus two energy-levels, with an energy separation of $2\mu H$ (Fig. 11.1). An equilibrium distribution is set up; the nuclei are distributed between the two levels

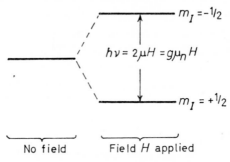

$$m_I = -\tfrac{1}{2}$$
$$h\nu = 2\mu H = g\mu_n H$$
$$m_I = +\tfrac{1}{2}$$

No field   Field H applied

FIG. 11.1. Energy-levels of nuclei with spin $\frac{1}{2}$ in magnetic field; resonance condition.

according to the Maxwell-Boltzmann law[4], so that there is a small excess of nuclei in the lower energy state.[5]

The spinning nuclei can absorb energy from a magnetic field at right angles to the main field.[6] Suppose that such a field is applied,

[4] Energy is exchanged between the nuclei and their surroundings by a mechanism mentioned later (p. 228), involving the components of magnetic moment at right angles to the field.

[5] The ratio of the numbers in the lower and higher states is $\exp(2\mu H/kt)$, since the energy-separation is $2\mu H$; this is much less than kT, so that the excess of nuclei in the lower state is only a few in a million. The observed resonance absorption depends on this small excess (see below); nevertheless the sensitivity of the method is such that it can easily be detected.

[6] This absorption of energy also involves the components of the magnetic moment at right angles to the field; its mechanism may be visualised in terms of nuclear precession. Cf., e.g., Roberts, ref. 1d, chapter 1; Jackman, ref. 1e, chapter 2; Pople, Schneider and Bernstein, ref. 1f, chapter 3.

alternating with a frequency ν such that the energy-quantum $h\nu$ is equal to the energy-separation $2\mu H$ of the two states. Energy will be absorbed in raising nuclei from the lower to the higher state. Some energy will be lost from nuclei in the higher state, but as there are fewer of these there will be a net absorption of energy. This absorption will occur only at the frequency ν such that:

$$h\nu = 2\mu H \qquad (11.1)$$

The absorption of energy from the oscillating field is thus a resonance phenomenon. If the field-strength H is varied, keeping the frequency ν constant, there is a sharp maximum in the power absorbed at a particular value of H, corresponding to the resonance condition 11.1. This maximum gives rise to a peak in the n.m.r. spectrum.

The height of the maximum, and therefore the accuracy with which it can be measured, depends on the relative numbers of nuclei in the upper and lower states, which depend on the field strength H. The sensitivity is thus increased by increasing H. An upper limit is set by the need for a stable field uniform over a volume of about 0·1 ml. It is now usual, in proton resonance work, to use a field of 10,000 to 25,000 gauss. The corresponding frequency, determined by equation 11.1, is in the radio region. For protons, as we shall see later, the value of μ is $1\cdot42 \times 10^{-23}$ erg/gauss, with which $H = 10^4$ gauss gives ν as $42\cdot6 \times 10^6$ c/sec. Radio-frequency oscillators and detectors must therefore be used. The reason why the frequency is lower than for electron-spin resonance, where it is in the microwave region, is that the magnetic moment of the proton ^{1}H is some 657 times smaller than that of the electron.

The value of the magnetic moment for the proton

The proton, like the electron, has spin $\frac{1}{2}$, and the relation between the resolved magnetic moment μ and the resolved angular momentum p for proton spin is analogous to that for electron spin (p. 197):

$$\mu/p = \tfrac{1}{2}ge/M_p c \qquad (11.2)$$

Here e is the electronic charge, M_p the mass of the proton, and c the velocity of light; g is a constant called the 'nuclear g-factor', which depends on the relative contributions of the spin and orbital angular momenta characteristic of the nucleus, and is determined experimentally. Since the quantized value of p is $\pm h/4\pi$, equation 11.2 gives:

$$\mu = \pm \tfrac{1}{2}g(he/4\pi M_p c) \tag{11.3}$$

This may be written in the form:

$$\mu = \pm \tfrac{1}{2}g\mu_n \tag{11.4}$$

Here μ_n is the 'nuclear magneton', $he/4\pi M_p c$, corresponding to the Bohr magneton (p. 197) but containing the proton mass instead of the electronic mass; its numerical value is $5 \cdot 0493 \times 10^{-24}$ erg/gauss. It is the magnetic moment that would be ascribed to a proton if it could be treated as a spinning spherical particle with its charge distributed uniformly over the surface. Such a model is over-simplified and gives only an order of magnitude for the nuclear magnetic moment. It is therefore necessary to insert the empirical constant g, which for the proton has been determined[7] as $5 \cdot 5854$. The resolved magnetic moment μ for the proton comes out to be $1 \cdot 42 \times 10^{-23}$ erg/gauss. It is much smaller than that of the electron ($9 \cdot 3 \times 10^{-21}$ erg/gauss); this is because of the larger mass of the proton, as may be seen by comparing equation 11.3 with the corresponding equation for electron-spin (10.3).

The condition for proton resonance (equation 11.1) may now be expressed in terms of g, after substituting the value of μ from equation 11.4:

$$h\nu = g\mu_n H \tag{11.5}$$

Substituting numerical values, we obtain for proton resonance:

$$\nu = 4 \cdot 26 \times 10^3 H \tag{11.6}$$

Nuclei other than protons

So far, the theory has been closely analogous to that for electron-spin resonance, because we have confined our attention to protons, for which the spin (like that of electrons) is $\tfrac{1}{2}$. Other nuclei have various values (see Table 11.1). In the general case, for a nucleus of

[7] By a molecular-beam method: Ramsey, *Molecular Beams* (Oxford, 1956), chapter 6; Rabi *et al.*, *Phys. Rev.* 1939, **55**, 526; **56**, 728.

spin I, the nuclear spin magnetic quantum number can take the values I, $I-1$, ... 0 ... $-I$, and there are $2I+1$ possible orientations, differing in energy by $\mu H/I$. The maximum component of the angular momentum in the direction of the field is given by

$$p = I(h/2\pi) \tag{11.7}$$

The general relation between this and the corresponding component of the magnetic moment μ is as before (cf. equation 11.2):

$$\mu/p = g(e/2M_p c) \tag{11.8}$$

Combining equations 11.7 and 11.8, we obtain:

$$\mu = gI(he/4\pi M_p c) \tag{11.9}$$

or in terms of the nuclear magneton,

$$\mu = gI\mu_n \tag{11.10}$$

Since the energy-separation is $\mu H/I$, the resonance condition is (in place of equation 11.1):

$$h\nu = \mu H/I \tag{11.11}$$

Substitution for μ (from equation 11.10) gives for the resonance condition:

$$h\nu = g\mu_n H \tag{11.12}$$

This has the same form as the condition for proton resonance (equation 11.5). The value of the nuclear g-factor depends on the nucleus concerned, and ranges considerably, as may be seen from Table 11.1. If we determine the frequency ν for resonance for a given compound, we can find g from equation 11.12, and this enables us to identify the nucleus concerned.

An alternative to the use of g-factors is to express the magnetic moment μ in terms of the 'magnetogyric ratio' γ, which is the ratio of magnetic moment to angular momentum, and is so called because it is related to the gyroscopic properties of the molecule:

$$\mu = \gamma I(h/2\pi) \tag{11.13}$$

Comparing equations 11.13 and 11.10, we see that γ is related to g by the equation

$$\gamma = g\mu_n/(h/2\pi) \tag{11.14}$$

The resonance condition in terms of γ is evidently:

$$\nu = \gamma H/2\pi \qquad (11.15)$$

Nuclei with spin $I = 0$ have no magnetic moment and give no n.m.r. spectrum. Such nuclei include ^{12}C and ^{16}O. A consequence is that the very many organic molecules containing only H, C and O atoms give an n.m.r. spectrum due to proton spin only. The nuclei that give the strongest signals are ^1H and ^{19}F. Relative sensitivites for various nuclei at constant field strength are shown in the last column of Table 11.1.

TABLE 11.1

Magnetic properties of certain nuclei[8]

ν = resonant frequency in megacycles per sec for a field of 10^4 gauss
g = nuclear g-value
μ = magnetic moment of nucleus = $gI\mu_n$
μ_n = nuclear magneton = 5.0493×10^{-24} erg/gauss

Nucleus	Atomic no.	Spin I	g	ν	μ/μ_n	Natural abundance (%)	Relative sensitivity at constant field
H	1	$\frac{1}{2}$	$+5.5854$	42.578	$+2.7927$	99.985	1.000
$^2H(D)$	1	1	$+0.8574$	6.536	$+0.8574$	0.015	2.45×10^{-2}
^{13}C	6	$\frac{1}{2}$	$+1.4044$	10.71	$+0.7022$	1.108	3.17×10^{-2}
^{14}N	7	1	$+0.4036$	3.077	$+0.4036$	99.635	3.74×10^{-3}
^{17}O	8	$\frac{5}{2}$	-7.5720	5.772	-1.8930	0.037	7.89×10^{-2}
^{19}F	9	$\frac{1}{2}$	$+5.254$	40.05	$+2.627$	100	0.858
^{31}P	15	$\frac{1}{2}$	$+2.262$	17.24	$+1.131$	100	0.104
^{35}Cl	17	$\frac{3}{2}$	$+0.5474$	4.172	± 0.8210	75.4	1.50×10^{-2}
^{37}Cl	17	$\frac{3}{2}$	$+0.4556$	3.472	$+0.6833$	24.6	9.50×10^{-3}
^{55}Mn	25	$\frac{5}{2}$	$+13.84$	10.55	$+3.461$	100	0.357
^{63}Cu	29	$\frac{3}{2}$	$+1.481$	11.29	$+2.221$	69.1	0.181
^{79}Br	35	$\frac{3}{2}$	$+1.399$	10.67	$+2.099$	50.52	0.157
^{81}Br	35	$\frac{3}{2}$	$+1.509$	11.50	$+2.263$	49.48	0.211
Electron	—	$\frac{1}{2}$	—	$27,994$	1.836	—	—

[8] Data mainly from Gutowsky, ref. 1*g*, p. 2674.

Experimental determination of n.m.r. spectra[9]

The basic features of the standard high-resolution apparatus for the study of proton magnetic resonance spectra are shown in Fig. 11.2. The specimen is placed in the gap of a powerful electromagnet, producing a stable and homogeneous field of 10,000 to 25,000 gauss; subsidiary coils enable this field to be varied by a few gauss. Surrounding the specimen is a cylindrical coil of wire; an oscillating radio-frequency field, at right angles to the main field, is produced by coupling this coil to an oscillator, operating at a fixed frequency of 40, 60 or 100 megacycles/sec. The power absorbed by the sample is detected by means of a radio receiver, tuned to the oscillator frequency; this is coupled either to a bridge of which the coil forms one arm (Fig. 11.2a), or to a separate coil surrounding the sample (Fig. 11.2b). The output is fed to the Y plates of an oscilloscope. The main field H is swept slowly through a region of perhaps 0·1 gauss including the resonance value. The X plates of the oscilloscope are fed synchronously with the field, so that the trace on the screen shows the change of absorption with H during the sweep. At resonance a peak appears.

The absorption spectrum commonly consists of a series of peaks, for reasons discussed below. The range of field strength that is commonly of interest in proton-resonance work is of the order of 0·05 gauss; expressed in terms of frequency (equation 11.6), this range is around 200 c/sec. The resolving power of the standard 60-Mc apparatus is better than 1 c/sec (about one in 10^8). The width of an individual proton-resonance peak, in the absence of chemical reaction, is of the same order. Lines are broadened by any inhomogeneity in the field; this effect is much reduced by spinning the sample.

The concentration of the species whose spectrum is being studied is made fairly high, of the order of 1 M, or at least 0·1 M, in order to obtain a reasonably strong signal. The applicability of the technique is therefore limited to species which are sufficiently soluble. Any solvent may be used, though naturally one with a simple n.m.r.

[9] For fuller accounts see, e.g., (a) Gutowsky, ref. 1g, part 4, chapter 4; (b) Pople et al., ref. 1f, chapter 4; (c) Jackson, ref. 1e, chapter 3. For recent advances see various papers in (d) Discuss. Faraday Soc. 1963, **34**.

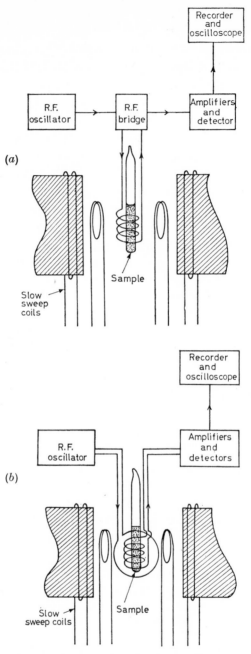

FIG. 11.2. Basic features of n.m.r. apparatus. (a) Single-coil system. (b) Nuclear-induction system. (From Jackman, *Applications of N.m.r. Spectroscopy*, Pergamon Press, 1959, by permission.)

spectrum is preferred. The volume required is less than 1 ml. The temperature can be varied over a wide range, from below $-100°$ to above $+100°$, by blowing pre-heated or pre-cooled gas round the sample. By this method the temperature can be controlled to about $\pm 1°$.

Features of n.m.r. absorption spectra

The following properties of the absorption spectrum may be measured. (i) The frequency region in which absorption occurs; this identifies the nucleus concerned, but is not otherwise of particular interest. (ii) The intensity of absorption, which is proportional to concentration; this has sometimes been used, like any other physical property, to follow changes in concentration during kinetic experiments.[10] (iii) The structure of the absorption band, which is characteristic of the substance, and (iv) the width and shape of individual lines. These last two features are the most important in kinetic work, and because of the high resolving power they can be studied in detail. We shall deal with them in turn.

The structure of proton magnetic resonance spectra

We first consider the structure of the absorption band.[11] Structure is observed when there are differences in the magnetic environments of protons within the same molecule; it may arise for two rather different reasons. For simplicity we shall confine the treatment to proton magnetic resonance, but the principles are of general application in n.m.r. work.[12]

(i) Chemical shifts

Compounds which contain equivalent hydrogen atoms and no other nuclei with magnetic moments, such as water or benzene, give a

[10] For some examples, see (a) Emerson, Grunwald, Kaplan and Kromhout, J. Amer. Chem. Soc. 1960, **82**, 6307; (b) Luz and Silver, J. Amer. Chem. Soc. 1961, **83**, 4518; 1962, **84**, 1095.
[11] For a fuller account, see, e.g Pople, Schneider and Bernstein, High-resolution N.m.r., ref. 1f, chapters, 5, 7, 8, 11.
[12] For application to nuclei other than protons, cf. ibid., chapter 12.

single proton resonance line, There are, however, slight differences
—a few parts per million—in the resonance frequencies of different
compounds. These differences are called 'chemical shifts'. They
suggest that the electronic environment has an effect on the resonance frequency.

Such an environmental effect is clearly shown in the spectra of

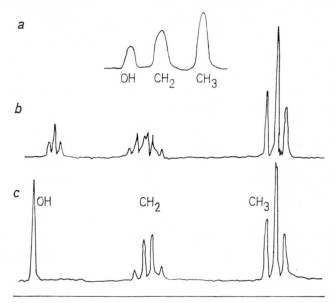

FIG. 11.3. Proton magnetic resonance spectrum of ethanol, showing the chemical shifts: (*a*) under medium resolution; (*b*) under high
resolution; (*c*) the same after addition of a little HCl, showing the
collapse of the fine structure of the OH line. The field increases
from left to right. (From Pople, Schneider and Bernstein, *High-
resolution N.m.r.*, McGraw-Hill, 1959, by permission.)

compounds containing chemically non-equivalent hydrogen atoms,
i.e. protons in different environments. Ethyl alcohol, for example,
contains protons in three different environments: one in the
hydroxyl group, two in the methylene group, and three in the
methyl group. The n.m.r. spectrum, which under low resolution
consists of a single line, is found under moderate resolution to
consist of three components (Fig. 11.3*a*). The areas under the three

components are approximately in the ratios $1:2:3$. The components may be assigned to the groups OH, CH_2 and CH_3 respectively. The frequency difference between (for example) the CH_2 and CH_3 components is proportional to the field strength. Numerically it is 2·45 ppm (parts per million), so that with a field of 10,000 gauss the separation in terms of field strength is 0·0245 gauss, or in terms of frequency (by equation 11.6) 109 c/sec. Proton chemical shifts in other compounds are of the same order; they range over about 11 ppm. Some values are shown in Fig. 11.4. Chemical shifts for other nuclei are larger, by more than an order of magnitude.[13]

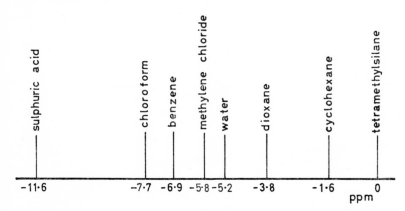

FIG. 11.4. Chemical shifts of some liquids giving single proton signals, relative to tetramethylsilane, at room temperature.

The interpretation of these chemical shifts is as follows. The magnetic field at the nucleus is not exactly equal to the applied field, because of the orbital motions induced by the field in the surrounding electrons. These motions are equivalent to currents, and produce a small secondary field which will act on the nuclei in addition to the applied field. Since the induced currents are proportional to the applied field H, the magnitude of the secondary field will also be proportional to H, and the local field H_N at the nucleus may be represented thus:

$$H_N = H(1 - \sigma)$$

[13] Tables of values are given in ref. 1f, chapters 5, 11, 12.

Here σ is a constant, independent of H but dependent on the nucleus and on its electronic environment. It is called the 'screening constant' or 'shielding constant', because the effect of the electronic motions is to screen the nucleus to some extent from the applied field. The effect of the reduced field will be to bring the nuclear-spin energy levels closer together (Fig. 11.5), so that resonance will occur at a lower frequency, according to equation 11.1. The shift will depend on the nucleus, on its electronic environment, and on the

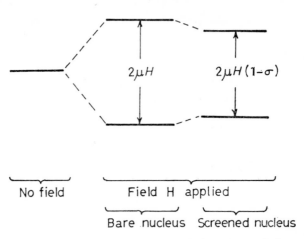

Fig. 11.5. Interpretation of chemical shifts: effect of electronic screening on spin energy-levels of nuclei with spin $\frac{1}{2}$ (not to scale).

field strength, but not necessarily on the temperature. All this is in agreement with the observed results.

(ii) *Fine structure due to spin–spin interaction*

An additional splitting of the resonance lines is often observed in the spectra of compounds containing non-equivalent protons (or other nuclei). For example, when the spectrum of ethanol is examined under high resolution each component shows a fine structure (Fig. 11.3b). The splitting is of the order of 10 c/sec. The interpretation is that the spins of nuclei can interact, by an indirect mechanism via the electrons in the molecule; the magnetic moment of a spinning nucleus tends to orient the spins of nearby electrons, which in turn orient the spins of other electrons and so those of other nuclei. The spin-interaction energies, represented by a spin–spin coupling constant J, lead to splitting of the resonance lines. The spins of the protons of the CH_2 group in RCH_2OH, for example, can interact with those of the OH group (Fig. 11.6).

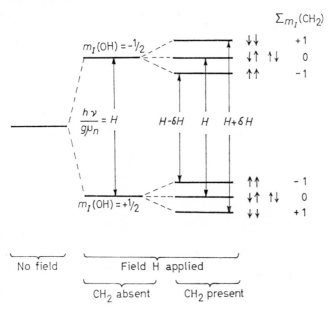

FIG. 11.6. Spin–spin interaction. The splitting of the energy-levels for the hydroxyl group protons in ethanol by spin–spin interaction with the protons of the methylene group. ($\delta H = Jh/g\mu_n = 2\pi J/\gamma$. J is positive.)

There are three possible configurations of the CH_2 group, represented by ↑↑, ↓↑or ↑↓, and ↓↓, which result in a splitting of the resonance line for the OH protons into three components, whose spacing is J c/sec. The middle component is the strongest, because the statistical weights if the three configurations are in the ratios 1:2:1.

The observed n.m.r. spectra can in general be interpreted in terms of chemical shifts and spin–spin interactions. The spectra and their interpretation are often complex; the treatment outlined above is only a first approximation, valid when the effects of spin–spin interaction are much less than those of chemical shifts. For fuller treatments the standard monographs may be consulted.[1] Because they are complex and specific, n.m.r. spectra are of great value in identifying molecular species and their configurations, especially in liquids and solutions, where other methods are less applicable. The resolving power of the standard instruments (better than 1 c/sec) is such that protons whose mean energies differs by as little as 10^{-11} cal mole^{-1} can be distinguished.

Nuclear-spin relaxation and line-widths in absence of reaction

The determination of rates of reaction by nuclear magnetic resonance methods depends, as we shall see in the next section, on measurements of line-shape and line-width. In this section we consider briefly the width of n.m.r. lines in the absence of reaction.[14] To do this we must first discuss two mechanisms of nuclear-spin relaxation.

Spin-lattice relaxation. Energy is exchanged between spinning nuclei and their surroundings. The observation of resonance would be impossible if the nuclei could not lose energy to their surroundings by radiationless transfer, for in that case the absorption of energy would cease when the numbers of nuclei in the upper and lower spin states had been equalized. The mechanism by which energy is exchanged, whether in solids or in liquids, is called 'spin-lattice relaxation' or 'longitudinal relaxation'. This can be understood in terms of the precession of the nucleus. The spinning nucleus, which is oriented at an angle to the axis of the field (p. 215), precesses about this axis, just as a gyroscope precesses under the torque of the gravitational field. The nucleus therefore comes under the influence of the fluctuating magnetic fields associated with the thermal motions of nearby magnetic dipoles. From time to time the resultant field at the nucleus is correctly oriented and phased to

---

[14] For fuller treatments of line-width see, e.g., (*a*) Pople, Schneider and Bernstein, ref. 1*f*, chapters 3, 8, 9; (*b*) Roberts, ref. 1*d*, chapter 1; (*c*) Jackman, ref. 1*e*, chapter 1.

induce a transition from one spin state to the other. When this happens, a nucleus in the upper spin state can 'relax' to the lower, or vice versa, and the energy lost or gained appears as a change in the translational or rotational energy of the surrounding molecules. The efficiency of spin-lattice relaxation can be expressed by a characteristic relaxation time T_1; this means that T_1 is the time required for the difference between the actual population of either state and its equilibrium value to be reduced by a factor e. For most liquids, the values of T_1 are of the order of 1 to 10 sec.

Spin–spin relaxation and T_2. A nucleus can also transfer its energy to a similar neighbouring nucleus, by a mutual exchange of spin. This is called 'spin–spin relaxation', or 'transverse relaxation'. It does not alter the populations of the spin states, and so leaves the energy-distribution unaltered. The corresponding relaxation time is commonly written T_2. For most liquids this turns out to be comparable with T_1, that is around 1–10 sec, in the absence of reaction.

Measurement of T_1 and T_2. The nuclear-spin relaxation times T_1 and T_2 may be measured by various methods.[14a] These involve transient measurements, rather than steady-state observations as in n.m.r. spectroscopy. A technique which is specially suited to short times, and has been used in kinetic work (see e.g. p. 252), is the *pulse* or *spin-echo method*.[15] It is possible for example to apply a succession of pulses which change the phases of all the spins by 90° and then by 180° several times at intervals of a few milliseconds; an 'echo' appears after the same interval, with an amplitude depending on T_2, which can thence be determined.

Mathematical theory of line-shape and line-width in absence of reaction. The natural line-width is related to the lifetime of a nucleus in a given spin state, by reason of the Heisenberg uncertainty principle. Just as for electron-spin resonance (p. 200), the finite lifetime is associated with an uncertainty in the spin energy level, and therefore in the resonance frequency, which leads to a finite line-width. A mathematical account of the dependence of the magnetic properties of the system on the relaxation times T_1 and T_2

[15] (a) Carr and Purcell, *Phys. Rev.* 1954, **94**, 630; (b) Reeves and Wells, *Discuss. Faraday Soc.* 1963, **34**, 177.

16

was given by Bloch. From the Bloch equations it is possible to derive an exact expression for the line shape and width, in terms of T_1 and T_2.[16] According to this expression the rate of absorption of energy at frequency ν, as a function of the difference between ν and the resonance value ν_0, is proportional to

$$T_2/[1 + 4\pi^2 T_2^2 (\nu_0 - \nu)^2 + \gamma^2 H_1^2 T_1 T_2] \tag{11.16}$$

Here H_1 is the amplitude of the oscillating magnetic field. If this is small, the term in T_1 drops out, and the absorption is proportional to

$$T_2/[1 + 4\pi^2 T_2^2 (\nu_0 - \nu)^2] \tag{11.16a}$$

This describes a symmetrical Lorentzian curve, with a maximum absorption at resonance ($\nu = \nu_0$), and a width at half-height of $1/\pi T_2$ in c/sec. Thus it is T_2 which primarily determines the natural width of an n.m.r. line in absence of reaction.

Other contributions to line-width in absence of reaction. In liquids of high viscosity such as glycerine (and in solids) there is a further contribution to the line-width. If the nuclei stay in the same relative position for a long time, they must be treated as being in slightly different fields, because of the local fields due to neighbouring magnetic dipoles. In most liquids, however, the dipolar interactions are averaged to zero by the rapid 'tumbling' motions of the molecules, and there is no appreciable broadening from this source. As regards the spontaneous emission of radiation, the upper energy level is quite long-lived, and the contribution to the line-width from this source is negligible compared with others.

In practice, the inhomogeneity of the magnetic field is usually the main factor affecting line-widths determined directly from n.m.r. spectra recorded by the standard types of apparatus, for liquids where no reaction occurs. These line-widths are commonly in the region of a few tenths of a cycle per second, and appreciably larger than $1/\pi T_2$. Determinations of the natural line-width can be made, however, by measuring T_2 by spin-echo or transient methods (p. 229).

[16] See, e.g., (a) Pople, Schneider and Bernstein, ref. 1f, pp. 31–37; (b) Roberts, ref. 1d, pp. 88 *seq.*

Line-widths and chemical reactions. Finally, line-widths are increased by reactions whose relaxation times are comparable with T_2. This is important for the determination of rates of reaction and is dealt with in the next section. It will be convenient, however to note one or two points here. When such a reaction occurs the line-width is increased by $\delta'\nu = 1/\pi\tau_{HA}$ (in c/sec), and so becomes $(1/\pi T_2 + 1/\pi\tau_{HA})$, where τ_{HA} is the mean lifetime of the proton in the environment HA which gives rise to the line, and is also the relaxation time for the forward reaction (pp. 62, 235). The line-width may also be expressed in terms of the measured relaxation time T_2', as $1/\pi T_2'$. Hence τ_{HA} is related to the transverse relaxation times measured in absence and in presence of reaction by the equation

$$\frac{1}{T_2'} - \frac{1}{T_2} = \frac{1}{\tau_{HA}} = \pi\delta'\nu \qquad (11.17)$$

The relaxation time for the reaction (τ_{HA}) and the relaxation times for nuclear spin must not be confused. When dealing with proton-transfer reactions, it is sometimes desirable to avoid the ambiguous term 'proton relaxation time' by using the phrase '^1H relaxation time' when nuclear relaxation is under consideration.

The determination of reaction rates from n.m.r. spectra[17]

General description and interpretation

Reaction rates can be inferred from the changes in n.m.r. spectra which can be brought about by addition of reagents or by change of temperature. We first give a semi-quantitative interpretation of the phenomena, and then cite the results of the full mathematical treatments.

[17] For reviews see (a) Roberts, ref. 1d, chapter 4; (b) Pople, Schneider and Bernstein, ref. 1f, chapter, 10, also chapters 13, 17, 18; (c) Meiboom, *Z. Elektrochem.* 1960, **64**, 50; (d) Loewenstein, Study of rate processes by n.m.r. techniques, in *Fluctuation, Relaxation and Resonance in Magnetic Systems*, ed. D. ter Haar (Oliver & Boyd, 1962), pp. 261–268; (e) Loewenstein and Connor, *Ber. Bunsen Gesell. Phys. Chem.* 1963, **67**, 280; (f) Strehlow, in *Investigation of Rates and Mechanisms of Reactions*, ed. Friess, Lewis and Weissberger (2nd edn., Interscience, 1963), part II, chapter 17.

Consider as an example an equimolar mixture of two substances HA and HB. If there is no interaction, the proton resonance spectrum will show two peaks separated by perhaps 100 c/sec, representing the characteristic chemical shifts of HA and HB. (We neglect spin–spin interactions for the moment.) Suppose now that exchange of protons can occur:

$$HA + H'B \rightleftharpoons H'A + HB$$

and can be accelerated by increase of temperature, or by addition of hydrogen ions. The changes in the n.m.r. spectrum, as the rate of exchange is progressively increased, are as follows. The two lines first broaden and approach each other (this is called 'lifetime broadening'), then coalesce to a single broad line. This subsequently narrows to a sharp line, at an intermediate position ('exchange narrowing'). These changes are illustrated by Fig. 11.7, which shows part of the proton resonance spectrum of a mixture of acetylacetone with acetic acid at various temperatures.[18] At $-8°$ there are two peaks attributable to OH protons with different chemical shifts, one for the OH group in the enol form of acetylacetone, the other for the OH group in acetic acid. As the temperature rises, the two lines broaden and coalesce.

The interpretation of such changes is qualitatively as follows. The initial broadening of each line is due to the shortening of the mean lifetimes of HA and HB molecules and therefore of ^{1}H nuclei in a given environment and spin energy level, by migration of protons. It is analogous to the broadening of e.s.r. lines by reaction (pp. 198–202). We have seen that the finite lifetime of the nucleus in a given energy-level leads to a finite line-width. Shortening of the lifetime by reaction correspondingly leads to an increase of line-width. The exact theory shows that if the mean lifetime of the proton in a given environment HA is τ_{HA}, the broadening $\delta'\nu$ of the HA line in c/sec is $1/\pi\tau_{HA}$. Hence if the observed broadening is of the order of 1 c/sec, which is not far from the limit of resolution, the mean lifetime τ is in the region of 0·1 to 1 sec.

This increase of width will not continue indefinitely. As the

[18] Schneider and Reeves, *N.Y. Acad. Sci.* 1958, **70**, 858.

exchange rate rises, the protons in the two environments no longer behave as independent systems; this is why the lines do not merely broaden, but approach each other, overlap, and finally merge. Separate lines are not observed unless $\tau > ca.\, 1/\Delta\nu_0$, where $\Delta\nu_0$ is the frequency-difference of the two chemical shifts in the absence

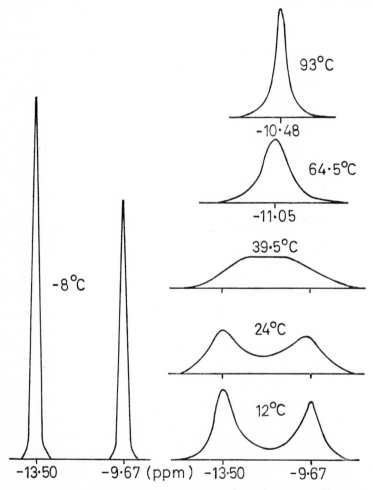

FIG. 11.7. Proton resonance spectra of acetylacetone + acetic acid (58:42) at various temperatures. Only the OH signals are shown. Chemical shifts are in ppm, relative to the methyl-group signal of the enol. (From Schneider and Reeves, ref. 18.)

of exchange. When $\tau \approx 1/\Delta\nu_0$, the proton takes up an averaged resonance frequency, and therefore gives rise to a single absorption line. There are random deviations from the averaged frequency; the higher the exchange rate ($\tau < 1/\Delta\nu_0$), the more nearly will these fluctuations average to zero, and the sharper will be the line. Thus the coalescence and subsequent narrowing of the line can be understood. Since $\Delta\nu_0$ is commonly of the order of 100 c/sec for proton resonance spectra, coalescence corresponds to a lifetime of ca. 10^{-2} sec, and measurements of subsequent narrowing permit estimates of lifetimes down to 10^{-3} or even 10^{-4} sec (p. 238).

The fine-structure due to spin–spin interaction can similarly disappear, if reactions involving the protons concerned are made to

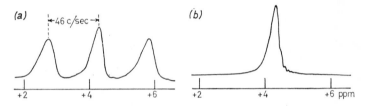

FIG. 11.8. Proton resonance in liquid ammonia (a) intensively dried (b) containing a trace of water. Displacements are in ppm relative to water. (From Ogg, ref. 27a.)

occur fast enough. The separate components are observed only if $\tau > ca.\Delta\nu_0^{-1}$, where $\Delta\nu_0$ is the frequency separation of the components. The phenomenon is analogous to the collapse of the hyperfine structure of e.s.r. spectra (p. 203). An example is illustrated in Fig. 11.8, which shows how the triplet line for the protons in liquid ammonia (p. 248) collapses to a singlet if a trace of water is present, because of the increased rate of exchange of protons. Another example is seen in Fig. 11.3c; the fine-structure of the OH-proton line in the spectrum of ethanol collapses when acid is added (p. 239). At intermediate rates of exchange the lines coalesce in a way parallel to that shown in Fig. 11.7. Since the separation of the components is usually smaller than that of chemical shifts, coalescence will occur at lower rates of exchange. The determination of rates of reaction in this way is of special interest in studies of exchange between similar molecules, where there is no difference of chemical shift.

Quantitative determination of lifetimes and rate constants from line-shapes[19]

The preceding section has shown the orders of magnitude of the reaction lifetimes that can be determined by n.m.r. methods. The quantitative derivation of rate constants may be done as follows. The system is described by the Bloch equations (p. 230) modified by the addition of terms containing the mean lifetime τ of the proton in each environment. Several methods of varying rigour are available for solving these modified Bloch equations.[20] Line shapes are then computed for various values of τ, and compared with the observed line-shapes until a match is obtained. The mean lifetime is related to a first-order rate constant; taking the reaction between HA and H'B (p. 232) as an example, the mean lifetime of the protons in the environment HA is (cf. equation 10.9, p. 201):

$$\tau_{HA} = -(HA)/[d(HA)/dt] = 1/k_{HA} \qquad (11.18)$$

The first-order rate constant k_{HA} is thus equal to $1/\tau_{HA}$.

It is not necessary to solve the equations for every particular system. For instance, the resonance line is often a simple doublet. It is often assumed that the numbers of HA and HB molecules are equal, and that the lifetime of the proton is the same in each of the two environments, so that the overall lifetime τ is given by $\tau_{HA} = \tau_{HB} = 2\tau$. It is then found that the calculated line-shape depends mainly on the value of $\tau \Delta \nu_0$, where $\Delta \nu_0$ is the frequency-separation of the peaks in the absence of any exchange reaction.

[19] For reviews see (a) Pople, Schneider and Bernstein, ref. 1f, chapter 10; (b) Loewenstein, ref. 17d; (c) Piette, in N.m.r. and E.p.r. Spectroscopy, ed. Varian Associates (Pergamon Press 1960), chapter 9. The fundamental paper is that of (d) Gutowsky, McCall and Slichter, J. Chem. Phys. 1953, 21, 279; later papers are those of (e) Gutowsky and Holm, J. Chem. Phys. 1957, 25, 1228; (f) Piette and Anderson, J. Chem. Phys. 1959, 30, 899. For analysis of a complex line-shape, see (g) MacLean and Mackor, Discuss. Faraday Soc. 1963, 34, 165.

[20] The method now favoured is due to McConnell, J. Chem. Phys. 1958, 28, 430; cf. ref. 19.

The transverse relaxation time T_2 also has some effect, but this is comparatively small and can be neglected when the line-width in absence of exchange (which depends on T_2, cf. p. 230) is small compared with the separation $\Delta\nu_0$. Some curves calculated for various values of $\tau\Delta\nu_0$ (with $T_2^{-1} = 0$) are shown in Fig. 11.9. The labour of fitting the curves can be reduced by plotting the calculated varia-

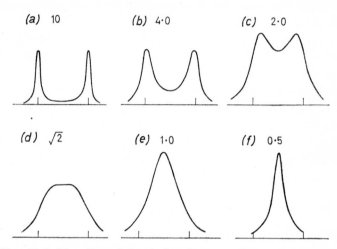

FIG. 11.9. The effect of chemical exchange on the n.m.r. spectrum of HA and HB. The rate of exchange increases from a to f. The intensities are not on comparable scales. The figures are values of $2\pi\tau\Delta\nu_0$, where $\Delta\nu_0$ is the initial separation of the lines and τ is the mean lifetime or relaxation time for the reaction. (From Pople, Schneider and Bernstein, *High-resolution N.m.r.*, McGraw Hill, 1959, by permission.)

tion with τ of such characteristics as the ratio of maximum height to central minimum of the curves.[21]

Equations for rates from line-width

For various special cases, simplified approximate expressions for τ, calculated on the above assumptions, can be written as follows.[19a,g]

[21] (a) Grunwald, Loewenstein and Meiboom, *J. Chem. Phys.* 1957, **27**, 630;
      (b) Loewenstein and Meiboom, *ibid.*, 1067; (c) Loewenstein, ref. 17d;
      (d) Loewenstein, *Tables of NMR Exchange Broadened Multiplets* (Weizmann Institute of Science, Rehovoth, Israel).

(i) *'Slow' exchange* $(\tau \Delta \nu \gg 1)$; *'lifetime broadening.'* Here the two peaks are distinct, but each is broadened, as in Fig. 11.9, *a*. If the broadening at half-height is $\delta' \nu$,

$$k = \tau^{-1} = 2\pi \delta' \nu \qquad (11.19)$$

(ii) *Intermediate rate of exchange* $(\tau \Delta \nu \approx 1)$ as in Fig. 11.9, *b* and *c*. If the peaks are separated by a frequency-interval $\Delta \nu$, compared with $\Delta \nu_0$ in the absence of exchange,

$$k = \tau^{-1} = 2^{1/2} \pi (\Delta \nu_0^2 - \Delta \nu^2)^{1/2} \qquad (11.20)$$

Coalescence of the lines (Fig. 11.9*d*) occurs at

$$k = \tau^{-1} = 2^{1/2} \pi \Delta \nu_0 \qquad (11.21)$$

(iii) *'Fast' exchange* $(\tau \Delta \nu \ll 1)$; *'exchange narrowing'*. There is a single line, as in Fig. 11.9, *e* and *f*. If at half-height this is broader by $\delta' \nu$ than the lower limit of line-width (corresponding to $\tau = 0$), the expression for τ comes out (provided $\tau \ll T_2$) to

$$k = \tau^{-1} = 4\pi \Delta \nu_0^2 / \delta' \nu \qquad (11.22)$$

Reaction rates in each of these three ranges have been determined. Equations 11.19 to 11.22 are often sufficiently close approximations, and have been widely used.

General comments on the kinetic applications of n.m.r.

The quantity measured by the n.m.r. methods is the mean life-time τ_A of some particular molecular species or configuration A, whence a first-order rate constant is found as $k_A = \tau_A^{-1}$. The measurements are made on systems in chemical equilibrium; they are well adapted to studies of exchange reactions, for example. The equilibrium is not disturbed, however, as it is when the relaxation methods described in chapters 4 and 5 are used. The n.m.r. method is thus specially useful for investigations of symmetrical exchanges; reactions too fast for isotopic methods can be studied. As the n.m.r. spectrum identifies directly the atoms that exchange, very detailed information about the mechanism can sometimes be obtained, accessible by no other method, for instance about the role of water in the reactions of amines (p. 244). Cross-checking is often possible; thus for amine solutions the several ${}^1H$ signals can be compared, and for water the ${}^1H$ and ${}^{17}O$ lines.

For the successful use of these methods, the n.m.r. spectrum must be relatively simple, so that accurate measurements of line-shape can be made and interpreted. Chemically the system must be simple enough to allow interpretation in terms of familiar types of reaction mechanism. To obtain an adequate signal with the present standard apparatus, the concentration of the absorbing species must be at least of the order of 0·1 M, so the solubility must be adequate; best of all is to study the ways in which the spectrum of the solvent is modified by solutes, as in many of the applications which follow. The volume required is under 1 ml.

The rate of reaction must be within the range where changes in line-shape are noticeable; this implies that $\tau \Delta \nu_0$ is in the region of 10 to 0·01. Taking the range of $\Delta \nu_0$ for proton resonance as 10 to 100 sec^{-1}, this gives the range of τ as 1 to 10^{-4} sec (in most applications it has been between 1 and 10^{-3} sec). The first-order rate constant must therefore lie between 1 and 10^3 or 10^4 sec^{-1}. The rate of reaction must be adjusted into this range, either by altering the concentration of the other reagent (which may be very low, as in the work on exchange reactions of amines and alcohols outlined below), or by altering the temperature or solvent. It will be noticed in the applications which follow that when very high second-order rate constants can be determined it is often because moderately short lifetimes, of the order of 10^{-3} sec, of one reagent are associated with very low concentrations of the other reagent. For nuclei other than the proton, chemical shifts and line-widths are larger, and shorter lifetimes can therefore be determined; lifetimes of about 10^{-7} sec have been found with ${}^{17}O$, and 10^{-5} sec with ${}^{63}Cu$. The standard deviation for many of the published rate constants is of the order of $\pm 10\%$; in some instances it is lower. Observations of coalescence on raising the temperature give less accurate results than measurements of line-shape, broadening, or exchange narrowing, but nevertheless yield much useful information.

The n.m.r. technique has been applied to a considerable number of reactions, including proton transfers, electron transfers, inversion of configuration, restricted rotation, and exchange of water between cations and solvent. We consider these in turn.

KINETIC APPLICATIONS OF N.M.R. METHODS

Proton transfers

Alcohols and aqueous alcohols[22]

The n.m.r. spectrum of pure anhydrous ethanol under moderately high resolution is shown in Fig. 11.3*b*. It consists of three lines, due to the protons of the hydroxyl, methylene and methyl groups respectively (p. 224). Each line is a multiplet; the splitting is due to spin–spin interaction with the protons of the neighbouring group (p. 227). The OH line is therefore a triplet; the CH_3 line is likewise a triplet, and the CH_2 line has a complex shape, because the quadruplet which would result from interaction with the methyl protons is modified by the influence of the OH proton.[22a] (The CH_3 line is also complex, but the details are here irrelevant.) If a little water is present, it gives rise to an additional single line between the methylene and hydroxyl lines.

If hydrogen chloride, or sodium hydroxide, is added to anhydrous ethanol, the spectrum changes (Fig. 11.3*c*). The hydroxyl triplet collapses to a single sharp line; correspondingly the methylene line becomes a simple quadruplet, because the spin–spin interaction with the hydroxyl proton disappears. These changes are complete at concentrations around 10^{-5} M; at lower concentrations, the line-shapes are similar, but the peaks are broader. In aqueous ethanol, the water line is broadened in presence of acid or base. The collapse of the multiplets and broadening of the water line on addition of acid or base may be attributed to exchange of the hydroxyl protons with neighbouring molecules. In alkaline solutions, the alcohol may exchange with OH^-, with OEt^-, or with water (reactions *a*, *b* and

[22] (*a*) Arnold, *Phys. Rev.* 1956, **102**, 136 (anhydrous ethanol, analysis of spectrum; effect of HCl and NaOH); (*b*) Luz, Gill and Meiboom, *J. Chem. Phys.* 1959, **30**, 1540 (ethanol and methanol plus HCl, NaOH and water); (*c*) Loewenstein, ref. 17*d*; (*d*) Loewenstein and Connor, ref. 17*e* (summary of rate constants); (*e*) Feldbauer and Weller, *Z. physik. Chem.* (*Frankfurt*), 1962, **32**, 263 (acetate buffers in ethanol); (*f*) Grunwald, Jumper and Meiboom, *J. Amer. Chem. Soc.* 1962, **84**, 4664 (revised values for methanol).

c below); in acid solutions, it may exchange with hydrogen ion, ethoxonium ion, or water (reactions *c*, *d* and *e*):

(*a*) $ROH + OH^- \overset{k_1}{\rightleftharpoons} RO^- + H_2O$

or $ROH' + HOH + RO^- \rightleftharpoons RO^- + HOH' + ROH$;

(*b*) $ROH + RO^- \overset{k_2}{\rightleftharpoons} RO^- + ROH$;

(*c*) $ROH + H'OH \overset{k_5}{\rightleftharpoons} ROH' + HOH$;

(*d*) $ROH + H_3O^+ \overset{k_3}{\rightleftharpoons} ROH_2^+ + H_2O$

or $ROH + H'OH + ROH_2^+ \rightleftharpoons ROH'H^+ + HOH + ROH$;

(*e*) $ROH' + ROH_2^+ \overset{k_4}{\rightleftharpoons} ROH'H^+ + ROH$.

The shape of the CH_2 line, when compared with theoretical curves, gives the overall first-order constant k_T, for exchange by all mechanisms. This is made up of the rate constants for exchange involving water (k_A) and for exchange involving ethanolic species only (k_B); hence $k_T = k_A + k_B$. The broadening of the water line gives k_A, by equation 11.19 (p. 237). Thus k_A and k_B can be evaluated. The shape of the OH line in aqueous ethanol depends on both k_A and k_B, and was not used to evaluate them,[22b] though it was successfully fitted to theoretical curves in an investigation of anhydrous ethanol.[22a] The lifetimes are in the region of 10^{-2} to 1 sec.

Both k_A and k_B give straight lines when plotted against the acid or base concentrations. From the slopes of the graphs, and a knowledge of the equilibrium constants governing the ratios $(OH^-)/(OEt)^-$[23a] and $(H_3O^+)/(EtOH_2^+)$,[23b] the second-order rate constants for the various reactions were determined (Table 11.2). The uncertainties are mostly of the order of $\pm 10\%$.

Methanol solutions can be treated somewhat similarly.[22b,f] At low rates of exchange, the spectrum under moderately high resolution consists of a CH_3 doublet and an OH quadruplet; in aqueous

[23] (*a*) Ballinger and F. A. Long, *J. Amer. Chem. Soc.* 1960, **82**, 795; Koivisto, *Acta Chem. Scand.* 1954, **8**, 1218; Caldin and G. Long, *J. Chem. Soc.* 1954, 3737. (*b*) Guss and Kolthoff, *J. Amer. Chem. Soc.* 1940, **62**, 1494.

solutions a water line appears in addition. The overall rate constant k_T can be found from the shape of the CH_3 line, and k_A from the broadening of the water line. The results are similar to those for ethanol, except that in neutral anhydrous methanol there is a contribution to the rate (with $\tau = 0.08$ sec) from an additional reaction which in ethanol is too slow to be observed:

$$ROH + ROH' \rightleftharpoons ROH' + ROH$$

The rate constants for several alcohols are collected in Table 11.2. They are mostly smaller by several powers of ten than the rate constants for the corresponding reactions of water (below).

TABLE 11.2

Rates of proton transfers in alcohols

k in l mole^{-1}sec^{-1}. Temp. $22 \pm 2°$ (24,8° for asterisked values[22f]).

Reaction	k			
	MeOH	EtOH	i-PrOH	i-BuOH
(a) $ROH + OH^- \rightleftharpoons RO^- + H_2O$	2.6×10^6	2.8×10^6	—	—
(b) $ROH + RO^- \rightleftharpoons RO^- + ROH$	7.4×10^8*	1.4×10^6	0.6×10^6	2.7×10^6
(c) $ROH + H'OH \rightleftharpoons ROH' + HOH$	<3	0.8	—	—
(d) $ROH + H_3O^+ \rightleftharpoons ROH_2^+ + H_2O$	$ca. \ 10^8$	2.8×10^6	—	—
(e) $ROH' + ROH_2^+ \rightleftharpoons ROH'H^+ + ROH$	3.5×10^9*	1×10^8	8×10^6	2×10^7

Proton transfers between water and hydrogen or hydroxyl ions[24]

The proton resonance spectrum of water consists of a single line, of width less than 1 c/sec. This is too narrow for direct steady-state measurements of the variation of width with pH, and transient methods of measuring line-width were used (p. 229).[24b] It was found that the line-width decreased in presence of either acid or base. The interpretation is as follows. The proton-resonance energy-levels are split by spin–spin interaction with ^{17}O (this was confirmed

[24] (a) Meiboom, Luz and Gill, *J. Chem. Phys.* 1957, **27**, 1411; (b) Meiboom, *idem*, 1961, **34**, 375; (c) Loewenstein and Szoke, *J. Amer. Chem. Soc.* 1962, **84**, 1157.

by experiments in which water enriched in ^{17}O was used), so that a multiplet would be expected in the absence of reaction. The single line is due to shortening of the mean lifetime of water molecules by a 'fast' exchange (cf. Fig. 11.9, e, f):

$$H_2O + H_3O^+ \underset{}{\overset{k_1}{\rightleftharpoons}} H_3O^+ + H_2O$$

$$H_2O + OH^- \underset{}{\overset{k_2}{\rightleftharpoons}} OH^- + H_2O$$

Line-widths for proton resonance were determined over a range of pH from 3 to 11, with concentrations of ^{17}O up to 0·8%. Line-widths for the ^{17}O resonance were also measured; these are much larger. The corresponding lifetimes were determined by means of the approximate equation for fast exchange (p. 237). The lifetimes are in the region of 0·1 to 1 sec, depending on the pH. The two reactions above account for all the observations. The rate constants at $25 \pm 1°$ are $k_1 = 1·_1 \times 10^{10}$ and $k_2 = 5·_5 \times 10^9$ l mole^{-1}sec^{-1}; these values are subject to an uncertainty of about 30%, largely because the line-splitting in absence of reaction cannot be directly measured. The lifetimes are much shorter than could have been determined by isotope-exchange methods; but the main reason why such large rate constants can be measured in this instance is that the concentrations of hydrogen or hydroxyl ions concerned are very small.

TABLE 11.3

Kinetic data for proton-transfers in water

Values of k and A in l mole^{-1}sec^{-1}; E in kcal mole^{-1}

Reaction	k at 25°	E	A
$H_3O^+ + H_2O$	1×10^{10}	$2·_6 \pm 0·3$	9×10^{11}
$OH^- + H_2O$	5×10^9	$4·_8 \pm 0·5$	2×10^{12}
$H_3O^+ + OH^-$	$1·4 \times 10^{11}$	$2–3$	9×10^{12}

Energies of activation were determined, from measurements in the temperature range 20° to 80°.[24c] These and other data are collected in Table 11.3, which also includes Eigen's value for the combination of hydrogen and hydroxyl ions (p. 72). The results are of interest in connection with the theory of proton transfers and ionic mobility in water (p. 269). The rate constants at 25° agree with those calculated from the anomalous mobilities of the hydrogen and hydroxyl ions, though the temperature-coefficients are somewhat higher.

Proton exchange in aqueous hydrogen peroxide[25]

The protons in water and hydrogen peroxide would be expected to give different chemical shifts, so that in the absence of exchange a mixture should show two lines. In practice a single line is always observed, whose width is strongly dependent on the concentrations of hydrogen peroxide and of hydrogen ion. This suggests that the protons of the two species are rapidly exchanged (cf. Fig. 11.9e, f), so that the resonance frequency represents an average of the two environments.

The estimation of the rate of this 'fast' exchange by equation 11.22 (p. 237) requires a knowledge not only of the line-width, which can be measured with comparative ease, but of the difference of chemical shifts in absence of exchange, which can only be estimated indirectly, from the variation with peroxide concentration of the position of the single observed line (it is about 200 c/sec). This makes the derived rate constants uncertain by a factor of about two. The line-width is a maximum at a pH of about 4·5, when it corresponds to a half-time of about 5×10^{-4} sec.

Exchange rates were determined over a pH range of 2·5 to 6·5, adjusted by addition of perchloric acid or sodium hydroxide. In the acid region (pH < 4), the rate is represented by the expression $k(H^+)(H_2O)$, with k equal to $1·6 \times 10^7$ l mole^{-1}sec^{-1}; the rate-determining step proposed is:

$$H_2O_2 + H_3O^+ \rightleftharpoons H_3O_2^+ + H_2O$$

In the alkaline region (pH > 5), the rate is given approximately by $k(H_2O_2)^2/(H^+)$, with k equal to $7·3 \times 10^7$ l mole^{-1}sec^{-1}; the rate-determining step appears to be:

$$HO_2H + H'OH + HO_2^- \rightleftharpoons HO_2H' + HOH + HO_2^-$$

[25] Anbar, Loewenstein and Meiboom, J. Amer. Chem. Soc. 1958, 80, 2630.

Since a termolecular collision is improbable, it is presumed that there is a preliminary equilibrium in which a complex is formed. The rates are comparable with those in ethanol, and like them are low compared with those in water (p. 241).

Proton-transfers in aqueous solutions of ammonium and methylammonium salts[26]

A thorough investigation of aqueous solutions of methylammonium chloride[26a] was the prototype of this series of studies, which has led to a remarkably detailed picture of the mechanisms concerned.

The solutions were acidified with HCl, so that nearly all the methylamine was present as $CH_3NH_3^+$. In strongly acid solution (pH 1), there is no indication of exchange, and the n.m.r. spectrum, shown in Fig. 11.10, consists of (i) a quadruplet due to the CH_3 protons, the line being split by their interaction with the NH_3^+ protons; (ii) a broad triplet for the NH_3^+ protons, split by interaction with ^{14}N (as in liquid ammonia, p. 248); and (iii) a single line due to the H_2O protons. As the pH is increased, the spectrum changes, no doubt because of protolytic exchange of the NH_3^+ protons. The peaks of the NH_3^+ triplet broaden and ultimately disappear, while those of the CH_3 quadruplet broaden and coalesce to a single broad line which then narrows. Either of these effects gives a measure of the mean lifetime of the NH_3^+ protons, the changes in the CH_3 line being the more accurately measurable. The H_2O line broadens, showing how long a proton remains bonded to water before returning to nitrogen. (At higher pH it narrows again, after coalescence with the NH_3^+ triplet.)

[26] (a) Grunwald, Loewenstein and Meiboom, *J. Chem. Phys.* 1957, **27**, 630 (methylamine); (b) Loewenstein and Meiboom, *J. Chem. Phys.* 1957, **27**, 1067 (diethylamine, triethylamine); (c) Meiboom, Loewenstein and Alexander, *J. Chem. Phys.* 1958, **29**, 969 (ammonia); (d) Emerson, Grunwald and Kromhout, *J. Chem. Phys.* 1960, **33**, 54 (ammonia); (e) Grunwald, Karabatsos, Kromhout and Purlee, *J. Chem. Phys.* 1960 **33**, 557 (methylamine); (f) Connor and Loewenstein, *J. Amer. Chem. Soc.* 1961, **83**, 560 (temperature coefficients for ammonia and methylamine); (g) Silver and Luz, *J. Amer. Chem. Soc.* 1961, **83**, 786 (trimethylphosphine); (h) Emerson, Grunwald, Kaplan and Kromhout, *J. Amer. Chem. Soc.* 1960, **82**, 6307 (lifetimes of H-bonded complexes).

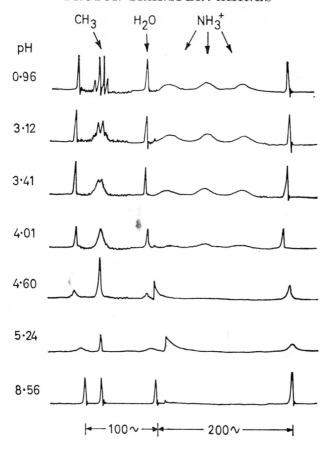

FIG. 11.10. Proton resonance spectra of aqueous methylammonium chloride solutions (4·47 M) at various pH. The lines at extreme right and left are repetitions of the water line. Different groups were recorded at different amplifications. (From Grunwald, Loewenstein and Meiboom, ref. 26a.)

The mechanisms that have to be considered include exchange between the methylammonium ion and water or hydroxyl ion:

(1) $CH_3NH_3^+ + H_2O \underset{}{\overset{k_4}{\rightleftharpoons}} CH_3NH_2 + H_3O^+$

(2) $CH_3NH_3^+ + OH^- \underset{}{\overset{k_5}{\rightleftharpoons}} CH_3NH_2 + H_2O$

17

and exchange with methylamine, either with or without the intervention of a molecule of water:

(3) $CH_3NH_3^+ + CH_3NH_2 \underset{}{\overset{k_6}{\rightleftharpoons}} CH_3NH_2 + CH_3NH_3^+$

(4) $CH_3NH'H_2^+ + HOH'' + CH_3NH_2 \overset{k_7}{\rightleftharpoons} CH_3NH_2 + H'OH + + CH_3NH''H_2^+$

The mean lifetime τ of the NH_3^+ protons was determined at a series of concentrations of amine (0·3 to 4·5 M) and of hydrogen ion (10^{-3} to 10^{-5} M), by fitting the observed CH_3 lines to theoretical line-shapes of the forms shown in Fig. 11.9. The lifetimes ranged from about 0·002 to 0·2 sec. The corresponding first-order constant k for the exchange (τ^{-1}) turned out to be proportional to the concentration of methylammonium ion and inversely proportional to that of hydrogen ion. This implied that only mechanisms 3 and 4 needed to be considered, and gave a value for $k_6 + k_7$. To determine their relative contributions, the variation of the width of the H_2O line was observed; this showed that reaction 4 contributed about 60% of the total exchange, at all concentrations, and so gave the individual values of k_7 and k_6. More precise values, corrected for viscosity changes, were obtained in some later work.[26e] Measurements of the NH_3^+ triplet gave less accurate results but confirmed those from the CH_3 and H_2O lines. The rate constants determined in this way are of the order of 10^8 l mole^{-1}sec^{-1}.

Dimethylammonium, trimethylammonium[26b] and ammonium[27c, d] ions have been investigated by the same methods. The results for the series of compounds are shown in Table 11.4. Most of the rate constants given are accurate to ± 10% or better; the best are within ± 4%, and are the most accurate rate constants so far obtained by n.m.r. methods. It will be seen that on passing from ammonia to trimethylamine the importance of mechanism 4 increases relative to mechanism 3, while mechanism 1 contributes appreciably only with ammonia and trimethylamine. This detailed information on the role of water in the reaction is typical of the n.m.r. method.

Temperature-coefficients have been measured for the reactions of ammonium and methylammonium ions.[26f] For reactions 3 and 4, the activation energies are zero within experimental error (± 0.5 kcal mole^{-1}), although the rate constants are well below the diffusion-controlled value of around 10^{10} 1 mole^{-1}sec^{-1} (p. 12). The corresponding entropies of activation are about -20 cal deg^{-1} mole^{-1}. These are relatively large decreases for reactions involving only one ion, and may be due to the steric requirements of the transition state.

TABLE 11.4

Rates of proton transfers in aqueous amine solutions

Second-order rate constant k in 1 mole^{-1}sec^{-1}.
E in kcal mole^{-1}. Temperatures as shown.

Reaction	k				E
	NH_4^+ $25°$	$CH_3NH_3^+$ $25° \pm 1$	$(CH_3)_2NH_2^+$ $22° \pm 1$	$(CH_3)_3NH^+$ $22° \pm 1$	
1. $RNH^+ + H_2O \overset{k_4}{\leftrightarrows}$ $RN + H_3O^+$	*	$<4 \times 10^{-3}$	$<4 \times 10^{-3}$	5.5×10^{-2}	12^a
2. $RNH^+ + OH^- \overset{k_5}{\leftrightarrows}$ $RN + H_2O^+$	3×10^{10}‡	3.7×10^{10}‡	3.1×10^{10}‡	2.1×10^{10}‡	—
3. $RNH^+ + RN \overset{k_6}{\leftrightarrows}$ $RN + RNH^+$	11.7×10^8	4×10^8	0.4×10^8	$<0.3 \times 10^8$	$0^{a,}$
4. $RNH^+ + H_2O + NR \overset{k_7}{\leftrightarrows}$ $RN + H_2O + H^+NR$	1×10^8	5.3×10^8	5.6×10^8	3.1×10^8	$0^{a,b}$

* The first-order rate constant is 24·6 sec^{-1}.
‡ See Table 4.2 of chapter 4 (p. 75).
a, NH_4^+; b, $CH_3NH_3^+$.

The temperature-coefficient of reaction 1 can be studied for ammonium ion solutions above $25°$[26f]; the energy of activation was found to be 12.2 ± 0.5 kcal mole^{-1}. As the equilibrium has $\Delta H \approx 12.4$ kcal mole^{-1}, the energy of activation for the reverse reaction $NH_3 + H_3O^+ \longrightarrow NH_4^+ + H_2O$ must be very small. In accordance with this conclusion, the rate constant found by combining the values of k_4 and the equilibrium constant[26d] is 4.3×10^{10} 1 mole^{-1} sec^{-1}. This is comparable with the value for $NH_4^+ + OH^-$ (3×10^{10} 1 mole^{-1}sec^{-1}) and indicates diffusion control.

By combining the rate of reaction 1 with isotopic exchange rates, it has been possible on certain assumptions to estimate the mean lifetime of hydrogen-bonded complexes between amines and water; the values given are in the region of 10^{-11} sec.[26h]

The details of reaction 4 are of interest.[26e] The proton-transfer from $CH_3NH_3^+$ to water is too slow (Table 11.4) to be the rate-determining step. Comparison of the rates for the various amines suggests that the slowest step is the transfer of a proton from water to CH_3NH_2, which is followed by rapid release of a proton from $CH_3NH_3^+$.

The corresponding reactions of the trimethylphosphonium ion, $(CH_3)_3PH^+$, were studied in a similar way by observing the shape of the CH_3 line. In this case the water line could not be used to distinguish mechanisms analogous to 3 and 4. It was found that reactions 1 and 3–4 would account for the observations, with rate constants $4\cdot6 \times 10^7$ and $1\cdot2 \times 10^2$ l mole^{-1}sec^{-1} respectively. These are much lower than for the analogous reactions of Me_3NH^+, in accordance with the lower basicity of trimethylphosphine compared with trimethylamine. The corresponding reactions of PH_4^+ are slow enough to be studied by the isotopic-labelling technique.

Proton-exchange in liquid ammonia[27]

This was one of the earliest reactions whose rate was estimated by n.m.r. methods. The proton resonance spectrum of liquid ammonia that has been intensively dried is a triplet (Fig. 11.8a, p. 234); this is because the proton energy levels are split by spin–spin interaction with ^{14}N, which has spin 1 and therefore has three spin states (p. 219). The separation between adjacent lines is relatively large, 46 c/sec. If a trace of water is present the triplet collapses to a single line (Fig. 11.8b). The reaction with potassamide is more controllable; as the concentration increases, the three peaks became less sharp, then coalesce (at about 10^{-7} M) to a single line, which becomes progressively sharper. The reaction is presumably:

$$NH_3 + NH_2^- \rightleftharpoons NH_2^- + NH_3$$

[27] Ogg, (a) *Discuss. Faraday Soc.* 1954, **17**, 215; (b) *J. Chem. Phys.* 1959, **22**, 560.

The first-order rate constant at coalescence is, by equation 11.21, about 200 sec^{-1}. The second-order rate constant is therefore of the order of 10^9 l mole^{-1}sec^{-1}, but as the concentration of NH$_2^-$ is not accurately known the result can only be approximate.

Protolysis of N-methylacetamide[28]

N-methylacetamide, $CH_3CONHCH_3$, is of special interest as the simplest representative of the grouping RCONHR' characteristic of peptides. Its n.m.r. spectrum at pH 5 contains, besides a broad NH line and a line due to C—CH$_3$ protons, two lines which are sensitive to pH: (i) a doublet due to N—CH$_3$ protons, split by reason of spin–spin interaction with NH protons, and (ii) a single line due to water. As the pH is either increased or decreased, the N—CH$_3$ peaks coalesce to a singlet, indicating that the rate of exchange of NH protons increases; the water line broadens, because of exchange of protons between water and NH. Exchange lifetimes τ were determined from the N—CH$_3$ line, much as for methylamine (p. 244). For low rates, the shape of the doublet was fitted to theoretical curves (p. 235); for high rates, the line-width was measured and equation 11.22 applied. The first-order constants thence obtained ($k = 1/\tau$) were found to be proportional to (H$^+$) in the acid range and to 1/(H$^+$) in the alkaline range, indicating that the effective mechanisms are:

(1) $CH_3CONHCH_3 + OH^- \; \underset{}{\overset{k_1}{\rightleftharpoons}} \; (CH_3CONCH_3)^- + H_2O$

(2) $CH_3CONHCH_3 + H_3O^+ \; \underset{}{\overset{k_2}{\rightleftharpoons}} \; (CH_3CONH_2CH_3)^+ + H_2O$

The rate constants are:

$$k_1 = (5 \cdot 2 \pm 1) \times 10^6 \text{ l mole}^{-1} \text{sec}^{-1} \text{ at } 21 \pm 1°$$

$$k_2 = (3 \cdot 8 \pm 0 \cdot 4) \times 10^2 \text{ l mole}^{-1} \text{sec}^{-1} \text{ at } 23 \pm 2°$$

An independent check of the mechanisms is provided by measurements on the broadening of the water line.

The N-protonation process 2 is only one of the possible paths for

[28] (a) Berger, Loewenstein and Meiboom, J. Amer. Chem. Soc. 1959, **81**, 62; (b) Takeda and Stejskal, J. Amer. Chem. Soc. 1960, **82**, 25.

the protonation by hydrogen ions. There could also be an O-protonation reaction 3, which would not affect the NH group and so would not be detected by the above method:

(3) $CH_3CONHCH_3 + H_3O^+ \rightleftharpoons (CH_3C(OH){=}NHCH_3)^+ +$
$$H_2O$$

There is independent evidence that reaction 3 does occur and is faster than 2. It is noteworthy that the n.m.r. method can thus be used to study one mechanism in a composite reaction.

Proton transfers in liquid hydrogen fluoride[19g]

Liquid hydrogen fluoride is an interesting solvent for the study of proton transfers; it has a high dielectric constant, and the temperature-range available is from $-110°$ to about $+50°$. The liquid contains HF_2^- and hydrogen ions formed by dissociation:

$$2HF \rightleftharpoons HF_2^- + H^+$$

Addition of boron trifluoride increases the concentration of hydrogen ions, and if water is also added it produces H_3O^+:

$$HF + H_2O + BF_3 \rightleftharpoons H_3O^+ + BF_4^-$$

The proton n.m.r. spectrum at room temperature then consists of a single peak; as the temperature is lowered below $-50°$, distinct peaks attributable to HF and H_3O^+ gradually separate. The coalescence of these peaks at higher temperatures is attributed to the proton-exchange reaction:

$$H_3O^+ + HF_2^- \rightleftharpoons H_2O + 2HF$$

The mean lifetime is found from the line-shape to be of the order of 0·1 sec. The rate constant for the exchange is then found (the equilibrium constants being known, and hence the concentrations) to be about 10^{11} l mole^{-1} sec^{-1}, with a small temperature-coefficient. This is similar to the values for the diffusion-controlled reactions of hydrogen ions in water (p. 262). The mechanism is no doubt similar; the ions are associated with the solvent by hydrogen bonding:

$$H_3O^+ \ldots FHF^- \longrightarrow H_2O + HF \ldots HF$$

Aromatic hydrocarbons ArH form carbonium ions ArH_2^+ when dissolved in liquid hydrogen fluoride. The rates of intramolecular proton migration, and of exchange with HF_2^-, can be determined by line-shape methods (p. 235) over wide ranges of temperatures. These reactions have larger energies of activation, in the region of 8 kcal mole^{-1}; this was to be expected, since C—H bonds must be broken and there is no assistance from hydrogen bonding.

Restricted rotation about single bonds

Amides (C—N bond).[29] Restriction of rotation about the C—N bond in such compounds as N,N-dimethylacetamide (I) is to be expected if there is some participation of the form II:

In form II, one of the methyl groups is *cis* to the oxygen atom and the other *trans*, so that the protons will be shielded to different extents and give different chemical shifts. In accordance with this expectation, the proton-resonance spectra of pure N,N-dimethyl-acetamide and N,N-dimethylformamide at room temperature show two peaks, attributable to the protons of the non-equivalent methyl groups. As the temperature is increased, the lines approach each other and coalesce. By fitting the line shapes to theoretical curves (p. 235), the lifetimes can be determined; they are of the order of 0·1 sec. The Arrhenius plots give energies of activation of 7 ± 3 and 12 ± 2 kcal mole^{-1} respectively for the two compounds.

Substituted ethanes (C—C bond).[30] Hindered rotation about the C—C bond in halogen-substituted ethanes has been demonstrated in a similar way. The ^{19}F resonance spectrum of $CCl_2Br.CF_2Br$ at room temperature consists of a single sharp line. On cooling, however, the line broadens, and at $-60°$ new lines begin to appear, which at $-80°$ are well resolved; they are identified as due to 'trans' and 'gauche' configurations.

[29] (a) Gutowsky and Holm, *J. Chem. Phys.* 1957, **25**, 1228; (b) Loewenstein and Connor, ref. 17e (summary of rate constants).
[30] (a) Nair and Roberts, *J. Amer. Chem. Soc.* 1957, **79**, 4565; (b) Abraham and Bernstein, *Canad. J. Chem.* 1961, **39**, 39.

Alkyl nitrites (O—N bond).[31] A series of alkyl nitrites has been studied[31a, b]; the behaviour of methyl nitrite is typical.[31c] At 20° the spectrum shows a single proton-resonance line, which splits into two below about −40°. At −60° the two new lines are well resolved. They are attributable to the different chemical shifts of the *cis* and *trans* forms I and II arising from hindered rotation about the O—N bond. The rate constant for the interconversion of these two forms has been determined from the line-broadening at various temperatures between −35° (where it is about 200 sec^{-1}) and +10°. The energy of activation, which may be identified with the height of the potential-energy barrier, is found to be 7–10 kcal mole^{-1}. Measurements have also been made by the spin-echo method.[31d]

Nitrosamines (N—N bond).[32] Dimethylnitrosamine provides an example of restricted rotation about a N—N bond, which has a partial double-bond character on account of the participation of the resonance form II:

The proton resonance spectrum at 25° shows two sharp resonances, separated by 19 c/sec. These coalesce at about 180°, when the rate constant must, by equation 11.21, be 84 sec^{-1}. Application of the equation for intermediate rates of exchange (equation 11.20) in the intervening temperature range gives a series of values of τ which yield a good Arrhenius plot. From this the activation energy is

[31] (a) Phillips, Looney and Smith, *J. Mol. Spect.* 1957, **1**, 35; (b) Piette and Anderson, *J. Chem. Phys.* 1959, **30**, 899; (c) Gray and Reeves, *J. Chem. Phys.* 1960, **32**, 1878; (d) Reeves and Wells, *Discuss. Faraday Soc.* 1963, **34**, 177; (f) Loewenstein and Connor, ref. 17e.
[32] Looney, Phillips and Reilly, *J. Amer. Chem. Soc.* 1957, **79**, 6136.

found to be 23 kcal mole^{-1} and the frequency-factor 0.7×10^{13} sec^{-1}.

Inversion of configuration

Cyclohexane and its derivatives[33]

Cyclohexane molecules have a chair configuration in which there are two non-equivalent sets of hydrogen atoms, the axial and the equatorial. As these are differently shielded, they will have different chemical shifts, and would be expected to give rise to two separate lines, if the molecule retained its configuration long enough. At room temperature, however, the n.m.r. spectrum of cyclohexane consists of a single line. This implies that chair-chair inversion occurs at a considerable rate:

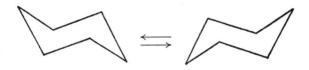

At lower temperatures the line broadens, and below $-65°$ it splits into a complex doublet. The separation of the two lines at $-106°$ is 27.6 c/sec, and this appears to be the limiting separation. The rate of inversion can therefore be determined. The equation for the lifetime at the temperature of coalescence ($-65°$) in this instance is $\tau^{-1} = \pi \Delta \nu_0$, instead of $2^{1/2} \pi \Delta \nu_0$ as in equation 11.21, because the two lines are coupled.[33b] The first-order rate constant at $-65°$ is $k = \tau^{-1} = 88$ sec^{-1}. Measurements of line-broadening over the range $-20°$ to $-70°$ gave $\Delta H^* = 9.0 \pm 0.2$ kcal mole^{-1} and $\Delta S^* = -8 \pm 1$ cal deg^{-1} mole^{-1}. These results are in reasonable agreement with the relaxation time of *ca.* 10^{-5} sec at room temperature determined by the ultrasonic absorption method (p. 101).

Perfluorocyclohexane has been studied in a similar way.[33c] The fluorine resonance line was observed. As chemical shifts for ^{19}F

[33] (a) Jensen, Noyce, Sederholm and Berlin, *J. Amer. Chem. Soc.* 1960, **82**, 1256; (b) Harris and Sheppard, *Proc. Chem. Soc.* 1961, 419; (c) Tiers, *Proc. Chem. Soc.* 1960, 389; (d) Anet, *J. Amer. Chem. Soc.* 1962, **84**, 671; (e) Loewenstein and Connor, ref. 17e (summary of rate constants).

are considerably larger than for ^1H, the lines were much wider than for cyclohexane. Measurements were made from $-66°$ to $+118°$, and the value $\Delta H^* = 7 \cdot 5 \pm 0 \cdot 3$ kcal mole^{-1} was found. For the related inversion of the tub-shaped molecule of cyclo-octatetraene, the coalescence of the doublet has been observed at $-10°$, at which the first-order constant is about 26 sec^{-1}.

Dioxane and dithiane derivatives[34]

Dioxane and dithiane have chair configurations, and like cyclohexane they can undergo inversions in which axial hydrogen atoms become equatorial and vice versa.

$$
\begin{array}{cc}
\text{H}_2\text{C---CH}_2 & \text{H}_2\text{C---CH}_2 \\
(\text{CH}_3)_2\text{C} \qquad \text{C(CH}_3)_2 & (\text{CH}_3)_2\text{C} \qquad \text{C(CH}_3)_2 \\
\text{O---O} & \text{S---S} \\
\text{I} & \text{II}
\end{array}
$$

The n.m.r. spectra of the tetramethyl derivatives I and II (3,3,6,6-tetramethyl-1,2-dioxane and -dithiane) at room temperature both show a single methylene line, which on cooling gives place to a well-resolved doublet attributable to the different chemical shifts of the two proton environments. The rate constants were evaluated from equations 11.20, 11.21 and 11.22 (p. 237). From the Arrhenius plots, the energies of activation were found to be 18·5 and 16·1 kcal mole^{-1} for I and II respectively; the corresponding values of ΔS^* were 14·4 and 6·7 cal deg^{-1}mole^{-1}.

Cyclic imines: trivalent nitrogen[35]

Attempts to isolate isomers attributable to the asymmetry of trivalent nitrogen have been unsuccessful. Substituted ethyleneimines (aziridines) such as I present favourable cases for the resolution of optical isomers, but this has not been achieved. This suggests that in these compounds there may be a rapid inversion,

[34] Claeson, Androes and Calvin, *J. Amer. Chem. Soc.* 1961, **83**, 4357.
[35] (a) Bottini and Roberts, *J. Amer. Chem. Soc.* 1956, **78**, 5126; (b) *ibid.*, 1958, **80**, 1203; (c) Loewenstein, Neumer and Roberts. *J. Amer. Chem. Soc.* 1960, **82**, 3599.

such as is known from infra-red and microwave spectra to occur in ammonia:

$$\text{I} \qquad\qquad \text{II} \qquad\qquad \text{III}$$

The rate of inversion has been determined by the n.m.r. technique. The two protons attached to the ring carbon atom in I are not equivalent, because one is *cis* and the other *trans* to the N-ethyl group. They will therefore give separate proton resonance signals if the rate of inversion is not too great. At room temperature the line occupying a position attributable to these protons is a singlet.[35a] As the temperature is lowered, this line broadens, and at about $-70°$ gives place to a doublet with a separation of about 50 c/sec. This shows (by equation 11.21) the lifetime of either configuration is of the order of 10^{-2} sec at $-70°$, and less at room temperature. Resolution of optical isomers therefore cannot be expected. A considerable series of cyclic imines has been examined and this conclusion appears to be general.[35b] Rates have been studied over a range of temperature for two of these compounds.[35c] For the N-methyl analogue of I, line-widths were measured near room temperature, and the corresponding lifetimes calculated from the equation for 'fast' exchange (p. 237); the energy of activation was found to be 6.4 ± 0.6 kcal mole^{-1}, and the frequency factor 1×10^{9} sec^{-1}. For the related compound III, which has a more complex spectrum, the corresponding values are 10 ± 1 kcal mole^{-1} and 5×10^{7} sec^{-1}; both of these are lower for solutions in methanol or carbon tetrachloride.

Hydration of cations

When paramagnetic cations are added to water, the ^{17}O resonance line is broadened, as well as the proton line.[36a, b, e] This may be

[36] (a) Connick and Poulson, *J. Chem. Phys.* 1959, **30**, 759; (b) Connick and Stover, *J. Chem. Phys.* 1961, **65**, 2075; (c) Pearson, Palmer, Anderson and Allred, *Z. Elektrochem.* 1960, **64**, 110; (d) Bernheim, Brown, Gutowsky and Woessner, *J. Chem. Phys.* 1959, **30**, 950; (e) Swift and Connick, *J. Chem. Phys.* 1962, **37**, 301. (f) For results on the analogous broadening of the ^{35}Cl line see Wertz, *J. Chem. Phys.* 1956, **24**, 484.

attributed, at least in part, to $^{17}OH_2$ molecules entering the first coordination shell of the paramagnetic cation. The strong magnetic field due to the unpaired electron, whose magnetic moment exceeds that of a nucleus by a factor of around 10^3, facilitates change of spin of nuclei close to it. The broadening depends on the lifetime τ of the ^{17}O nucleus between changes of spin, and is therefore related to the rate constant (τ^{-1}) for exchange of water molecules between the bulk solvent and the first coordination shell of the cation (actually the observed broadening gives only a lower limit for the rate of exchange). A general theory has been developed.[36c, e] The assumption that most of the broadening is due to exchange of solvent molecules is supported by the fact that it is a minimum for the ion $Cr(H_2O)_6^{+++}$, despite its large paramagnetic moment; this ion is known from isotopic-dilution experiments to exchange water only slowly in aqueous solution (p. 24, ref. 20e).

Water enriched in ^{17}O was used,[36b, e] so as to increase the signal. The line-width increased linearly with the concentration of added salt. By making observations at a series of temperatures, and fitting theoretical equations to the results, it was possible to determine rate constants for the reaction:

$$(1) \quad M(H_2O')^{n+} + H_2O \xrightarrow{k_1} M(H_2O)^{n+} + H_2O'$$

The values found for aqueous solutions of perchlorates of various cations at room temperatures are shown in Table 11.5. They are discussed below, and further in Chapter 12 (p. 276).

TABLE 11.5

Rate constants, etc., for exchange of water by cations[36e]

k_1 in sec^{-1}; ΔH^* in kcal $mole^{-1}$; ΔS^* in cal $deg^{-1}mole^{-1}$

Cation	k_1	ΔH^*	ΔS^*
Mn^{++}	3.1×10^7	8.1	+2.9
Fe^{++}	3.2×10^6	7.7	−3.0
Co^{++}	1.1×10^6	8.0	−4.1
Ni^{++}	2.7×10^4	11.6	+0.6
Cu^{++} equatorial	1.0×10^4	11	−4
axial	2×10^8	5	−4
Fe^{+++}	$> 2 \times 10^4$	—	—

Some interesting comparisons may be made with the rates of other processes. (a) The rates of reaction 1 for the divalent ions can be compared with Eigen's values (p. 97) for the rate of formation of inner sulphate ion-pairs:

(2) $(M^{++}H_2O) + SO_4^{--} \longrightarrow (M^{++}SO_4^{--}) + H_2O$

There is a fairly close parallelism. This is in accord with the view that the rate-determining step is the partial loss of a water molecule from the first coordination shell (cf. p. 278).[36b, 36e, 37]

(b) In the reactions of ferric ion with chloride or with thiocyanate ion, one water molecule in the first coordinate sphere is replaced, just as in reaction 1. In 0·1 M perchloric acid, the apparent second-order rate constant for Cl^- is $1·9 \times 10^2$, and for SCN^- $3·3 \times 10^2$ l mole$^-$ sec^{-1} (p. 50); for H_2O, taking account of 6-coordination, it comes out as not less than $2·6 \times 10^3$ l mole^{-1} sec^{-1}, which is considerably larger. This result is consistent with the view that the rate-determining step here is not the loss of a water molecule (cf. p. 278).

(c) The rate of reaction 1 for Mn^{++}, determined from the ^{17}O resonance, can be compared with the rate of replacement of protons in the first coordination sphere; this rate is derived from measurements of ^1H relaxation times in aqueous manganous solutions.[36d] The two values are compatible; the rate constants are 4×10^7 l mole^{-1} sec^{-1} for ^1H and $3·1 \times 10^7$ for ^{17}O. This is consistent with the assumption that when protons enter or leave the first coordination shell it is because an entire water molecule is exchanged.[36b]

An independent method has been used by Taube[38] to estimate rates of exchange of water in the coordination shell. The ^{17}O resonance line in water is appreciably shifted in position (as well as broadened) by addition of paramagnetic ions such as Co^{++} at a concentration of say 0·2 M. This shift depends on the rapid circulation of all the water molecules in and out of the first coordination shells of the cobalt ions. If there is also present in the solution another cation, the spectrum should be a single line if this cation exchanges water rapidly with the bulk solvent; but if it exchanges

[37] Cf. Basolo and Pearson, *Mechanisms of Inorganic Reactions* (Wiley, 1959), p. 163.
[38] Jackson, Lemons and Taube, *J. Chem. Phys.* 1960, **32**, 553.

slowly enough, a second line should appear, characteristic of the bound water of the cation. Both types of behaviour were observed. Cations which showed one line were Mg^{++}, Sn^{++}, Ba^{++}, Hg^{++}, and Bi^{+++}; it was concluded that in these the exchange was too fast to be observed. Cations which showed two lines were Al^{+++}, Ga^{+++}, Be^{++}, and $Co(NH_3)_5(H_2O)^{+++}$; the last named is known from isotopic labelling work to exchange its bound water only slowly ($t_{1/2} = 28$ hours). From the separation of the two lines, it may be concluded by applying equation 11.21 that the lifetime for exchange between the hydration shell and the bulk solvent is greater than 10^{-4} sec for Al^{+++}, Ga^{+++} and Be^{++}. For the aluminium ion, there is confirmatory evidence from the isotopic-dilution technique (p. 26) that the lifetime is actually greater than 0·02 sec.

Halide complexes[39]

Cadmium-bromide complex ions.[39a, b] The bromine nuclei ^{79}Br and ^{81}Br both possess a large quadrupole moment, and the free ions in solution give a single resonance line, of considerable breadth. If the Br^- ions become covalently bound to some other ion, such as Cd^{++}, the signal becomes so broad as to make detection difficult. If the lifetime of Br^- is shortened by reason of fast complexing with Cd^{++}, the line is broadened. By measuring the line-width, the lifetime of the Br^- ion was determined for various concentrations of KBr (up to 4 M) in presence of various concentrations of $CdBr_2$ (10^{-6} to 10^{-2} M). Thence, from an independent knowledge of the equilibrium constants, the rate constants of the following reactions were found.

(1) $Cd^{++} + Br^- \rightleftharpoons CdBr^+$ (K_1)

(2) $CdBr^+ + Br^- \rightleftharpoons CdBr_2$ (K_2)

(3) $CdBr_2 + Br^- \rightleftharpoons CdBr_3^-$ (K_3)

The results, extrapolated to zero ionic strength, are shown in Table 11.6. They may be compared with those obtained for the cadmium cyanide complex (p. 189).

[39] (a) Hertz, *Z. Elektrochem.* 1960, **64**, 53; (b) *Z. Elektrochem.* 1961, **65**, 36; (c) Myers, *J. Chem. Phys.* 1958, **28**, 1027; (d) Muetterties and Phillips, *J. Amer. Chem. Soc.* 1959, **81**, 1084.

TABLE 11.6

Rates of formation and dissociation of $Cd^{++}-Br^-$ complexes.
k_f^o *refers to forward reaction, k_b^o to back reaction,*
at 25° and zero ionic strength

Reaction	K (mole l^{-1})	k_f^o (l mole^{-1} sec^{-1})	k_b^o (sec^{-1})
1	0·007	$1·4 \times 10^9$	1×10^7
2	0·01	1×10^8	1×10^6
3	0·21	$2·8 \times 10^7$	6×10^6

Formation of tri-iodide ion. The resonance line for ^{127}I in aqueous solutions of iodide ion is broadened by addition of iodine, no doubt by the reaction

$$I^- + I_2 \rightleftharpoons I_3^-$$

Assuming the mechanism to be as shown, and making use of the known value of the equilibrium constant, the rate constants of the forward and reverse reactions can both be determined. The values obtained, at about 35° and ionic strength 0·5 to 2 M, are respectively $(4·1 \pm 0·4) \times 10^{10}$ l mole^{-1} sec^{-1} and $(7·6 \pm 0·8) \times 10^7$ sec^{-1}.

Exchange in SF_4.[39d] The resonance spectrum for ^{19}F in SF_4 at $-98°$ shows two triplets; as the temperature is raised these broaden and coalesce at about $-45°$. This is attributed to exchange of fluorine between non-equivalent positions. The exchange appears to be intermolecular, possibly via a dimeric fluorine-bridged structure. Application of the equation for intermediate rates (equation 11.20) to the spectra at temperatures below $-47°$ gives the activation energy as $4·5 \pm 0·8$ kcal mole^{-1} and the frequency factor as $10^{8 \pm 1}$ sec^{-1}. Other fluorine compounds were also studied.

Electron-transfer reactions[40]

Cuprous-cupric electron-transfer.[41] The resonance line for ^{63}Cu in a solution of cuprous chloride (1 M) in strong hydrochloric acid

[40] For a review see Halpern, *Quart. Rev. Chem. Soc.* 1960, **15**, 207; cf. p. 52.
[41] McConnell and Weaver, *J. Chem. Phys.* 1956, **25**, 307.

(12 M) is a single line of Lorentzian shape. When a little cupric chloride is added, the line is broadened. This broadening is attributed to electron-exchange. The cupric ion is paramagnetic, so that the field near it will be different from that near the diamagnetic cuprous ion (p. 256) and the resonance frequency will be different. The energy-levels will therefore become uncertain if the Cu^+ ion is liable to be converted to Cu^{++} by rapid electron transfer, and so the line will broaden. The equation for 'slow' exchange (p. 237) will apply.[42] The method can be applied generally where one of the reactants is paramagnetic.

In the cuprous-cupric exchange, the line-width is doubled (from 8 to 17 gauss) when the concentration of Cu^{II} is 10^{-3} M. The first-order rate constant comes out to about 10^5 sec^{-1}. The possibility of observing so high a value is due to the exceptional width and broadening of the lines for ^{63}Cu. If we assume a bimolecular reaction between Cu^I and Cu^{II}, the second-order rate constant is evidently about 10^8 l $mole^{-1}sec^{-1}$. This is the highest value so far observed for electron-exchange between inorganic ions, and is comparable with those of the naphthalene ion exchanges studied by the e.s.r. method (p. 210). The mechanism of the reaction is uncertain.

Vanadium $V^{IV}-V^V$. In a similar study,[43] the resonance line for $^{51}V^V$ in strongly acid solution was found to be broadened by addition of V^{IV}. Lifetimes of the order of 10^{-4} to 10^{-3} sec were found for V^V, and attributed to electron-exchange.

Manganate-permanganate.[44] The ^{55}Mn nucleus is very suitable for n.m.r. investigations, since it has a high natural abundance and sensitivity (Table 11.1, p. 220). The electron-exchange between MnO_4^- and MnO_4^{--} has been investigated[44a] by the same method as the cuprous-cupric exchange, by measuring the broadening of the

[42] The investigators used an equation for the first-order constant k equivalent to $k = \sqrt{3}\pi\delta'\nu$, instead of $2\pi\delta'\nu$ as given on p. 237; this is because they made use of the line-width between inflection points instead of the width at half-height.

[43] Giuliand and McConnell, *J. Inorg. Nucl. Chem.* 1959, **9**, 171.

[44] (a) Myers and Sheppard, *J. Amer. Chem. Soc.* 1961, **83**, 4739; (b) Britt and Yen, *J. Amer. Chem. Soc.* 1961, **83**, 4516; (c) Sheppard and Wahl, *J. Amer. Chem. Soc.* 1957, **79**, 1020.

[55]Mn resonance lines for MnO_4^- (0·15 to 0·3 M) in presence of MnO_4^{--} (0·007 to 0·15 M) and applying the equation for 'slow' exchange (p. 237). The first-order rate constant at 30° is in the region of 10^3 sec^{-1} and is proportional to the concentration of MnO_4^{--}, as would be expected for the reaction:

$$MnO_4^- + MnO_4^{--} \rightleftharpoons MnO_4^{--} + MnO_4^-$$

The second-order rate constant in the temperature range 6° to 30° is in the region of 10^4 l mole^{-1}sec^{-1}. The Arrhenius plot gives the energy of activation for solutions 1 M in K$^+$ as 8·3 kcal mole^{-1}. The results are in reasonable agreement with measurements of relaxation times by the pulse method[44b] (p. 229), and with measurements by the isotopic-labelling technique at considerably lower concentrations[44c] (p. 25).

Tetramethyl-p-phenylenediamine.[45] An electron-transfer reaction analogous to that between naphthalene and its negative ion, but too slow to be examined by the e.s.r. technique, is that between N,N,N′,N′-tetramethyl-p-phenylenediamine (TMPD) and the ion derived from it by addition of one electron (Wurster's blue). The proton resonance spectrum of TMPD dissolved in acidified D_2O consists of two lines, one due to the ring and one due to the methyl protons. On adding Wurster's blue, the lines broaden; the broadening is the same for both lines, and increases linearly with the concentration, to about 30 c/s at 2×10^{-3} M. This broadening is assumed to be due to electron-exchange. (The possibility of thermal paramagnetic relaxation is excluded by the fact that the breadth of the water line remains constant.) Assuming that the reaction is bimolecular, the second-order rate constant comes out to about $2·5 \times 10^4$ l mole^{-1}sec^{-1}.

[45] Bruce, Norberg and Weissman, *J. Chem. Phys.* 1956, **24**, 473. Footnote 42 applies here also.

CHAPTER 12

Some General Topics in the Mechanisms and Energetics of Reactions in Solution

Introduction

In this chapter we shall take up certain problems which have recurred in the preceding pages. Some of these problems are primarily mechanistic; thus we shall consider the mechanisms of proton-transfer, the kinetic effects of hydrogen bonding, and the mechanisms for the reactions of aqueous metallic cations with ligands, including the exchange of water between the first co-ordination shell and the bulk solvent. Other problems are concerned with the energetics of reactions, such as diffusion control, the activation energies of fast reactions, and the interpretation of the Arrhenius equation.

Rates and mechanisms of fast proton-transfer reactions

Reactions involving hydrogen or hydroxyl ions [1]

Our understanding of proton-transfer processes has been much enlarged in recent years by studies on fast reactions, especially those of Eigen and his school. Let us first consider proton-transfers from hydrogen ion or to hydroxyl ion:

$$A^- + H_3O^+ \underset{k_1}{\overset{k_2}{\rightleftarrows}} AH + H_2O \qquad (12.1)$$

[1] For reviews see (*a*) Eigen, *Z. Elektrochem.* 1960, **64**, 115; (*b*) Bell, *Quart. Rev. Chem. Soc.* 1959, **13**, 169; (*c*) Bell, *The Proton in Chemistry* (Methuen, 1959), chapters 8 and 9; (*d*) Eigen, *Pure and Applied Chemistry*, 1963, **6**, 97, reprinted in *Coordination Chemistry: Seventh International Conference* (Butterworths, for I.U.P.A.C., 1963), p. 97; (*e*) Eigen, *Angewandte Chem.* 1963, **75**, 489.

TABLE 12.1

Fast reactions of hydrogen ions

$$AH + H_2O \underset{k_2}{\overset{k_1}{\rightleftharpoons}} A^- + H_3O^+$$

Rate constants in l mole^{-1} sec^{-1} at 18–25°, in water.
The rate constant actually measured (k_1 or k_2) is indicated under 'Method'.
ROH^{3-} = 3-hydroxypyrene-5:8:10-trisulphonate; ImH$^+$ = imidazole cation; InH$^-$ = chlorphenol red anion.
* Indicates excited state.

Acid AH	pK	$\log_{10} k_1$	$\log_{10} k_2$	Method	See page
Oxygen and nitrogen acids					
H$_2$O	15·7	−4·6	11·1	Electric impulse (k_2)	75
(CH$_3$)$_3$NH$^+$	9·8	1·0	10·8	N.m.r. (k_1)	244
ROH^{3-}	7·3	3·1	10·4	Flash (k_2)	110
H$_2$S	7·0	3·9	10·9	Electric impulse (k_2)	75
ImH$^+$	7·0	3·2	10·2	Temp. jump (k_2)	66
InH$^-$	6·1	4·4	10·5	Temp. jump (k_2)	66
CH$_3$CO$_2$H	4·8	5·9	10·7	El. imp.; electrochem. (k_2)	75 186
C$_6$H$_5$CO$_2$H	4·2	6·4	10·6	Electric impulse (k_2)	75
p-NO$_2$.C$_6$H$_4$OH	3·4	7·2	10·6	Electric impulse (k_2)	75
HF	3·3	7·7	11·0	Electric impulse (k_2)	75
β-naphthol*	3·1	7·6	10·7	Fluorescence (k_2)	159
H$_3$O$_2$$^+$	ca. 3	7·2	ca. 10	N.m.r. (k_1)	243
HSO$_4$$^-$	1·6	9·4	11·0	Ultrasonics (k_2)	98
CF$_3$CO$_2$H	0·2	ca. 11	ca. 11	Raman broadening	200
8-cyanonaphthol*	−0·8	10·3	9·5	Fluorescence (k_1)	159
H$_3$O$^+$	−1·7	10·$_0$	10·$_0$	N.m.r. (k_1)	241
Carbon acids					
CH$_3$COCH$_3$	20	−9·3	10·7	Bromination (k_1)	
CH$_2$(CO$_2$C$_2$H$_5$)$_2$	13·3	−4·6	8·7	,, ,,	
CH$_2$(CN)$_2$	11·2	−1·8	9·4	,, ,,	
CH$_3$COCH$_2$COCH$_3$	9·0	−1·8	7·2	,, ,,	
C$_2$H$_5$NO$_2$	8·6	−7·4	1·2	,, ,,	
CH$_3$COCH$_2$NO$_2$	5·1	−1·4	3·7	,, ,,	
CH$_2$(NO$_2$)$_2$	3·6	−0·1	3·5	,, ,,	

$$AH^+ + OH^- \underset{k'_2}{\overset{k'_1}{\rightleftharpoons}} A + H_2O \qquad (12.2)$$

Some results for reactions of hydrogen ion (equation 12.1), when AH is an oxygen or nitrogen acid, are summarized in Table 12.1, along with a few results for carbon acids.[1b, 2] Since the equilibrium constants are known independently, the rate constants k_1 and k_2 are both known. Some results for reactions of hydroxyl ion (equation 12.2) are shown in Table 12.2.

TABLE 12.2

Fast reactions of hydroxyl ions

$$AH^+ + OH - \underset{k_2}{\overset{k'_1}{\rightleftharpoons}} A + H_2O$$

Rate constants in 1 mole^{-1} sec^{-1} at 18–25° in water.
Im = imidazole; Acr = acridine; ROH = cresol red; DH^{3-} = 3-acetoaminopyrene-5:8:10-trisulphonate.
* Indicates excited state.

Acid AH$^+$	pK	log$_{10} k'_1$	Method	See page
H$_2$O	15·7	9·7	N.m.r.	241
AcrH^{+*}	10·7	10·3	Fluorescence	159
(CH$_3$)$_3$ NH$^+$	9·8	10·3	Electric impulse	75
ROH	9·4	9·6	Temp. jump	66
NH$_4^+$	9·25	10·5	Electric impulse	75, 99
DH^{3-*}	7·1	9·2	Fluorescence	159
ImH$^+$	7·0	10·4	Electric impulse	75
H$_3$O$^+$	−1·7	11·1	Electric impulse	75

The rate constants k_2 for the reactions of hydrogen ion show marked differences according to whether the proton becomes attached to (i) carbon or (ii) to oxygen or nitrogen.

[2] Other results will be found in Tables 4.1, 4.2, 9.1, 9.2, 11.2 and 11.4. Those in Table 12.1 are chosen to show the variety of the acids and of the methods used. For a collection of results on 58 reactions, see Eigen, ref. 1e.

(i) When AH is a carbon acid, $R_1R_2R_3CH$, the recombination of its ions, which is the forward reaction in equation 12.1, has a rate constant k_2 well below 10^{10} 1 mole^{-1} sec^{-1}, except for the very weakest acids (Table 12.1). The energy of activation is considerable. The rate constant depends on the chemical nature of the activating groups R, as well as on the pK (compare the values for acetylacetone

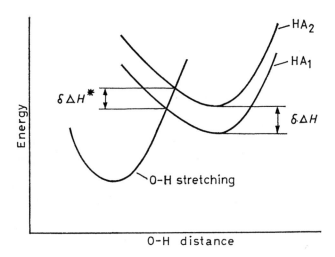

FIG. 12.1. Potential-energy diagram for the transfer of a proton from H_3O^+ to an anion A_1^- or A_2^-.

and nitroethane). For a series of similar acids, containing various substituents, the rate constant is found to be related to the dissociation constant of the acid (K_a) by the Brønsted relation, which in its differential form may be written $d\ln k_2 = \alpha\, d\ln K_a$, where α is a constant.

The simplest interpretation of the Brønsted relation [3] is in terms of an appreciable potential-energy barrier to reaction. A potential-energy diagram (Fig. 12.1) may be constructed for the

[3] Bell, (a) Acid-base Catalysis (Oxford, 1941), chapter 8; (b) The Proton in Chemistry (ref. 1c), chapter 10.

transfer of a proton from H_3O^+ to the various anions such as A_1^- and A_2^-, on the reasonable assumption that the potential-energy curves for the stretching of A_1—H and A_2—H bonds have the same shape and the same equilibrium A–H distance. Changes in potential energy are approximated to changes in enthalpy. It is assumed that other contributions to the enthalpy of activation ΔH^* (due to repulsion, etc.; see p. 287 below) are the same for A_1H and A_2H. The geometry of the figure shows that on changing from one anion to another the changes in ΔH^* are proportional to the changes in ΔH. That is, $\delta(\Delta H^*) = \alpha\delta(\Delta H)$, where α is a constant for the series and lies between 0 and 1. From this equation we can derive the Brønsted relation, if we suppose that the variations of rate are due solely to those of ΔH^* (ΔS^* being constant), and that variations of equilibrium constant are due solely to those of ΔH (ΔS being constant)[4]; for in that case $\delta\ln k = \delta\Delta H^*$, $\delta\ln K = \delta\Delta H$, and so $\delta\ln k = \alpha\delta\ln K$. This derivation of the Brønsted relation from the potential-energy diagram is not the whole story, but it appears to be on the right lines, and shows the importance of ΔH^* in these reactions.

The characteristics of the reactions producing carbon acids appear to be associated with the considerable and varied electronic rearrangements which occur in the ionization of these acids.[1b] These reorganizations are indeed responsible for the acidity, since they allow the negative charge of the anion to reside on oxygen or nitrogen rather than carbon. The kinetic results show that such a change of bonding is associated with a finite enthalpy of activation. This depends on the type of activating group, which therefore influences the rate. The variation in rate along a series of similar substances may be ascribed to the different inductive effects of the substituents.

(ii) When AH is an oxygen acid ROH, or a nitrogen acid $RR'NH$, matters are very different. The rate constant (k_2 in Table 12.1) for the forward reaction involving hydrogen ion,

$$A^- + H_3O^+ \xrightarrow{\ k_2\ } AH + H_2O \tag{12.3}$$

[4] A less restrictive condition is that ΔS^* is linearly related to ΔH^*, and ΔS to ΔH. Alternatively, changes in potential energy may be approximated to changes in free energy rather than enthalpy; cf. Bell, ref. 3b.

is much the same for all the acids studied, although their dissociation constants vary over 17 powers of ten. There is no systematic variation with the type of molecule, nor with substituents. Minor individual differences are attributable to differences of charge type, steric factors (cf. p. 76) or diffusion coefficients. It is also remarkably high, in the region of 10^{10} to 10^{11} 1 mole^{-1} sec^{-1}. A high and uniform value is found also for the reactions involving hydroxyl ion (k_1' in Table 12.2);

$$AH^+ + OH^- \xrightarrow{k_1'} A + H_2O \qquad (12.4)$$

This behaviour is to be expected if the potential-energy barrier is very low. This explanation is supported by the fact that the rate constants agree quite well with the calculated value for a diffusion-controlled reaction, which is determined solely by the rate at which the reacting species can come together; for a reaction between singly-charged ions of opposite sign, this is between 10^{10} and 10^{11} 1 mole^{-1} sec^{-1} (p. 13). The observed Arrhenius activation energy is 2–3 kcal mole^{-1}, as expected for a diffusion process (p. 288).

The very low energy-barrier for oxygen and nitrogen acids can be understood as follows. The reactions of hydrogen and hydroxyl ions in water are unique in that they can come about simply by the shift of protons along hydrogen bonds, without the need for removal of the solvation sheath as in other ionic processes (p. 276). The mechanisms suggested by Eigen[5] for reactions (12.3) and (12.4) are:

Such processes would be expected to have unusually low potential-energy barriers. The contribution from stretching of covalent bonds appears from calculation to be small, and may be

[5] (a) Eigen, Z. Elektrochem. 1960, 64, 115; (b) Eigen and De Maeyer, Proc. Roy. Soc., A, 1958, 247, 505; (c) Eigen and De Maeyer, in Structure of Electrolytic Solutions, ed. Hamer (Chapman and Hall, 1959).

reduced to zero by the effect of the coulombic forces. [6] No electronic rearrangement is involved, so there is no contribution from changes of bonding within AH, as with carbon acids. There is no desolvation, and the contribution from repulsion will be small (p. 287). Any slight resultant barrier may well be effectively lowered by quantum-mechanical tunnelling (p. 272).

Independent evidence for a low energy-barrier comes from the rate of the reaction $H_3O^+ + OH^-$ in pure ice,[7] where the hydrogen-bonded structure is already set up. The observed rate constant is 10^{13} to 10^{14} l mole^{-1} sec^{-1}, so that the reaction has a half-time comparable with that of a vibration, and the effective energy barrier must be very low. This accounts also for the abnormal mobility of the proton in ice, which is 10^7 times that of Li$^+$ for example.

The reaction between hydrogen and hydroxyl ions in water,

$$H_3O^+ + OH^- \longrightarrow 2H_2O \qquad (12.5)$$

is treated by Eigen more fully as follows.[5] The experimental rate constant is $(1\cdot4 \pm 0\cdot2) \times 10^{11}$ l mole^{-1} sec^{-1}; for the corresponding reaction in D_3O^+ with OD^- in D_2O, it is smaller by a factor of $1\cdot7$, which agrees with the ratio of the diffusion coefficients in the two solvents (p. 65n). The rate constant for a reaction between ions whose rate is controlled by diffusion can be calculated (p. 10) in terms of the distance of closest approach of the reactant ions (a). For instance, the values of the rate constant in H_2O when $a = 0, 2\cdot7$ Å, and $7\cdot5$ Å are calculated as 8×10^{10}, $8\cdot6 \times 10^{10}$, and $1\cdot3 \times 10^{11}$ l mole^{-1} sec^{-1} respectively. Eigen concludes that the experimental value indicates a reaction distance of 6–8 Å, corresponding to 2–3 hydrogen bonds. Once the ions have approached within this distance by diffusion, the reaction is completed by the rapid movements of protons along hydrogen bonds as in ice. This type of mechanism presumably applies to all the fast reactions of hydrogen and hydroxyl ions.

[6] Huggins, *J. Phys. Chem.* 1936, **40**, 723.

[7] The rate was measured by a dissociation-field method using the saturation current, rather than a relaxation method as in water (p. 72), by Eigen and de Maeyer, *Z. Elektrochem.* 1956, **60**, 1037; cf. ref. 5b.

A similar mechanism consisting of proton-transfers along hydrogen bonds accounts for the abnormal mobility of hydrogen ions in water.[5b] Two processes must be involved: the formation of the hydrogen-bond structure by rotation of water molecules, and the proton-transfer within the bond. The first step is rate-determining in water, the second in ice. The second step may involve quantum-mechanical tunnelling. It is of interest that in alcohols, where the mobility of the hydrogen ion is much less abnormal, the rate constants for protolysis are found by nuclear magnetic resonance (p. 239) to be much less than in water.

Fast proton-transfer reactions not involving hydrogen or hydroxyl ion

Diffusion-controlled reactions. The rates of a number of other fast reactions involving transfer of a proton between oxygen or nitrogen atoms have been determined by fluorescence quenching (p. 160) or by nuclear magnetic resonance (p. 247). Table 12.3 shows some of the results, collected in the order of the equilibrium constants K; results for two reactions of fluorescent molecules with hydrogen and hydroxyl ions have been added for comparison.[8] At the end of the table are some results for reactions of the large triply-charged anion DH^{3-} (3-acetylaminopyrene-5:8:10-trisulphonate).

The reactions are all very fast compared with those of carbon acids with comparable equilibrium constants. For reactions with $K < 1$, there is a rough parallelism between K and the rate constant k. For most of the reactions with $K \geqslant 1$, involving two uncharged molecules or a molecule and an ion, the rate constants approach the limiting diffusion-controlled value k_D (about 10^{10} l $mole^{-1}$ sec^{-1}); deviations can be understood in terms of simple steric considerations.[9] For these reactions, therefore, the energy barrier appears

[8] Results obtained by the fluorescence-quenching method are taken from (a) Weller, *Z. Elektrochem.* 1960, **114**, 55; cf. (b) *Progress in Reaction Kinetics*, vol. I, ed. Porter (Pergamon Press, 1961), p. 187. Those obtained by n.m.r. methods are from the papers of Meiboom, Loewenstein *et al.* (see p. 244).

[9] The value of k_D was calculated from equation 1.3, taking the encounter distance as 7·5 Å; thence the ratio k/k_D (also called the reaction probability, p. 148) was found, and compared with the value calculated from steric factors; see ref. 8b.

TABLE 12.3

*Fast reactions of oxygen and nitrogen acids, not
involving hydrogen or hydroxyl ions*

$$AH + B \underset{k_2}{\overset{k_1}{\rightleftharpoons}} A^- + BH^+$$

Rate constants in 1 mole^{-1} sec^{-1} at 25° in water.

Acr = acridine; ROH = β-naphthol; DH^{3-} = 3-acetylaminopyrene-
5:8:10-trisulphonate; HOAc = acetic acid; Im = imidazole; H$_2$In =
chlorphenol red.

*Indicates excited state.

AH + B	Transfer	$\log_{10} K$	$\log_{10} k_1$	Method
AcrH$^+$* + OH$^-$	NH → O	3·3	10·3	Fluorescence
RO$^-$* + H$_3$O$^+$	OH → O	2·8	10·7	,,
ROH* + C$_2$H$_5$CO$_2^-$	OH → O	2·1	9·3	,,
ROH* + C$_3$H$_7$CO$_2^-$	OH → O	2·0	9·2	,,
ROH* + OAc$^-$	OH → O	1·9	9·3	,,
RO$^-$* + H$_3$PO$_4$	OH → O	1·7	9·3	,,
Acr* + NH$_4^+$	NH → N	1·4	8·8	,,
Acr* + H$_3$BO$_3$	OH → N	1·4	8·6	,,
ROH* + HCO$_2^-$	OH → O	0·9	9·4	,,
NH$_3$ + NH$_2^-$	NH → N	0	8·7	N.m.r.
NH$_4^+$ + NH$_3$	NH → N	0	9·1	,,
CH$_3$NH$_3^+$ + CH$_3$NH$_2$	NH → N	0	8·6	,,
(CH$_3$)$_2$NH$_2^+$ + (CH$_3$)$_2$NH	NH → N	0	7·6	,,
ROH* + H$_2$PO$_4^-$	OH → O	−0·7	8·8	Fluorescence
Acr* + Mg(H$_2$O)$_n$	OH → N	−0·8	8·0	,,
RO$^-$* + HCO$_2$H	OH → O	−0·9	8·4	,,
AcrH$^+$* + NH$_3$	NH → N	−1·4	7·3	,,
RO$^-$* + HOAc	OH → O	−2·0	7·5	,,
DH^{3-}* + (CH$_3$)$_2$NH	NH → N	4·9	8·7	,,
DH^{3-}* + CH$_3$NH$_2$	NH → N	4·3	8·7	,,
DH^{3-}* + (CH$_3$)$_3$N	NH → N	2·9	8·3	,,
DH^{3-}* + NH$_3$	NH → N	2·3	8·4	,,

to be very low. The mechanism can be visualized as the formation
of an encounter complex in which the reactants are linked through
hydrogen-bonded water molecules (AH...OH$_2$...OH$_2$...OH$_2$...B),
followed at once by the transfer of a proton from the acid to water
and thence to the base.

For some of the reactions, however, including those of the ion DH^{3-} shown in Table 12.3, the rate constant k is markedly less than k_D and the deviations are too large to be attributed to steric factors. These are reactions where AH is a relatively weak acid, and it has been suggested[8b] that the rate-determining step is the transfer of a proton from water to the base B.

Transition from diffusion-controlled to slower reactions. Consider a proton-transfer reaction for which the exponent α of the Brønsted

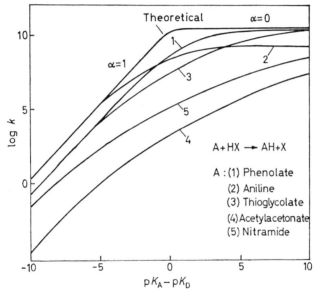

FIG. 12.2. Transitions from slower reaction to diffusion-controlled reaction; plots of log k against difference of pK of reactants. The curve marked 'theoretical' refers to reactions with only a diffusion barrier. From Eigen, ref. 1d, by permission. For details see ref. 1e, figs. 8–12.

relation lies between 0 and 1 for the range of acids and bases that give rates accessible to conventional methods. If the range of pK is extended so that the rate constant is increased, a value of pK will eventually be reached beyond which the reaction is so fast as to be diffusion-controlled, and the rate constant k becomes independent of acid strength, so that $\alpha = 0$. A sufficient extension of the range of pK in the other direction will lead to the reverse reaction becoming diffusion-controlled, with a rate constant k_2 independent of acid strength; then $k_1 = Kk_2 = K \times$ constant, and so $\alpha = 1$. Thus if the complete range can be studied, the value of α will vary from 0 to 1. The linear Brønsted plots usually observed must owe their linearity to their restricted range, as indeed has long been recognised.[1b] Observations on fast reactions showing the transition have recently been reported by Eigen (Fig. 12.2).[1d, 1e]

Quantum-mechanical tunnelling in proton-transfer reactions

Proton-transfer reactions are unique in that it is possible to detect non-classical kinetic behaviour.[10] Since a particle of mass m and velocity v is associated according to the Broglie relation with a wavelength h/mv, the representation of a reaction by the motion of a particle surmounting a col should strictly be replaced by one in which a wave is incident on an energy-barrier. On solving the resulting equation, one finds that, for systems with energy less than the height of the barrier, there is a transmitted as well as a reflected wave; that is, there is a finite probability of 'penetrating' the barrier, which on classical theory would be impossible. By taking into account the distribution of energies which the incident wave may have, the rate of reaction for a given barrier can be calculated. Solutions of varying exactness have been obtained for energy-barriers of various shapes. The shape that is mathematically most convenient is parabolic, but for any reasonable barrier the same general conclusions emerge. The predicted effects of tunnelling increase as the Broglie wavelength increases, i.e. as the mass decreases. This is why these predictions are specially relevant to proton-transfer reactions; the wavelength associated with the proton at ordinary temperatures is 1 to 2 Å, which is much greater than for other atoms, and is comparable with the width expected for an energy-barrier such as that represented in Fig. 12.1. Two main effects are predicted. (i) Above room temperature a plot of $\log k$ against $1/T$ will be approximately linear, in accordance with the Arrhenius equation $k = A \exp(-E_A/RT)$; but as the temperature is reduced, the plot will deviate from linearity and the rate

[10] Bell, (a) *Acid-base Catalysis* (Oxford, 1941), chapter 8; (b) *The Proton in Chemistry* (ref. 1c), chapter 11.

will be increasingly higher than that calculated from the Arrhenius equation. (ii) The observed A-factor for a proton-transfer (A_H) may be considerably less than for the corresponding deuteron-transfer (A_D); this is a result for which no alternative interpretation is known. These effects should increase markedly with decrease of the width of the energy-barrier, and to a less extent with increase of its height.

These predictions were made by Bell and others in the 1930's, but no unequivocal instance was reported until 1956. Both the effects mentioned have now been observed. The most thoroughly investigated instance is the base-catalysed bromination of the cyclic ketone 2-carbethoxycyclopentanone in heavy water, a reaction which is catalysed by bases generally and is undoubtedly controlled by a proton-transfer from $\geqslant$CH to the base. Bell and his co-workers found the largest effects for catalysis by fluoride ion, involving a CH...F transfer; here $A_D/A_H = 24 \pm 4$. [11] The Arrhenius plot for the proton-transfer deviates from linearity; at $-20°$, in 5·2 M sodium bromide solutions, the observed rate is about 75% faster than that calculated by extrapolating the linear Arrhenius plot obtained at higher temperatures. [12] The two sets of experiments can be quantitatively interpreted by fitting to them the theoretical equations derived for a parabolic barrier. The width of the barrier at its base is calculated as 1·17 Å, and the height is about 20% greater than the observed activation energy.

These deviations from a linear Arrhenius plot are exceptionally large. Earlier work on various CH...O transfers at temperatures ranging down to about $-100°$ (refs. 12, 13, 14 on pp. 19, 20) had shown no appreciable deviations. A combination of improved low-temperature methods with flow techniques has extended the usable temperature-range, and a curvature of the Arrhenius plot in the expected direction has been found for the reactions of the trinitro-benzyl ion with acetic acid (range $+20°$ to $-115°$) [13a] and with hydrofluoric acid (range $+25°$ to $-90°$), [13b] and for the reaction

[11] Bell, Fendley and Hulett, *Proc. Roy. Soc. A*, 1956, **235**, 453.
[12] Hulett, *idem*, 1959, **251**, 274.
[13] (*a*) Caldin and Harbron, *J. Chem. Soc.* 1962, 3454; (*b*) Caldin and Kasparian, unpublished work.

of 4-nitrobenzyl cyanide with ethoxide ion (range $-60°$ to $-124°$).[13b] The deviations of the rate constants at the lowest temperatures from those calculated by extrapolating the linear parts of the Arrhenius plots are about 45%, 120% and 100% respectively, compared with experimental uncertainties of a few per cent. For these reactions the width of the energy-barriers calculated to fit the results is around 1·6 Å; this is considerably wider than for the reaction studied by Bell and his collaborators, in accordance with the much lower temperatures at which deviations become appreciable.

Before attributing these deviations to quantum-mechanical tunnelling, it is of course necessary to consider for each reaction the alternative explanations for non-linear Arrhenius plots, such as a change in the mechanism of reaction, change of solvation in the transition state (p. 289), and change of solvent structure.

The values quoted for the widths of the energy barriers are obtained by using the equations for a parabolic barrier. As the barrier is probably bell-shaped rather than parabolic, too much reliance should not be put on the absolute values; but the relative values for a series of similar reactions should allow significant comparisons to be made. From the results so far, it may be tentatively concluded that there may be a difference in the widths of the barriers for C—H...O and C—H...F transfers, but much more work will be needed to determine the effects of differences of reaction type, substrate, solvent, temperature and experimental method.

Such studies of Arrhenius plots over long temperature ranges can evidently provide sensitive indications of the effects of substituents and other factors on the dimensions of the transition state. Measurements of isotope effects can also provide information on the stiffness of the transition state with respect to transverse vibrations.[11] Thus the configurations of transition states and the shapes of energy surfaces in their neighbourhood may be investigated.

Kinetic effects of hydrogen bonding

We have seen (p. 267) that the high rate constants found for reactions of hydrogen or hydroxyl ions in water (10^{10} to 10^{11}

1 mole^{-1} sec^{-1}) are attributable to the possibility of proton shifts along a system of hydrogen bridges. If this system is blocked, as when the donor proton is involved in an internal hydrogen bond, the reaction may be 10^3 or 10^4 times slower. An example is the reaction of OH$^-$ with the enol form of acetylacetone, where the rate constant is $1\cdot6 \times 10^7$ 1 mole^{-1} sec^{-1}.[1d] This can be understood as due to a prior equilibrium in which about 1 in 10^4 of the enol is present in a non-chelated form.

Other instances of the kinetic effect of an equilibrium involving hydrogen bonds may be found in the temperature-coefficients of the fluorescence of acridine in aqueous mixtures (p. 163) and of the dielectric absorption of water and of glycine in water (p. 103); the apparent energy of activation may be interpreted as the value of ΔH for the equilibrium.

Rates of formation and dissociation of hydrogen bonds have been determined in a few instances. The cyclic dimer of benzoic acid, containing two equivalent hydrogen bonds, has been investigated by an ultrasonic method (p. 99). In carbon tetrachloride solution, where solvation effects do not appear to be important, the rate constant for association at 25° has a high value (about 5×10^9 1 mole^{-1} sec^{-1}) which suggests diffusion control; the value found for ΔH^* is about 3 kcal mole^{-1}, which is quite close to that for diffusion (p. 288). For the dissociation, however, ΔH^* is much higher, about 13 kcal mole^{-1}. The formation of the hydrogen-bonded complex between pyridine and 3-hydroxypyrene (p. 161) has a rate constant in the region of 10^{10} 1 mole^{-1} sec^{-1} in organic solvents, and is no doubt diffusion-controlled. From this rather scanty evidence, it appears that the formation of hydrogen bonds is fast compared with normal chemical processes, but that their dissociation may contribute appreciably to the energy of activation of a reaction.

Replacement of solvent molecules in the coordination shells of metal cations

We have seen above that hydrogen and hydroxyl ions are exceptional in that they can react with other ions in water by a special mechanism which does not require the removal of the solvating water molecules. Any other association reaction of an ion requires the removal and replacement of a water molecule in the coordination sphere.

Exchange between solvent and solvated metal cations

The simplest instance of such a reaction is the exchange of solvent molecules between a solvated metal cation and the bulk solvent. The most direct measurements of the rates of such reactions are those of Taube on isotopic exchange, which show measurable rates of exchange and considerable energies of activation for Al^{+++} ion in water and for Mg^{++}, Co^{++} and Ni^{++} in methanol (p. 26). The ultrasonic absorption spectra of aqueous solutions of various divalent metal sulphates give rate constants of 10^5 to 10^7 sec^{-1} for the dissociation of a water molecule from the coordination shell (p. 97). These values are supported by the results of n.m.r. work (p. 255). The energies of activation are 5 to 12 kcal mole^{-1}.

It follows that in a fast reaction involving the attachment of a ligand to one of these divalent or trivalent cations, the rate-determining step may be the loss of a solvating water molecule. In that case the rate would be expected to be much the same for all ligands, and for these cations this is observed. When other cations are surveyed, however, it emerges that there are three types of behaviour; these are outlined in the next few paragraphs.

Reactions of ligands with solvated metal cations in aqueous solutions

These reactions are being systematically surveyed by Eigen and his co-workers, mainly by relaxation methods.[14] The results so far available are shown in Fig. 12.3. This is taken from a recent review[14a] which includes the results of several investigations not yet published in full, and supplements the results reported in earlier chapters. In the interpretation of these results[14a] it is suggested that three different mechanisms may be distinguished, depending on the relative rates of loss of coordinated water from the ion, attack by ligand, and hydrolysis.

[14] For reviews see Eigen (a) in *Coordination Chemistry*, ref. 1d, pp. 97–106; (b) in *Advances in the Chemistry of Co-ordination Compounds*, ed. Kirschner (Macmillan, 1961), pp. 371–378. Cf. also above, p. 17, ref. 6; p. 49, ref. 63; p. 51, ref. 67; p. 67, refs. 7, 8; p. 70, refs. 14, 15; p. 94, ref. 16; p. 255, ref. 36.

(i) *Ligand attack as the rate-determining step.* For ions of the alkali metals (Li⁺, Na⁺, K⁺, Rb⁺, Cs⁺) and alkaline-earth metals (Ca⁺⁺, Sr⁺⁺, Ba⁺⁺), the rate constants for loss of water are high ($> 10^7$ sec⁻¹) with all the ligands used, and there is some variation from one ligand to another. This indicates that the loss of water

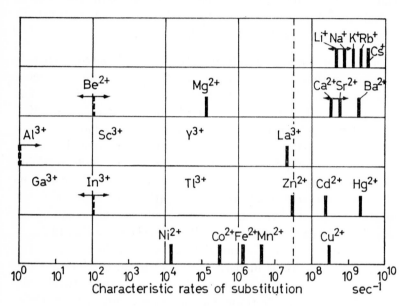

FIG. 12.3. Characteristic rate constants (in sec⁻¹) for the dissociation of water molecules from the inner coordination spheres of metal cations. From Eigen, ref. 14a, by permission.

molecules from the coordination sphere of the ions is easy, so that there is fast exchange with the solvent, and the rate-determining step is the attachment of the ligand.

In each group the rate increases with the size of the ion, though by less than a power of ten. The variations in rate from one ion to another are attributable to the differences in the electrostatic potential (size/charge) of the ions, which measures their electrostatic attraction for ligand dipoles.

With the alkali metals, it was necessary to use strongly-complexing agents such as EDTA, nitrilotriacetate, and adenosine

19

triphosphate; the rates were very high and were measured by the ultrasonic-absorption method.[14a] For the alkaline-earth metals, the rate constants with such chelating agents[14a, b] are of the same order as that for calcium ions with sulphate (p. 97). Zinc, cadmium and mercury ions react about as fast as calcium, but do not show marked differences between ligands; for instance, the reactions of cadmium with bromide ion (p. 258) and with EDTA (p. 191) both have rate constants about 10^9 l mole^{-1} sec^{-1}.

(ii) *Loss of coordinated water as the rate-determining step.* There is a group of cations for which the rate contants are less than 10^7 sec^{-1} and practically independent of the nature of the ligand. For example, with Mg^{++} the rate constant is about 10^5 sec^{-1} for reaction with SO_4^{--}, $S_2O_3^{--}$ and CrO_4^{--} (see Table 5.2, p. 97) and for adenosine di- and triphosphate.[14b] This indicates that the removal of water from the coordination shell of the cation is the rate-determining step. This group includes, besides Mg^{++}, most of the divalent ions of the first series of transition elements (the other series have not yet been studied). Preliminary results indicate that some of the trivalent rare-earth cations also fall in this class (see Fig. 12.3).

Electrostatic effects are enough to account for the results on the rare earths. The rates increase with the size of the ion, and are smaller than those for divalent ions. This type of explanation breaks down, however, for the transition-metal series Mn^{++}, Fe^{++}, Co^{++}, Ni^{++}, Cu^{++} (cf. p. 97). The cation with the smallest radius is Cu^{++}, which shows the highest rate constant; the explanation may be that the square planar configuration leads to greater lability of the axial water molecules, compared with the octahedral configuration of the other cations. A relatively low rate is shown by Ni^{++}, and also by V^{++}; this is probably due to crystal-field stabilization of the transition state.

(iii) *Hydrolysis as the rate-determining step.* In a third group of cations, the hydrolysis of a water molecule in the coordination shell appears to be rate-determining. The rates are comparatively low, and vary with the ligand. Examples of such cations are Fe^{+++} (p. 49), Al^{+++} (pp. 26, 71) and Be^{++} (p. 98). The rate constants for the reactions of Fe^{+++} with various anions show a broad parallelism with the basicity of the anion (p. 50; Table 3.2.) This suggests that the rate-determining step is

$$(Fe.H_2O)^{+++} + B^- \longrightarrow FeOH^{++} + BH$$

followed by

$$FeOH^{++} + BH \longrightarrow FeB^{++} + H_2O$$

This mechanism will only occur when the rate of hydrolysis exceeds the rate of substitution in the unhydrolysed cation; it may be expected to occur with the more hydrolysable divalent and trivalent metal cations.

Diffusion control of rates of reaction

Simple theory of diffusion-controlled rates

In nearly every chapter of this book we have come across rate constants of the order of 10^{10} l mole^{-1} sec^{-1}. These can be understood, as we noted in chapter 1 (p. 12), as limiting values determined by the rate at which the reactant molecules meet by diffusion through the solution. A simple theory due to Smoluchowski, in which the molecules are treated as spherical particles moving in a continuous fluid, led to an expression for the rate constant (equation 1.3), in terms of the diffusion coefficients (D_A, D_B) and radii (r_A, r_B) of the molecules. The equation may be written as follows, if we put $D_{AB} = D_A + D_B$ and $r_{AB} = r_A + r_B$:

$$k_D = 4\pi N° D_{AB} r_{AB} \text{ ml mole}^{-1} \text{sec}^{-1} \qquad (12.6)$$

$$= 4\pi D_{AB} r_{AB} \text{ ml molecule}^{-1} \text{sec}^{-1} \qquad (12.7)$$

Assuming the validity of the Stokes-Einstein equation for the motion of molecules in liquids, Debye obtained the diffusion-controlled rate constant in terms of the viscosity (equation 1.8) as:

$$k_D = 8RT/3\eta \text{ ml mole}^{-1} \text{sec}^{-1} \qquad (12.8)$$

$$= 8RT/3000\eta \text{ l mole}^{-1} \text{sec}^{-1} \qquad (12.9)$$

These equations 12.6 to 12.9 apply to reactions involving at least one uncharged molecule; for reactions between ions they must be corrected by a factor depending on the charges and the distance of closest approach (see equation 1.9, p. 12).

Equation 12.9 not only predicts rate constants of the right order of magnitude in water and ordinary organic solvents; it predicts also that these high rate constants will be sensitive to the viscosity of the solvent, and will exhibit relatively low temperature-co-efficients determined by that of the viscosity. [15] We have seen that where these predictions have been tested they are at least qualitatively fulfilled, as in studies on the fluorescence quenching of anthracene (p. 155), on the recombination of iodine atoms by photochemical and flash methods (pp. 140, 108), and on triplet-state decay (p. 112).[16]

Deviations from equation 12.9 may occur because the Stokes-Einstein equation is not exact; we have noticed one instance where equation 12.7 gives better agreement with experiment (p. 156). Measurements of diffusion coefficients will permit the wider use of equation 12.7.

Extended theory of the effects of diffusion on reaction rates

The theory of the influence of diffusion rates on the kinetics of reactions has been critically reviewed and its assumptions analysed by R. M. Noyes.[17a] Equation 12.7 is shown to be an approximate form of the limiting case of a more general equation.

The revised calculation, like Smoluchowski's, starts from Fick's laws (p. 167), but assumes a more realistic boundary condition. The result is expressed in equation 12.10, in which k_{obs} is the observed second-order rate constant, and k is the value which would be observed if the equilibrium distribution of molecules were maintained, instead of being disturbed by reaction:

$$k_{obs} = \frac{4\pi D_{AB}r_{AB}}{1 + (4\pi D_{AB}r_{AB}/k)} \text{ ml molecule}^{-1}\text{sec}^{-1} \qquad (12.10)$$

[15] For a table of the temperature-coefficients of viscosity in the form $\eta = A \exp(B/RT)$, see Moelwyn-Hughes, *Physical Chemistry* (Pergamon Press, 1957), p. 696. For many organic liquids B lies in the range 1–3 kcal mole^{-1}.

[16] Some recent work by flash methods on the quenching of naphthalene triplets by 1-iodonaphthalene or oxygen has shown that the rate constant is proportional to T/η when the solvent or temperature is changed, except in long-chain paraffin solvents (Osborne and Porter, *Proc. Sixth International Symposium on Free Radicals*, Cambridge, 1963).

[17] (a) R. M. Noyes, in *Progress in Reaction Kinetics* (Pergamon Press, 1961), pp. 129–160. The improved equation is due to (b) Collins and Kimball, *J. Colloid Sci.* 1949, **4**, 425; (c) Collins, *idem*, 1950, **5**, 499.

This equation is to be compared with Smoluchowski's equation 12.7. Its derivation assumes that there are no intermolecular forces between molecules not in contact; consequently it does not apply to reactions between ions. Apart from this it is a general equation, relating to all values of k. Two limiting cases are of special interest.

Rate constant for equilibrium distribution. For the observed rate constant k_{obs} to approximate to the value for equilibrium distribution k, the condition is evidently:

$$k \ll 4\pi D_{AB} r_{AB} \text{ ml molecule}^{-1} \text{sec}^{-1} \qquad (12.11a)$$

This condition will be satisfied within 1% for small molecules in ordinary solvents (for which $D_{AB} \approx 10^{-5}$ cm^{2}sec^{-1} and $r_{AB} \approx 10^{-8}$ cm) if k is less than 10^{-14} ml molecule^{-1}sec^{-1}, or about 10^7 l mole^{-1} sec^{-1}. Reactions with rate constants lower than this will not be appreciably affected by diffusion rates, unless they involve viscous solvents or very large molecules. If the A-factor has its normal value of about 10^{11} l mole^{-1}sec^{-1}, this implies that diffusion can be ignored as a rate-determining factor when the energy of activation is greater than about 6 kcal mole^{-1}.

Rate constant for reaction at every encounter. Equation 12.10 would become identical with Smoluchowski's equation (12.7) if:

$$k \gg 4\pi D_{AB} r_{AB} \text{ ml molecule}^{-1} \text{sec}^{-1} \qquad (12.11b)$$

For small molecules in ordinary solvents, this implies that $k \gg 10^9$ l mole^{-1}sec^{-1}. As the fastest reactions not involving ions have rate constants of about 10^{10} l mole^{-1}sec^{-1}, this condition is not fulfilled. Equation 12.7 must therefore be regarded as only an approximation for these reactions. The difference between equations 12.7 and 12.10 is little greater than the experimental errors, however; for the recombination of iodine atoms, for example, it amounts to a factor of 1·35, which is just large enough to be experimentally significant.

Intermediate rate constants. Rate constants lying between these two limits of about 10^7 and 10^{10} l mole^{-1}sec^{-1} should be affected by diffusion rates approximately according to equation 12.10. If k_{obs} is 10^8 l mole^{-1}sec^{-1}, for example, the equation indicates that, if we assume the same values of D_{AB} and r_{AB} as above, the difference between k_{obs} and the equilibrium-distribution value k is of the order of a few per cent.

Time-dependence of rate constants. A consequence of the disturbance of the equilibrium distribution of reactant molecules by a fast reaction is that after the initiation of reaction a finite time will be required before the value of the observed rate constant is steady. The equations for the time-variation of k_{obs} have been solved.[17a] At time t, the expression for k_{obs} in equation 12.10 must be multiplied by the following factor:

$$1 + [r_{AB}/(\pi D_{AB}t)^{1/2} (1 + [4\pi D_{AB}r_{AB}/k])] \qquad (12.12)$$

With solvents and reactants of ordinary molecular dimensions, at room temperature, the rate constant predicted by this expression may differ from the steady-state value by 1% at times of the order of 10^{-7} sec, and by 10% at 10^{-9} sec. These deviations may become just significant when half-lives of the order of 10^{-8} sec or less are concerned, as for instance in ultrasonics, fluorescence and e.s.r. work (cf. Table 1.1). Corrections for them have indeed been applied by Weller to results obtained by fluorescence methods (pp. 149, 160). Such methods might be applied to test the predictions of equation 12.12 for the transient values of observed rate constants.[18]

Effects of structure of solvent. It appears from Noyes' review[17a] that in the calculation of the effects of diffusion, leading to equation 12.7, the most questionable assumption is that the diffusive displacements of solute molecules are always random. When two solute molecules are close together, this is probably not so; their motions are likely to be mutually influenced by the structure of the solvent. Some of the kinetic evidence on the effects of solvent structure must now be mentioned.

Encounter and collision : cage effects

When two reactant molecules A and B, diffusing through the solutions, reach adjacent positions, the event may be called an encounter. The number of encounters per second, when A and B are at unit concentration, is called the encounter number; in water

[18] Non-equilibrium distributions of reagents are commonly encountered in radiation chemistry; cf. Monchick, Magee and Samuel, *J. Chem. Phys.* 1957, **26**, 935.

and solvents of comparable viscosity, as we have seen, it is of the order of 10^{10} 1 mole^{-1}sec^{-1}. This may be compared with the collision number, which would be expected to be around 10^{11} 1 mole^{-1}sec^{-1}, as in a gas. [19] This is an order of magnitude higher than the encounter number. The reason no doubt is that, once two reactant molecules have reached adjacent positions by diffusion, they are hemmed in by a 'cage' of solvent molecules, and collide with each other several times before one of them changes places with a solvent molecule and so breaks up the encounter. [20] It appears then that, in water and ordinary organic solvents, reactant molecules (or their products), undergo between one and ten collisions within the solvent cage before separating.

This concept of a molecular cage may be illustrated by a mechanical model of the liquid. A number of balls are agitated on a horizontal surface and their contacts are recorded electrically.[21] When there are few balls, occupying little of the available surface, collisions occur at random intervals, as in a gas. As more balls are added, to simulate increase of the density and viscosity, the collisions begin to occur in groups; the average number of collisions per encounter increases, while the frequency of encounters decreases. The collision frequency, which is the product of the two, is thus larger than the encounter frequency. Moreover, it is nearly constant over a considerable range of 'density'; this shows why the rates of reactions which occur only at a small fraction of collisions are insensitive to the viscosity of the solvent. [22] When a reaction occurs at practically every collision, however, its rate depends only on the encounter rate, and therefore depends on the viscosity.

Direct experimental support for the cage model may be found in the low quantum yields observed in some primary photochemical

[19] (a) Bell, *Trans. Faraday Soc.* 1939, **35**, 324; (b) Fowler and Guggenheim, *Statistical Thermodynamics* (Cambridge, 1939), p. 533.

[20] The cage picture was introduced by Rabinowitch, *Trans. Faraday Soc.* 1934, **30**, 120; see also refs. 21 and 22 below.

[21] (a) Rabinowitch and Wood, *Trans. Faraday Soc.* 1936, **32**, 1381; (b) Fairclough and Hinshelwood, *J. Chem. Soc.* 1939, 594.

[22] For some calculations of reaction rates from the cage model, see (a) Fowler and Slater, *Trans. Faraday Soc.* 1938, **34**, 81; (b) Bradley, *J. Chem. Soc.* 1937, 1185.

processes already mentioned in this book. When iodine in solution is dissociated by a flash, the quantum yield is much less than unity; this indicates that most of the iodine atoms recombine before escaping from the solvent cage (pp. 109, 140). In photochemical polymerization, also, measurements of the rate of initiation (p. 124) show that the quantum yield is often less than unity, and varies with the initiator, monomer and medium[23]; these effects may be attributed to recombination of the fragments formed by cleavage of the initiator molecule, before they have time to escape from the cage.

Diffusion, according to the cage model, occurs by molecular displacements, in which a molecule escapes from its cage. In such displacements it would be expected that the molecule would have to overcome a potential energy barrier. This idea was applied to the calculation of diffusion coefficients by Rabinowitch and by Eyring.[24] The result is expressed in equation 12.13, where D is the diffusion coefficient, λ is the root-mean-square displacement, and ΔH^* and ΔS^* are the enthalpy and entropy of activation for the displacement:

$$D = \lambda^2(kT/h)\exp(\Delta S^*/R)\exp(-\Delta H^*/RT) \qquad (12.13)$$

Comparison with experimental values of D shows that in ordinary solvents at room temperature ΔH^* is of the same order of magnitude as RT; thus the energy required for a molecular jump is of the same order as the thermal energy of a molecule.[25]

Proximity effects[26]

The theory of diffusion-controlled reactions previously outlined (pp. 279–282) deals satisfactorily with the random displacements of

[23] Walling, *Free Radicals in Solution* (Wiley, 1957), pp. 76–79.
[24] (a) Rabinovitch, *Trans. Faraday Soc.* 1937, **33**, 1225; (b) Glasstone, Laidler and Eyring, *The Theory of Rate Processes* (McGraw Hill, 1941), pp. 516 *seq.*
[25] On the question whether diffusive displacements are comparable with molecular-dimensions or much smaller, see Noyes, (a) *J. Chem. Phys.* 1955, **23**, 1982; (b) *J. Amer. Chem. Soc.* 1956, **78**, 5486.
[26] (a) R. M. Noyes, *Z. Elektrochem*, 1960, **64**, 153 (review with references); (b) Booth and Noyes, *J. Amer. Chem. Soc.* 1960, **82**, 1868; (c) Meadows and Noyes, *ibid.*, 1872.

solute molecules when they are far removed from each other. When two solute molecules are separated by only one or two solvent molecules, however, their displacements will no longer be independent. Calculations suggest that when the molecule centres are separated by about two molecular diameters, displacements that carry solute molecules away from each other are probably more frequent than those that carry them towards each other; but that the converse is true when the separation is reduced to less than about 1·5 molecular diameters.

There is some experimental support for these ideas. For instance, they account for the fact that in the photochemical dissociation of iodine in presence of a scavenger (p. 140) the quantum yield is higher at the shorter wavelengths (higher energy) and lower at the longer wavelengths (lower energy) than the values calculated from simple theory. It is suggested that when the separating iodine atoms have relatively high velocity they may travel one or two molecular diameters and become separated by solvent molecules before they lose their excess energy; the higher quantum yield implies that diffusion together is then less probable than the simple theory predicts. When the velocity of separation is relatively low, some of them are turned back towards each other by the solvent cage, so that the quantum yield is low. Another piece of evidence for this latter effect is that in the quenching of the fluorescence of anthracene the encounter diameter in solution appears to be larger than the collision diameter in the gas phase; this suggests that in solution molecules that have approached within a certain distance are forced together by the solvent cage (p. 156). The further improvement of the theory of diffusion control will require calculations taking account of 'proximity effects' such as these.

The interpretation of Arrhenius energies of activation

Factors contributing to the Arrhenius energy of activation

When the rate constant k of a reaction has been determined at a series of temperatures over the range convenient for conventional methods, a plot of log k against $1/T$ is usually linear within experimental error. The results may then be represented empirically by the Arrhenius equation:

$$k = A \exp\left(-E_A/RT\right) \tag{12.14}$$

where A and E_A are independent of temperature. E_A may be called the Arrhenius activation energy; it is obtained from the slope of the Arrhenius plot of $\log k$ against $1/T$, since by equation 12.14:

$$d\ln k/d(1/T) = -E_A/R \tag{12.15}$$

The molecular interpretation of E_A is suggested by a theorem in statistical mechanics which shows that it is the difference between the average energy of the reacting complexes and the average energy of all the colliding pairs of reactant molecules present.[27]

This suggests that each pair of colliding reactant molecules will react only if its energy exceeds a certain critical value. The simplest form of collision theory then gives for the rate constant:

$$k = PZ \exp\left(-E/RT\right) \tag{12.16}$$

Here E is a critical energy,[28] Z is the collision number (proportional to $T^{1/2}$), and P is a factor taking account of steric and other non-energetic conditions for effective collision.[29] If activation in F internal degrees of freedom is envisaged, this expression for k must be modified to:

$$k = PZ[(E/RT)^F/(F!)] \exp\left(-E/RT\right) \tag{12.16a}$$

The transition-state theory leads to the equation:

$$k = \kappa(kT/h) \exp\left(\Delta S^*/R\right) \exp\left(-\Delta H^*/RT\right) \tag{12.17}$$

in which ΔH^* and ΔS^* are the enthalpy and entropy of activation,

[27] Hinshelwood, *Kinetics of Chemical Change* (Oxford, 1940), p. 53.
[28] If this critical energy is assumed to be entirely kinetic energy of the molecules along the line of centres, it may be identified with E. If the kinetic energy in all directions is considered, or if other degrees of freedom are taken into account, the relation is less simple. Cf. Fowler and Guggenheim, *Statistical Thermodynamics* (Cambridge, 1939), chapter 12.
[29] Hinshelwood (a) ref. 27; (b) *The Structure of Physical Chemistry* (Oxford, 1950), p. 376.

and κ is a transmission coefficient.[30] Both these theoretically-derived equations 12.16 and 12.17 are experimentally indistinguishable from equation 12.14. For the Arrhenius activation energy E_A they give respectively:

$$E_A = E + \tfrac{1}{2}RT \simeq E \qquad (12.18)$$

$$E_A = \Delta H^* + RT \simeq \Delta H^* \qquad (12.19)$$

Both of them interpret the Arrhenius parameter E_A in terms of a critical energy.

It has long been recognized that this critical energy may be made up of several distinct contributions.[31] General chemical experience indicates that the *energies of the bonds broken and formed* in the reactant and product molecules usually play an important part in determining E_A; but there is no general or exact correlation of E_A with bond dissociation energies, especially in solution. This suggests that other contributions are also significant. Short-range *repulsion forces*, due to the interpenetration of electron shells, are set up when atoms approach each other closely. The contribution of this effect also has proved difficult to estimate in general; only for the transfer of protons, which have no valency electrons, is it possible to be confident that the contribution will be small.[32] *Electrostatic interactions* between ions or dipoles appear to have an important effect; in several series of related reactions in solution, changes in E_A up to 7 kcal mole^{-1} can be correlated with variations in the dipole moments of the reactants, or with the order of the inductive effects of substituents.[33]

Reorganization of solvent molecules is a fourth factor which must also play a part. If the formation of the transition state leads to a change in the number or magnitude of ionic charges, or in the distribution of charge, then reorientation of solvent molecules is to be

[30] Glasstone, Laidler and Eyring, *Theory of Rate Processes* (McGraw Hill, 1941), chapter 4. A factor involving activity coefficients may also be needed, especially for ionic reactions.

[31] For references and discussion, see Caldin, *J. Chem. Soc.* 1959, 3345.

[32] Bell, *Trans. Faraday Soc.* 1944, **37**, 493.

[33] (a) Hinshelwood, Laidler and Timm, *J. Chem. Soc.* 1938, 848; (b) Laidler, *Chemical Kinetics* (McGraw Hill, 1950), pp. 137–143; (c) Moelwyn-Hughes, *Kinetics of Reactions in Solution* (Oxford, 1947), chapters 5 and 7.

expected. The magnitude of the A-factor can be interpreted in this way for many reactions,[34] and so can the variation of the A-factor of a given reaction when the pressure is increased[35] or when the solvent is varied.[36] Such reorganizations of solvent involve energy changes and will contribute to E_A. The most direct evidence that they do so comes from measurements of E_A for a given reaction in different solvents; the variations may be as much as 4 to 7 kcal mole^{-1}.[37]

These solvent effects are attributable to the overall difference in solvation between the reactants and the transition state. There is, however, another aspect of solvation changes in reaction. If the reactant molecules are surrounded by a sheath of solvent molecules, they cannot approach close enough to begin forming the transition state unless at least one solvent molecule is detached from each. Calculations suggest that the electrostatic energy required to remove water from an ion is considerable; for hydroxide ion, as an example, it comes out to about 21 kcal mole^{-1}.[38] The experimental results on solvent exchange summarized above (p. 276) show that the energy of activation is 5–12 kcal mole^{-1} for the replacement of water in the coordinate shell of some divalent ions, and probably more for a trivalent ion. Preliminary desolvation may therefore contribute appreciably to the energy of activation of some reactions involving ions.

Finally, we have seen that for diffusion-controlled reactions (p. 279) the value of E_A is determined by the *temperature-variation of the diffusion coefficient*, which according to the Stokes-Einstein formula is related to that of the viscosity η, or more exactly that of T/η. For small molecules in ordinary solvents,

[34] Bell, *J. Chem. Soc.* 1943, 629.

[35] (*a*) Hamann, *Physico-chemical Effects of Pressure* (Butterworths, 1957), chapter 9; (*b*) Burrell and Laidler, *Trans. Faraday Soc.* 1955, **51**, 1497.

[36] (*a*) Bell, ref. 34; (*b*) Pearson, *J. Chem. Phys.* 1952, **20**, 1478; (*c*) Caldin and Peacock, *Trans. Faraday Soc.* 1955, **51**, 1217.

[37] For references to nine reactions (mostly ionogenic) showing these effects, see ref. 31.

[38] (*a*) Moelwyn-Hughes and Glew, *Proc. Roy. Soc, A*, 1952, **212**, 260; (*b*) Latimer, Pitzer and Slansky, *J. Chem. Phys.* 1939, **7**, 108; (*c*) Franklin, *Trans. Faraday Soc.* 1952, **48**, 443.

diffusion control may thus give rise to an Arrhenius energy of activation in the region of 1 to 3 kcal mole^{-1}. Diffusion rates will not, however, contribute to the value of E_A if it is above about 6 kcal mole^{-1}, assuming the A-factor to be normal (p. 281).

E_A as temperature-dependent, and its relation to the height of a potential-energy barrier

Most Arrhenius plots are linear within experimental error, even over extended temperature ranges, and in this section so far we have assumed that E_A does not vary with temperature. If this is the case, E_A can be identified with its value at $0°K$, and is a measure of the height of the potential-energy barrier, taking no account of thermal energy. We saw, however, that for certain proton transfers the plot is non-linear because of quantum-mechanical tunnelling, and that even when the curvature is not detectable over a moderate temperature-range the height of the energy-barrier may be 20% higher than the value of E_A (p. 273). This is a rather special case in practice, but it raises the general question of the linearity of Arrhenius plots and the relation of E_A to the height of the barrier. [39]

The collision theory and the transition-state theory both predict that E_A will vary with temperature, particularly in ionic reactions where there is a considerable change in the number of orientated or 'frozen' solvent molecules. On the transition-state theory, E_A represents ΔH^* which will vary with temperature according to the general relation:

$$dE_A/dT = d(\Delta H^*)/dT + R = \Delta C_p^* + R \approx \Delta C_p^* \quad (12.20)$$

Here ΔC_p^* is the difference of heat capacities between the reactants and the transition state, and may be appreciable for ionic reactions. On the collision theory, the generalized equation (12.16a) for activation in F internal degrees of freedom gives:

$$dE_A/dT \approx -(F - \tfrac{1}{2})R \quad (12.21)$$

Since the ion-solvent bonds must be included in estimating the number of degrees of freedom, F may be considerable for reactions involving ions.

[39] Cf. Bell, *Acid-base Catalysis* (ref. 3a), pp. 175 *seq.*

Accurate work by conductimetric methods on solvolyses by Robertson and his co-workers has shown that E_A does vary for these reactions. It has also been shown to vary for the inversion of sucrose in hydrochloric acid, for which the transition state may involve the participation of water. In many of these instances the variation is approximately linear with temperature, giving an effectively constant value for dE_A/dT of -20 to -50 cal deg^{-1} mole^{-1} in the temperature-range investigated.[40] It seems likely, therefore, that E_A at these temperatures differs from its (hypothetical) value at $0°K$ by several kilocalories per mole.

It is clear that for these reactions E_A may include an appreciable amount of thermal energy besides the potential energy which is measured by the value of E_A at $0°K$. This may also be true, moreover, for reactions giving apparently linear Arrhenius plots, since the value of dE_A/dT could be as large as -10 cal mole^{-1} deg^{-1} before producing deviations detectable by ordinary kinetic experiments, and this might lead to a difference of up to 3 kcal mole^{-1} between E_A and the potential energy. The observed values of E_A for such reactions cannot therefore be simply identified with the height of the potential-energy barrier. This would be justified, however, as a first approximation for reactions involving no change in ionic charge, and especially for comparisons of a series of related reactions at the same temperature, as on p. 265.

The status of the Arrhenius equation and of Arrhenius parameters

In conclusion, it is interesting to summarise the refinements that have come about in our understanding of the Arrhenius equation (12.14), partly as a result of the study of fast reactions.

Interpretation of the Arrhenius equation. The successful representation of the temperature-dependence of most reaction rates by the Arrhenius equation is interpreted both by the collision theory (equation 12.16) and by the transition-state theory (equation 12.17).

[40] For some values and references, see (a) Moelwyn-Hughes, *Kinetics of Reactions in Solution* (2nd edn., Oxford, 1947), pp. 56 *seq.*; (b) Robertson, Heppolette and Scott, *Canad. J. Chem.* 1959, **37**, 803; (c) Kohnstam, in *The Transition State* (Chem. Soc. Special Pub. No. 16, 1962), p. 179. For the effect on E_A, cf. (d) Bell, in *Handbuch der Katalyse*, ed. Schwab (Springer, 1940), vol. ii, p. 334.

The simple forms of both theories assume that the equilibrium spatial distribution of the molecules is maintained. We have seen that this is normally a good approximation for observed rate constants up to around 10^7 l mole^{-1} sec^{-1}, but that it is not true for diffusion-controlled reactions. The collision theory is able to handle these reactions by identifying the reaction rate with the encounter rate, which is calculated by diffusion theory. The transition-state theory is in greater difficulty because it is primarily concerned with what happens during a collision, and gives no detailed account of what leads up to it.

Both theories assume also that the equilibrium energy distribution is maintained. Calculations have been made by various authors for gas reactions,[41] and suggest that deviations may become appreciable if E/RT is less than about 5, a condition that could be fulfilled at high temperatures or with fast reactions. In solution, the solvent molecules will maintain the equilibrium distribution much more closely, and although detailed calculations do not seem to have been made it is unlikely that deviations will be important in fluid solvents.

Interpretation of Arrhenius parameters. For many purposes it is permissible to interpret the Arrhenius energy of activation on the simple assumptions (*a*) that it is independent of temperature, (*b*) that it represents the height of a potential-energy barrier, and (*c*) that this height is determined by the stretching of chemical bonds in the reactant molecules, as in Fig. 12.1. We have seen in this chapter that none of these assumptions is quite accurate. The value of E_A for a reaction is in principle temperature-dependent, and for some reactions the variation is detectable by careful measurements. In consequence E_A may not be identified exactly with the height of a potential-energy barrier, though no great error is likely to arise if the relative values for a series of reactions at a given temperature are interpreted in terms of potential-energy changes. Finally, the extension of chemical bonds in the reactant molecules is only one of the factors contributing to E_A, which include also repulsion, desolvation, ion–dipole interactions, and diffusion. For fast

[41] For reviews see (*a*) Montroll and Schuler, *Advances in Chemical Physics*, vol. I (Interscience, 1958), p. 368; (*b*) Careri, *ibid.*, p. 129.

reactions it may be outweighed by one of these; in the preceding pages we have encountered many instances where the rate-controlling step is diffusion, and some where it is desolvation. The study of fast reactions will doubtless throw light on these and similar energy terms, which may be only small contributions to the activation energies of reactions studied by conventional kinetic methods, but become important when E_A is relatively small.

Appendix

Least reaction half-time accessible	10^{-10} sec
Lifetimes of electronically-excited singlet states	10^{-8} sec
Period of molecular rotation	10^{-11}–10^{-12} sec
Thermal relaxation time in solution	10^{-12}–10^{-13} sec
Period of molecular vibration	10^{-13}–10^{-14} sec
Period of orbital motions of electrons	10^{-15} sec

TABLE 13.2

Diffusion-controlled rate constant for reaction between ions, compared with that for uncharged molecules

Values of $[k_D(\text{ions})]/[k_D(\text{molecules})] = \delta/(e^{\delta} - 1)$, for ions of charges z_A and z_B, with distance of closest approach a (in Å), for water at 25°. See page 12.

$z_A z_B$	$[k_D(\text{ions})]/[k_D(\text{molecules})]$			
	a (Å)			
	2·0	5·0	7·5	10·0
$+2$	0·005	0·17	0·34	0·45
$+1$	0·10	0·45	0·60	0·69
-1	3·7	1·9	1·6	1·4
-2	7·1	3·0	2·2	1·9

Index of Subjects

night